Wave Propagation in Periodic Structures

Wave Propagation in Periodic Structures

Electric Filters and Crystal Lattices

L. BRILLOUIN

Honorary Professor, Collège de France, Paris

Watson Laboratory, International Business Machines, New York

SECOND EDITION

WITH CORRECTIONS AND ADDITIONS

DOVER PUBLICATIONS, INC.

WAVE PROPAGATION IN PERIODIC STRUCTURES

PRINTED IN THE UNITED STATES OF AMERICA

Printed and Bound in the U. S. A.

Dedicated to My Wife

WHOSE FAITH AND LOVE HAVE NEVER FAILED

THROUGH HARDSHIP AND SORROW

PREFACE

Some readers may be surprised or even disturbed at the mixture of problems assembled in this book. These problems actually extend from electrical engineering to electromagnetism and wave mechanics of the spinning electron, but the link connecting this variety of problems will soon be discovered in their common mathematical background.

Waves always behave in a similar way, whether they are longitudinal or transverse, elastic or electric. Scientists of the last century always kept this idea in mind. When Lord Kelvin built up his model for a dispersive medium or when Lord Rayleigh discovered radiation pressure, they never failed to try the same methods again and again on all conceivable types of waves. This general philosophy of wave propagation, forgotten for a time, has been strongly revived in the last decade and represents the backbone of this book.

All problems discussed deal with periodic structures of various kinds, and they all lead to similar results: these structures, be they electric lines or crystal lattices, behave like band-pass filters. If energy dissipation is omitted, there is a sharp distinction between frequency bands exhibiting wave propagation without attenuation (passing bands) and those showing attenuation and no propagation (stopping bands). These general properties are defined for an infinite unbounded medium, but they bear a very close relation to *selective reflections* shown by a bounded medium. A wave striking from outside may be partly reflected from the surface, if the second medium is able to transmit the corresponding frequency. The amount of reflection depends upon how well the media are matched at their common boundary. But when the frequency falls inside a stopping band of the reflecting medium, there is no longer any matching problem; the wave cannot be transmitted, and hence it must be totally reflected. This same explanation applies to electric filters, rest rays, anomalous optical reflections, and selective reflection of X rays or electrons from a crystal. In the case of rest rays, the theory was developed by M. Born and his school; for X rays, it corresponds to Bragg's reflections and P. P. Ewald's now classical investigations summarized in his book "Kristalle und Roentgen Strahlen" (Springer, 1923), and a paper in the *Annales de l'Institut Poincaré* (vol. 7, p. 79, 1938). Many practical examples of electric filters may be found in the treatises of K. S. Johnson and T. E. Shea, in the collection of books from the Bell Telephone Laboratories (van Nostrand). The general connection between stopping bands and selective reflection is exemplified in the definition of the *zones* for a crystal lattice, a theory first developed by the author in his original papers and in a book "Quantenstatistik" (Springer, 1931). A general discussion of the zone theory is found in the present book and will serve as an introduction to Mott and Jones, "Theory of Metals and Alloys" (Oxford, 1936), and to F. Seitz's "The Modern Theory of Solids" (McGraw-Hill, 1940), where the theory is applied to many practical discussions.

Apart from physical and engineering problems, the general theory developed in this book bears a close connection with many problems of applied mathematics, such as the Mathieu functions and Mathieu's and Hill's equations.

The author discussed these general problems in his lectures at the Collège de France (1937–1938) and at the University of Wisconsin (1942), when Mary Hewlett Payne very kindly proposed to write down her notes and to prepare them for publication. Circumstances resulted in great delays before this could be completed, and the author's present duties would never have permitted him to undertake such a work if Mrs. Payne had not made a really excellent record of his lectures, so that very few corrections and additions were necessary on her manuscript. Let her find here the author's very best thanks for her valuable collaboration.

LÉON BRILLOUIN.

NEW YORK, N. Y.,
January, 1946.

CONTENTS

Chapter IV

Mathematical Treatment of More Complicated One-dimensional Lattices

Chapter V

Energy Velocity, Energy Flow, and Characteristic Impedance

Chapter VI

Two-dimensional Lattices

Chapter VII

Three-dimensional Lattice

Chapter X

CONTINUOUS ELECTRIC LINES

WAVE PROPAGATION IN PERIODIC STRUCTURES

CHAPTER I

ELASTIC WAVES IN A ONE-DIMENSIONAL LATTICE OF POINT MASSES: EARLY WORK AND INTRODUCTION

1. Historical Background; Eighteenth Century

The first work done on a one-dimensional lattice was that of Newton[1] in his attempt to derive a formula for the velocity of sound. Newton assumed that sound was propagated in air in the same manner in which an elastic wave would be propagated along a lattice of point masses. He assumed the simplest possible such lattice, *viz.*, one consisting of equal masses spaced

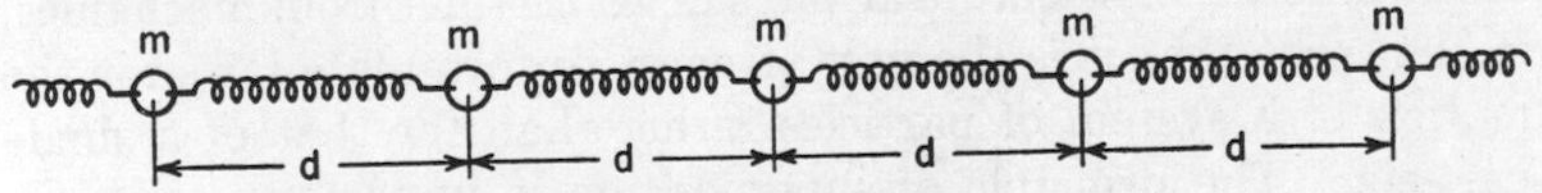

FIG. 1.1.

equally along the direction of propagation (Fig. 1.1). Neighboring masses were assumed to attract one another with an elastic force with constant e. Taking m to be the mass of each of the particles and d to be the distance between neighboring particles in the state of equilibrium, Newton obtained for the velocity V of propagation of an elastic wave

$$V = d\sqrt{\frac{e}{m}} = \sqrt{\frac{ed}{\rho}} \qquad \rho = \text{density} \qquad (1.1)$$

To compare this result with the experimental value of the velocity of sound in air, Newton took ρ to be the density of air and ed to be the isothermal bulk modulus of air. The theoretical value thus computed was smaller than the experimental value. In 1822 Laplace pointed out that the expansions and condensations

[1] NEWTON, "Principia," Book II, 1686.

associated with sound waves take place adiabatically and that, therefore, the adiabatic elastic constant should be used instead of the isothermal. A computation using the adiabatic constant in Newton's formula gave excellent agreement with experiment. It should be mentioned that Newton's formula holds only for wave lengths large compared with d.

The reason why Newton considered the one-dimensional lattice of Fig. 1.1 was that at that time a continuous structure represented an insoluble problem, and nothing was known about partial differential equations. Hence, a model had to be chosen that would lead to a number of simultaneous equations of motion of the usual type.

The work on one-dimensional lattices was continued in a series of letters, starting in 1727, between John Bernoulli in Basel and his son Daniel in St. Petersburg at that time. They showed that a system with n point masses has n independent modes of vibration, *i.e.*, n proper frequencies. Later (1753), Daniel Bernoulli formulated the principle of superposition, which states that the general motion of a vibrating system is given by a superposition of its proper vibrations. This investigation may be said to form the beginning of theoretical physics as distinct from mechanics, in the sense that it is the first attempt to formulate laws for the motion of a system of particles rather than for that of a single particle. The principle of superposition is important, as it is a special case of a Fourier series, and in time it was extended to become a statement of Fourier's theorem.

The laws of vibrating strings were first discovered empirically, and in 1713 Taylor started a theoretical investigation. Euler's treatment of the continuous string by means of partial differential equations (1748) was much more complete. He took the string to be along the x axis and to be vibrating in some plane perpendicular to this axis. The result he obtained was that the displacement of the string was given by an arbitrary function of $(x \pm vt)$, where v is the velocity of propagation of the wave and t is the time, provided that the function satisfied certain continuity conditions. Euler's result started a controversy lasting until 1807. If one takes Euler's result and the principle of superposition together, one must conclude that any arbitrary function of $(x \pm vt)$ may be described by a superposition of sine and cosine functions, since it is well known that the proper vibrations of a string are given by sine and cosine functions. This is, of course, merely a statement of Fourier's theorem, but Fourier's theorem was not proved until 1807, and to Euler's mind the theorem was almost an absurdity. Since he could not doubt the validity of his solution to the problem of the vibrating continuous string, Euler refused to accept the principle of superposition.

The Bernoullis had given the problem of the one-dimensional lattice of point masses a fairly complete treatment. Euler had solved the problem of the vibrating continuous string. The task of treating the continuous string as a limiting case of the one-dimensional lattice of point masses still remained. This problem was solved by Lagrange in 1759.

Lagrange followed Euler in refusing to accept the principle of superposition. This is very strange, since Lagrange's paper practically contains the principle of the Fourier series. A number of examples of trigonometric series were already known at the time, but it was not believed that such expansions could be used to represent any arbitrary function. In a paper on celestial mechanics, Clairaut (1754) actually had the proof, but it remained unnoticed; and it was left for Fourier to give the general statement and to emphasize its great practical and theoretical importance.

All this work at the end of the eighteenth century is most interesting since it cleared the way for a number of modern problems in theoretical physics as well as for pure mathematics:

Proper functions, proper values; first discovered in connection with proper vibrations of strings, plates, etc.

Fourier expansion; expansion in series of proper functions.

Partial differential equations.

Wave propagation.

Atomic theory of solids and crystal structure.

Lagrange's paper was often quoted by the famous electrical engineer Pupin, who discovered in Lagrange's theory the solution of an important problem of electrical engineering, the loaded cable.

2. Historical Background; Nineteenth Century. Cauchy, Baden-Powell, and Kelvin

In 1830, Cauchy used Newton's model in an attempt to account for dispersion of optical waves. Cauchy assumed that light waves were just elastic waves of very high frequency. He obtained the result that for waves with wave length large compared with the distances between the point masses in the one-dimensional lattice, the velocity was independent of wave length. For shorter wave lengths and hence for higher frequencies, however, he showed that the velocity of propagation was a function of wave length. The result is correct for elastic waves; however, it did not agree quantitatively with values obtained experimentally for light waves.

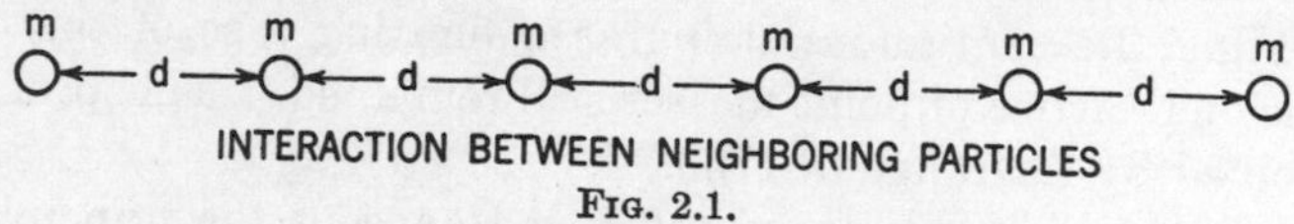

FIG. 2.1.

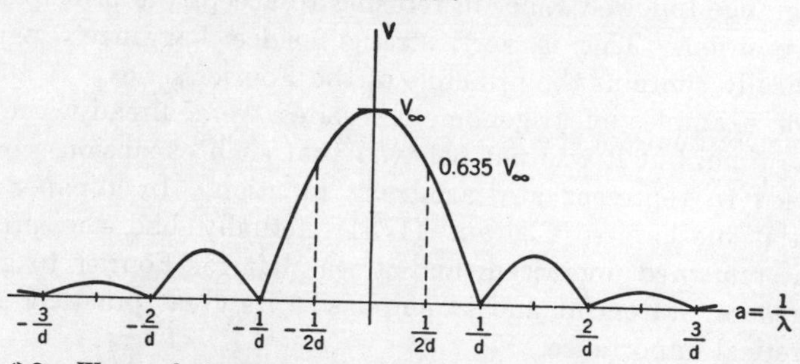

FIG. 2.2.—Wave velocity V as a function of a along the row of particles shown on Fig. 2.1.

In 1841, Baden-Powell computed the velocity of a wave propagating along one axis of a cubic lattice structure as a function of wave length. This is equivalent to considering a wave propagating along a one-dimensional lattice of point masses. Baden-Powell's lattice consisted of point masses of mass m spaced along a straight line at distance d from one another (see Fig. 2.1). Then he assumed each mass to be elastically bound to each of its neighbors with the restoring force the same for all masses. His equation for the propagation velocity V of the wave as a function of wave length is

$$V = V_\infty \frac{|\sin \pi d/\lambda|}{\pi d/\lambda} \tag{2.1}$$

where λ is the wave length and V_∞ is the velocity for infinite wave length. The curve of V plotted against reciprocal wave length is shown in Fig. 2.2. It is evident that if velocity is a function of wave length, the frequency must also be a function of the wave length. However, Baden-Powell neglected to consider the frequency as a function of the wave length and thus missed a very important point. The curve of velocity as a function of reciprocal wave length appears to be perfectly normal at the point $\lambda = 2d$; not so, however, for the frequency vs. reciprocal-wave-length curve. This point was noted by Kelvin, who gave a detailed discussion in 1881.[1]

Kelvin assumed the same lattice that Baden-Powell treated (see Fig. 2.3). Let us number the particles in such a way that

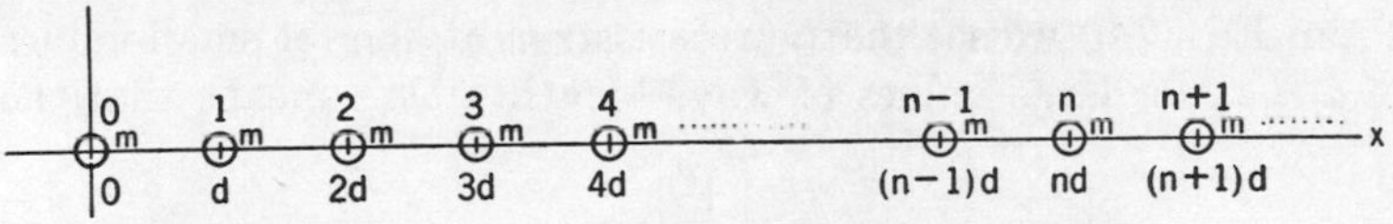

FIG. 2.3.

the x coordinate of the nth particle in its equilibrium position is given by

$$x_n = nd \tag{2.2}$$

In a sine wave, we obtain for y_n, the displacement of the nth particle,

$$y_n = A \cos 2\pi(\nu t - ax) = A \cos 2\pi(\nu t - and) \tag{2.3}$$

where ν is the frequency, a the wave number or reciprocal wave length, A an arbitrary constant, and t the time. Now in Eq. (2.3) we may replace a by

$$a' = a \pm \frac{m}{d} \qquad m \text{ an integer} \tag{2.4}$$

without changing the value of the displacement. This means that ν must be a periodic function of a with period $1/d$.

Now the phase velocity V, with which the waves propagate, is given by

$$V = \frac{\nu}{a} \tag{2.5}$$

Therefore, if we draw a curve of $\nu = \nu(a)$ as a function of a, the phase velocity for a given wave length will be given by the slope of the line drawn from the origin to the point on the $\nu(a)$ curve corresponding to the given wave length. The function $\nu(a)$ may

[1] "Popular Lectures," vol. I, p. 185.

be calculated and turns out to be

$$\nu(a) = B\,|\sin \pi a d| \tag{2.6}$$

where B is a constant that is a function of the constants of the lattice. From Eq. (2.6) we see that

$$V = \left|\frac{\nu(a)}{a}\right| = B\left|\frac{\sin \pi a d}{a}\right| = V_\infty \frac{|\sin \pi a d|}{|\pi a d|} \tag{2.7}$$

in agreement with Baden-Powell's equation (2.1), if we take

$$V_\infty = \pi\, dB \tag{2.8}$$

From Eq. (2.6) we see that $\nu(a)$ is a straight line for small values of a, *i.e.*, for large values of wave length. This means that the

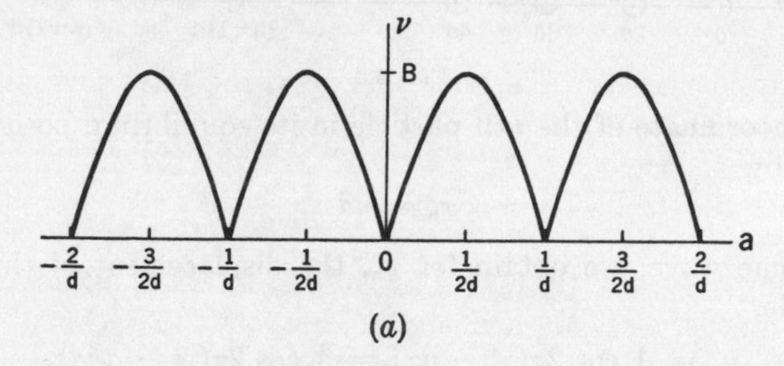

(*a*)

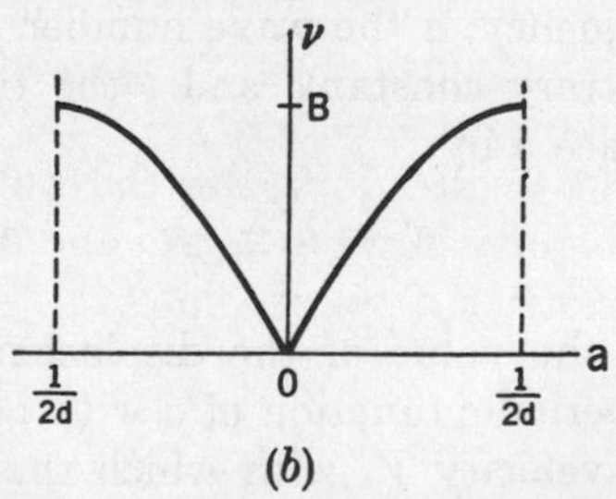

(*b*)

FIG. 2.4.—Frequency ν as a function of $a = 1/\lambda$ for the row of particles shown on Fig. 2.1.

velocity of propagation should be constant for large wave lengths, in agreement with the earlier calculations.

The curve of ν vs. a is shown in Fig. 2.4*a*. The periodicity of ν as a function of a means that for a given frequency the wave length is not completely determined. In fact, any a', where a' is defined by Eq. (2.4), will give the same ν. The ambiguity in wave length results in an ambiguity in the direction of propagation—an uncertainty both in magnitude and in direction. This is easily seen by referring to Eq. (2.7).

The physical meaning of the ambiguity in wave length may be seen from Fig. 2.5. The solid circles give the equilibrium positions of the point masses and the open circles the displaced positions at some instant. Through the displaced positions are drawn three possible sine waves. All three waves give equally good descriptions of the motion, as far as observation of the

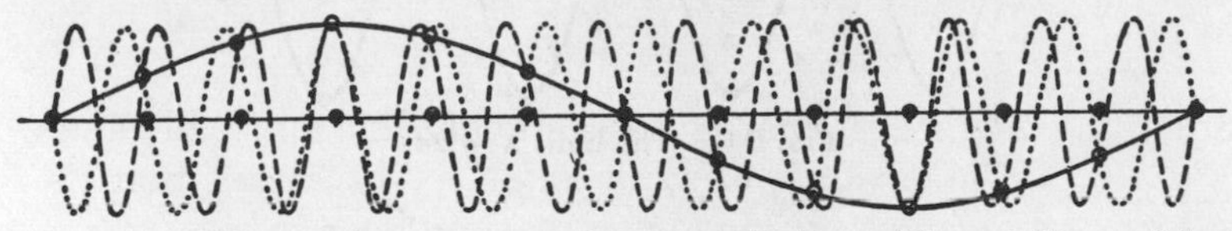

FIG. 2.5.—Different sine curves passing through the position of the particles.

points is concerned. The solid line gives the wave form for the only value of a such that

$$-\frac{1}{2d} \leqq a \leqq \frac{1}{2d} \tag{2.9}$$

Changing a by $1/d$ will take a out of this interval, as is immediately obvious. The dashed curve corresponds to $a + (1/d)$, and the dotted curve to $a - (1/d)$. A glance at the diagram shows that the solid and the dashed curves must propagate in the same direction for a given motion of the particles, and the dotted curve propagates in the opposite direction.

From now on, we shall adopt the convention expressed by Eq. (2.9). All ambiguity in wave length and direction of motion is removed if we restrict a to this interval, except in the two special cases where

$$a = \pm \frac{1}{2d} \tag{2.10}$$

We shall discuss these special cases shortly. The convention is not so arbitrary as might appear at first sight. It allows any wave length such that

$$\infty \geqq \lambda \geqq 2d \tag{2.11}$$

to have either direction of propagation, and excludes only wave lengths that lie in the interval

$$0 \leqq \lambda \leqq 2d \tag{2.12}$$

If we had a continuous strurture so that the motion of all points lying on a straight line could be observed, the wave lengths included in the interval (2.11) would be the only ones observed, since in this case $d = 0$. Thus there will be no inconsistency in what we mean by wave length when we go from a continuous to a

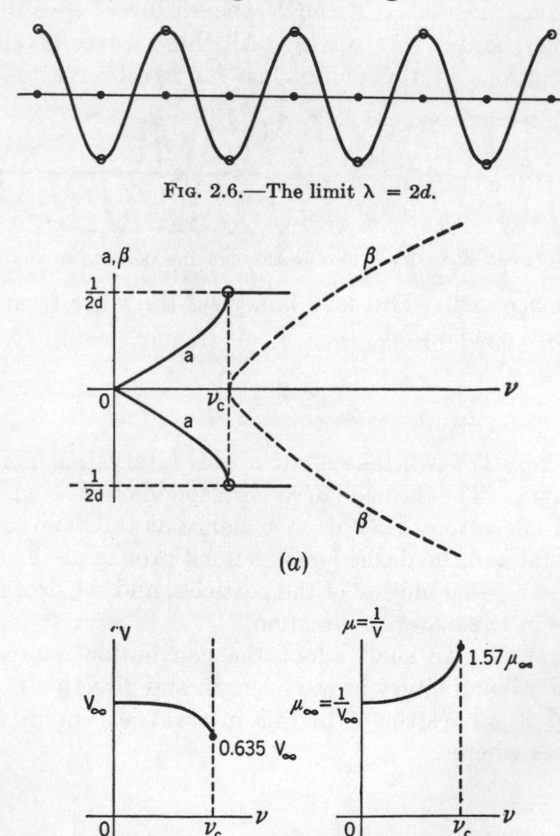

FIG. 2.6.—The limit $\lambda = 2d$.

FIG. 2.7.

discontinuous structure, and vice versa. Furthermore, the allowed interval contains a complete period of $\nu(a)$, so that none of the frequencies that can be propagated are omitted.

The special case noted in Eq. (2.10) is shown in Fig. 2.6. Here there is no way of distinguishing between the two possible wave numbers allowed by our convention, or between the two possible directions of propagation. In fact, the wave might even be considered as a standing wave, *i.e.*, a superposition of the two allowed wave numbers. The wave length is, of course, in both cases $2d$.

Engineers frequently find it convenient to use other curves giving essentially the same information as our ν vs. a curve. The one of greatest interest is the attenuation curve (Fig. 2.7a). The solid part of the curve is our ν vs. a curve rotated through 90 deg. The dotted, or β, part gives the attenuation β for frequencies higher than those that may be propagated. The attenuation will be discussed in detail in a later chapter. A lattice such as this, which allows propagation of all frequencies up to a maxi-

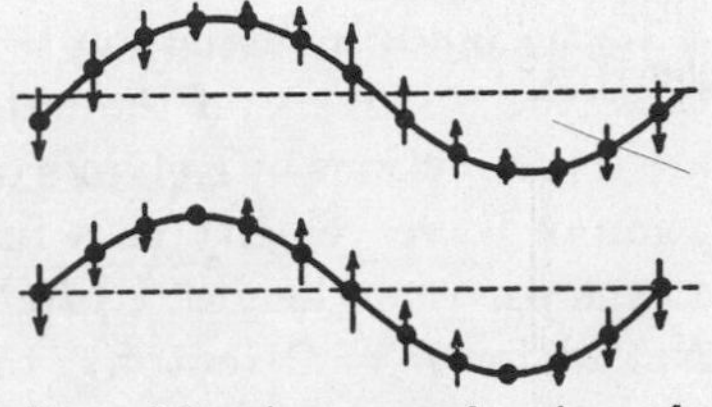

FIG. 2.8.—An example given by Lord Kelvin.

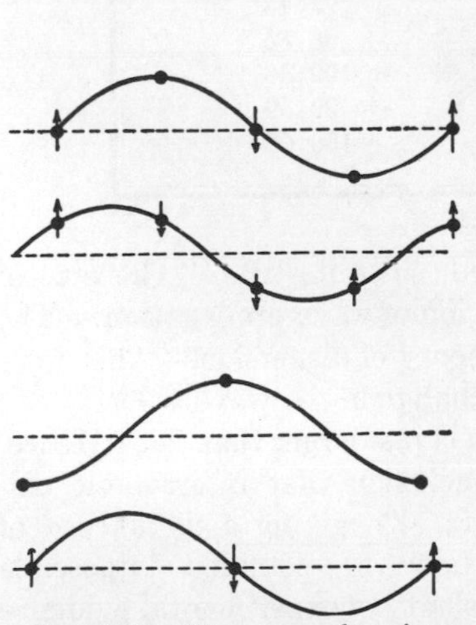

FIG. 2.9.—Other examples given by Lord Kelvin. The lower vibration corresponds to the limit $\lambda = 2d$.

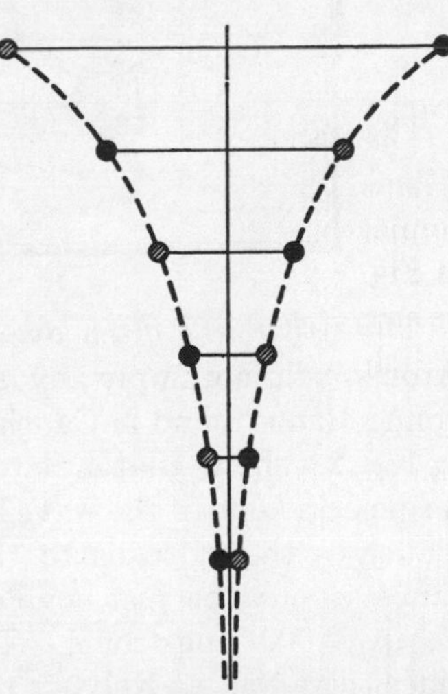

FIG. 2.10.—Attenuation of the wave for a frequency above cutoff (Lord Kelvin).

mum, or critical, frequency ν_c and damps all others, is called a *low-pass filter*; *i.e.*, it will pass low frequencies and stop higher frequencies. Figures 2.7b and 2.7c give V, the phase velocity, and μ, the index of refraction or reciprocal of phase velocity, as functions of frequency. Both curves terminate at the critical frequency, as phase velocity is not defined for attenuated waves. The curves shown in Figs. 2.7*a*, *b*, and *c* are very useful for some practical purposes. However, in general, we shall find the ν vs. a curve (Fig. 2.4*b*) most useful for our analytical discussions.

Lord Kelvin's discussion is of great significance, since it contains the discovery of the cutoff frequency. Figures 2.8 to 2.11 are reproductions of Kelvin's original drawings and show the variation of wave velocity as a function of $N = \lambda/d$, the number of atoms per wave length. Modes of vibration are shown for large N and for $N = 2$ (cutoff), together with the attenuated wave corresponding to a frequency above cutoff. All this shows how clearly Kelvin understood the problem.

N	W
2	63,64
4	90,03
8	97,45
12	98,86
16	99,36
20	99,59
∞	100,00

FIG. 2.11.

The paper was often overlooked, since its title, "The Size of Atoms," did not imply any discussion of wave propagation. The connection is found in Cauchy's theory of dispersion. The curve in Fig. 2.2 shows that a material change in the wave velocity can be expected only if the wave length is just larger than $2d$. Hence, Cauchy's theory leads to the conclusion that interatomic distances should be just smaller than $\lambda/2$, giving a distance d of about 2,000 angstroms. This, however, sounded impossible since there was, at Kelvin's time, plenty of experimental evidence that interatomic distances could not amount to more than a few angstrom units. The thickness of oil films on water, for instance, had been measured and was quite well known.

Kelvin's conception of the molecular structure of matter may be illustrated by the following quotation:

I believe that by imagining each molecule to be loaded in a certain definite way by elastic connection with heavier matter . . . we shall have a rude mechanical explanation for refractive dispersion. . . . It is not seventeen hours since I saw the possibility of this explanation.[1]

This was a remarkable guess, which led Kelvin to the discovery of the modern refraction formula, usually known as the *Lorentz formula.*

3. Later Work on Models Similar to That Treated in Sec. 2

After analyzing Baden-Powell's work and discussing the critical wave length and frequency, Kelvin proceeded to devise a theory

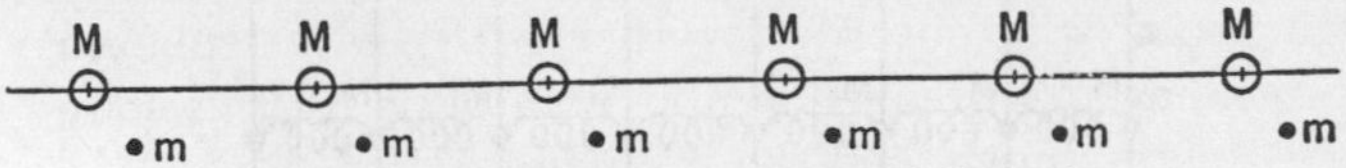

FIG. 3.1.—Kelvin's model for optical dispersion.

of dispersion based on a more complicated lattice than Baden-Powell's. He used the lattice shown in Fig. 3.1. Each of the masses in this model is supposed to have a small mass associated with it. The large masses are taken to have mass M and are the large circles in Fig. 3.1, while the small masses have mass m and are represented by dots. Each of the large masses interacts with the nearest large masses and with the small mass associated with it, so that there are two elastic constants in the system. Introducing two masses effectively doubles the number of degrees of freedom of the system, and hence one would expect to find twice as many proper vibrations as if there were only one mass. The curve of ν vs. a is shown in Fig. 3.2. The curve is restricted to values of a between $\pm 1/2d$. It is seen that for each a there are two modes of vibration of the system, so that

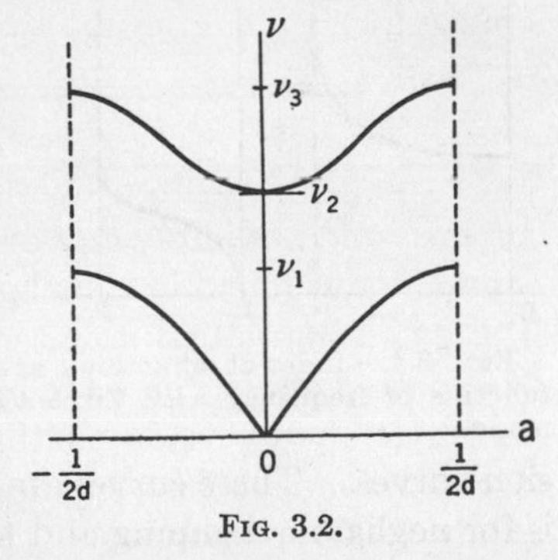

FIG. 3.2.

we do indeed have twice the number of modes obtained by Baden-Powell for his model with one mass. Frequencies below ν_1 and between ν_2 and ν_3 are propagated by the lattice, and all others are stopped. This lattice is an example of a *band-pass* filter. The interval between ν_1 and ν_2 is known as a *stopping band,* while that between ν_2 and ν_3 is known as a *passing band.* The frequencies ν_1 and ν_2 are very near the proper frequency of oscillation of one iso-

[1] *Op. cit.,* p. 194.

lated M-m molecule. This resonance frequency has nothing to do with the distance between molecules, and a material change in wave velocity is obtained when the resonance frequency lies in the near ultraviolet, just above the optical spectrum. Thus Kelvin explains refraction and escapes Cauchy's paradox.

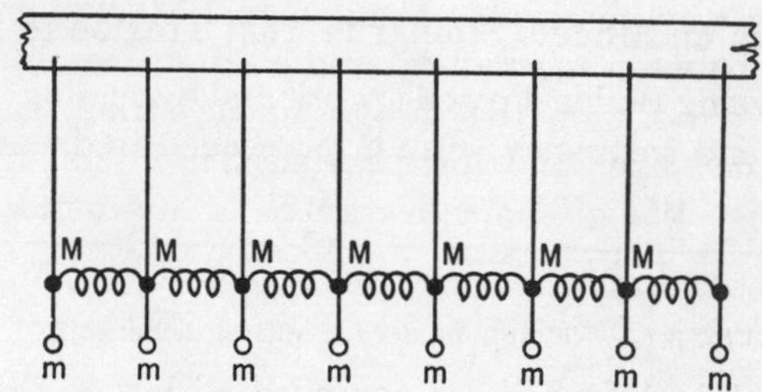

FIG. 3.3.—Vincent's model of the first mechanical filter.

Vincent[1] built a mechanical model to which Kelvin's theory was assumed to apply. The model is shown in Fig. 3.3. The large masses M are suspended from a beam on strings of equal length and connected to one another by springs. The small masses m are each suspended from one of the large masses. This model is evidently equivalent to Kelvin's more abstract scheme and was the *first mechanical filter* to be built. The motion of the system was observed for different frequencies. Vincent plotted curves of index of refraction μ against the frequency for comparison with standard dispersion curves. These curves are shown in Fig. 3.4. The solid curve is for negligible damping and the dotted curve for large damping. It is to be noted that the dotted curve is a typical anomalous dispersion curve. Vincent's curve of ν vs. a agreed with Kelvin's curve. The ratio $V = \nu/a$ can be measured on Fig. 3.2 and curve 3.4 obtained for $\mu = 1/V$ as a function of frequency ν.

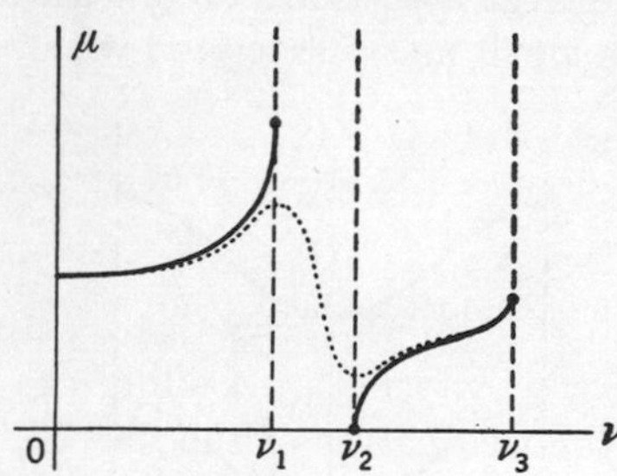

FIG. 3.4.—Index of refraction μ as a function of frequency ν for Vincent's model.

Kelvin's paper received little notice, and the analogy between the propagation of electromagnetic radiation and the propagation of elastic waves along a loaded string was forgotten.

[1] *Phil. Mag.*, **46**, 537 (1898).

In 1887, Heaviside noted that increasing the inductance per unit length of a cable should reduce the attenuation of waves propagating along the cable. However, he discussed no experimental details. Two years later, in 1889, Vaschy tried loading a very long cable with four inductances, an experiment much too crude to give any observable result. In 1900, Pupin developed the analogy between mechanical and electric lines and, referring to Lagrange's work on the discontinuous string, succeeded in building loaded lines and low-pass electric filters. The line is shown in Fig. 3.5*a*. The inductances L' were spaced so that

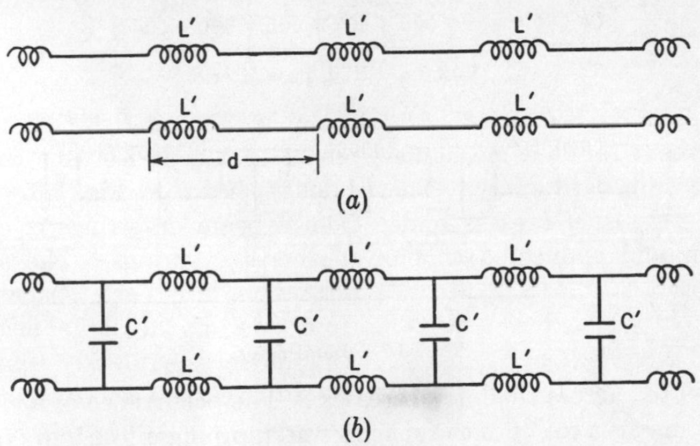

FIG. 3.5.—Low-pass electric filter and loaded line.

there were about ten inductances per wave length. Calling the capacitance per section d between the two halves of the line C', Pupin obtained a critical frequency of

$$\nu_m = \frac{1}{\pi \sqrt{2L'C'}} \tag{3.1}$$

Figure 3.5*b* shows an equivalent line with the capacitance of the line lumped and placed along the line as indicated.

The first high-pass electric filter (*i.e.*, a line passing all frequencies higher than a certain critical frequency and stopping all others) was built by Campbell in 1906. The line is shown in Fig. 3.6. Campbell followed up his high-pass filter by designing various band-pass filters. Figure 3.7 is the band-pass filter analogous to Vincent's mechanical band-pass filter.

It is somewhat easier than in the analogous mechanical lines to see why the electric lines mentioned above should pass some frequencies and stop others. The impedance offered by an electric circuit to a current passing through it is proportional to νL and inversely proportional to νC where ν is the frequency, L is the inductance, and C is the capacitance. Thus in the low-pass filter shown in Fig. 3.5*b* the impedance offered by the coils L' increases with the frequency, while the impedance of the capacities

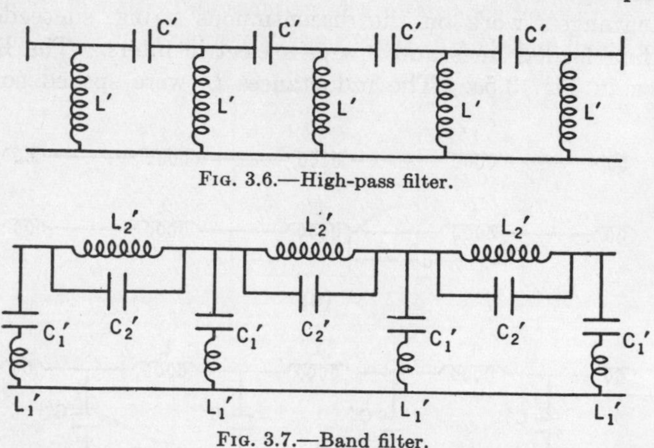

FIG. 3.6.—High-pass filter.

FIG. 3.7.—Band filter.

connected across the line decreases. The occurrence of a critical frequency is a result of the spacing and lumping of the inductances and capacities. In the high-pass filter the low frequencies will be shunted to the returning line through the inductances while the high frequencies will be passed. Again, the occurrence of a critical frequency is due to the discontinuous nature of the structure. These problems will be discussed in detail in a later section.

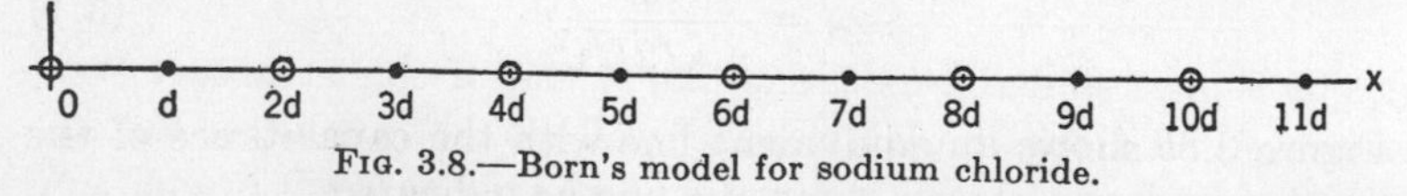

FIG. 3.8.—Born's model for sodium chloride.

In 1912, Born investigated the propagation of waves in crystals and rediscovered Kelvin's analysis. Using the model shown in Fig. 3.8, with large masses M and small masses m alternating at the points along the x axis defined by nd, where d is the distance between nearest neighbors, he obtained the curves shown in Figs. 3.9*a* and *b*. Figure 3.9*a* shows ν as a function of a. There are two branches to the curve because we have effectively doubled the number of degrees of freedom of the system by adding another constant. The additional constant is, of course, the second value for mass. We shall find that in general the number of branches will equal the number of different masses occurring in the model; *i.e.*, the number of frequencies corresponding to a given wave number is equal to the number of degrees of freedom associated with each element or cell of the lattice. In this case the cell consists of a large mass and either of its neighboring small masses. If there were two different masses between

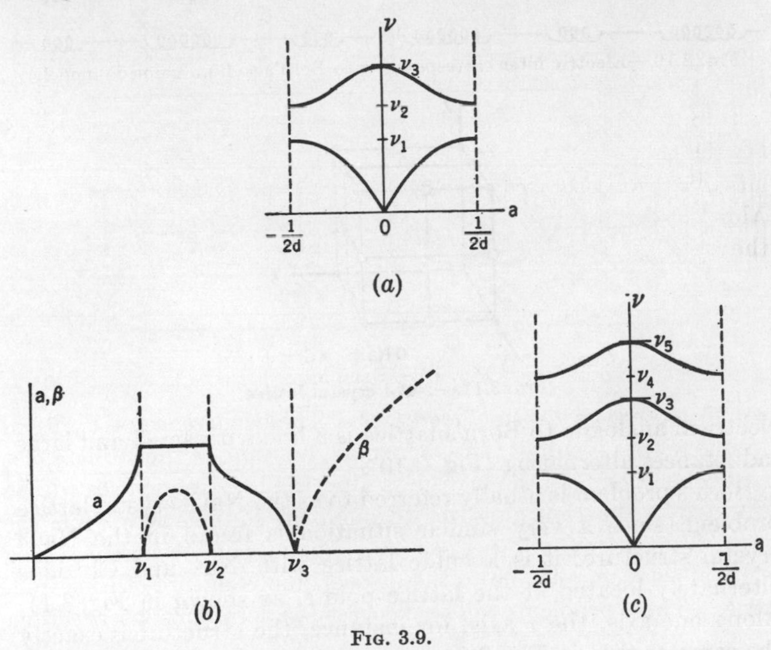

FIG. 3.9.

a given mass and the next one like it, and if this structure were repeated all along the lattice, each cell would have three degrees of freedom, and the ν vs. a curve would have one lower branch and two upper branches as in Fig. 3.9*c*. This property of discontinuous media will be discussed in greater detail later.

In general, the lower branch is called the *acoustical* branch. It corresponds to motion of the particles such that in each short section of the line all particles move in the same direction at a given instant. The upper branches are called *optical* branches and correspond to one or more types of particles moving in the direction opposite to that of the others at any given instant. In Born's model, where we have only two types of particle, the optical branch corresponds to the motion of the large masses in one direction while the small masses move in the other.

Figure 3.9*b* is the attenuation curve for Born's model and represents the generalization of Fig. 2.7*a*. There are one stopping band and two passing bands associated with this model. The

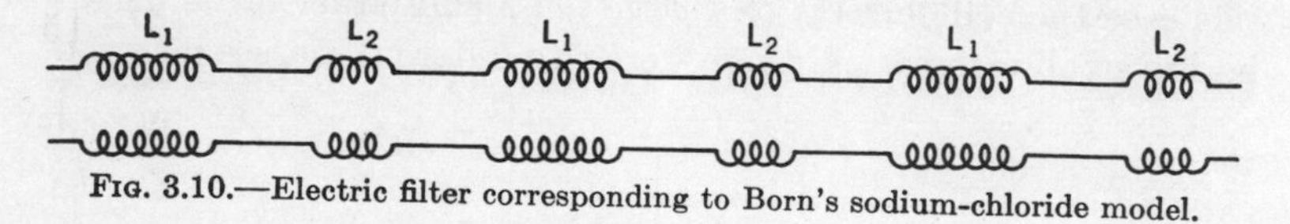

FIG. 3.10.—Electric filter corresponding to Born's sodium-chloride model.

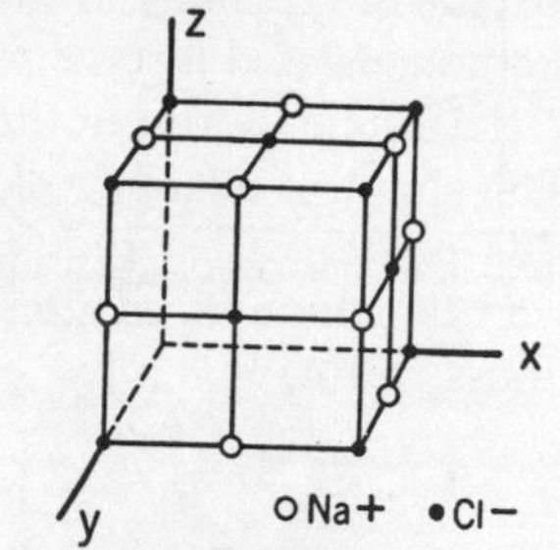

FIG. 3.11.—NaCl crystal lattice.

electrical analogue to Born's lattice is a line with small and large inductances alternating (Fig. 3.10).

Born's problem is usually referred to as the NaCl crystal lattice problem, since a very similar situation is found in the NaCl crystal structure: it is a cubic lattice with Na^+ and Cl^- ions alternately located at the lattice points, as shown in Fig. 3.11. Along one axis, the x axis, for instance, the structure is exactly the same as that in Fig. 3.8.

CHAPTER II

PROPAGATION OF WAVES ALONG ONE-DIMENSIONAL LATTICES. GENERAL RESULTS AND QUALITATIVE DISCUSSION

4. General Remarks

Before proceeding to the mathematical treatment of waves propagating along a one-dimensional lattice, we shall make some general remarks about the problem and discuss some particular cases qualitatively. The simplest example of a one-dimensional lattice is Baden-Powell's model with equal masses spaced uniformly in a line. If we take the masses along the x axis, the x coordinate of the nth mass will be given by

$$x = nd + \psi_n \tag{4.1}$$

where ψ_n is the displacement of the nth particle from its equilibrium position. ψ_n may be taken to represent transverse or longitudinal displacement, or any other quantity whose value may be defined at the points occupied by the masses but not elsewhere (electric polarization, for instance); *i.e.*, we may regard ψ_n as a property associated with point mass n. This property is propagated as a wave if the physical problem admits a solution of the type

$$\left.\begin{aligned} \psi_n = Ae^{2\pi i(\nu t - and)} = Ae^{i(\omega t - kn)} \\ a = \frac{1}{\lambda}, \qquad k = 2\pi ad, \qquad \omega = 2\pi\nu \end{aligned}\right\} \tag{4.2}$$

where ν is the frequency, t the time, a the wave number, λ the wave length, d the period of the lattice, ω the angular frequency, k the product of the wave number and the period of the lattice multiplied by 2π, and A a constant amplitude. The quantity k is the change in phase in passing from a point n to its right-hand neighbor $n + 1$:

$$\psi_{n+1} = \psi_n e^{-ik} \tag{4.3}$$

Thus k is essentially defined as an angle and can be known only as *modulus* 2π. The *same solution* of the problem is obtained for

$$k \quad \text{or} \quad k' = k + 2m\pi \tag{4.4}$$

when m is a positive or negative integer. Equations of the physical problem must yield the same value of ω or ν for every equivalent k or k', which means that the frequency ν is a periodic function of k or a:

$$\left.\begin{aligned} \omega &= f(k) \qquad \text{period } 2\pi \text{ in } k = 2\pi a d \\ \nu &= F(a) \qquad \text{period } \frac{1}{d} \text{ in } a \end{aligned}\right\} \tag{4.5}$$

This is a general and direct consequence of the periodic and discontinuous structure of the one-dimensional line. It was explained in Chap. I in Eq. (2.4) by saying that if ψ could be measured between particles, the uncertainty in k or a would be eliminated, but since ψ is measured only at the discrete points nd, the condition (4.5) is unavoidable.

On account of the periodic properties of the line, it is sufficient to discuss the properties of the functions f or F inside one period of k or a. The most convenient choice is

$$\left.\begin{aligned} -\pi \leqq k \leqq \pi \\ -\frac{1}{2d} \leqq a \leqq \frac{1}{2d} \end{aligned}\right\} \tag{4.6}$$

since a wave always propagates in the same way to the right and to the left. This means that the functions f and F have the additional property of being *even* functions. Positive k means a wave propagating to the right; negative k a wave propagating to the left. If k_0 is a positive number in the fundamental interval (4.6), it represents a wave going to the right, and so does $k_0 + 2\pi$; but $k_0 - 2\pi$ is negative and represents a wave going to the left (Fig. 2.5). Hence, the uncertainty is not only in the magnitude of a or k but also in the direction of propagation.

The limitation (4.6) means

$$\lambda = \frac{1}{|a|} \geqq 2d \tag{4.7}$$

The shortest wave length is thus equal to twice the distance between particles and corresponds to a certain *critical frequency* or *cutoff frequency* ν_m that is characteristic of the structure. In many important cases ν_m is the maximum frequency, and the system works as a *low-pass filter* for all frequencies

$$\nu \leqq \nu_m \tag{4.8}$$

Frequencies above ν_m are strongly attenuated. Condition (4.8) is, however, not the only possible one, and other situations may arise when ν_m would be a minimum. The system as a whole is always a filter, but it can be of the low-pass, high-pass, or band-pass type.

These general results, plus a direct discussion of the waves corresponding to the limiting cases, $\lambda = \infty$, $a = 0$, and $\lambda = 2d$, a maximum, may in a number of instances give enough information to enable one to describe, at least qualitatively, the general properties of the structure. In the next few sections we shall apply this discussion to specific examples of one-dimensional lattices.

5. A Lattice of Free Particles

By a lattice of free particles we mean particles in a one-dimensional lattice with no forces present except those due to interactions of the particles among themselves For purposes of this discussion we shall limit the interactions to nearest neighbors. An example of this is a loaded elastic cord with the masses distributed uniformly, where the elasticity of the cord remains constant along its length and plays the part of the interaction forces.

Let us first consider longitudinal displacements. The case $a = 0$ corresponds to infinite wave length. In this case the lattice as a whole is displaced, and no change in the distance between masses occurs. Thus no force is brought into play. The frequency is zero. For $a \neq 0$, but still very small, the wave length is large compared with the distance between masses, and hence the waves are propagated as if the lattice were a continuous string. The velocity of propagation of waves along a continuous string is constant for all wave lengths; *i.e.*, for long wave lengths, the frequency is proportional to $|a|$. A rigorous treatment shows that the velocity decreases for wave lengths comparable with the distance between masses. Now if a wave is to be propagated at all, the frequency must be a periodic function of a. Furthermore, the curve of ν vs. a must be symmetrical about the origin. If it were not, the frequencies for a given wave length propagating in opposite directions would be different, a fact that would be in contradiction with the symmetry of the structure. If ν is to be both periodic and symmetrical about the origin, there must be a maximum in the value of ν at $1/2d$, since the period of ν is $1/d$. Thus we obtain a curve of the general shape of that in Fig. 2.4*a*. We shall, of course, justify the exact shape mathematically in a later section.

The remarks made on the longitudinal vibrations also apply to transverse vibrations. Qualitatively, they may be treated in just the same way. Quantitatively, however, there is a difference. The velocities of propagation for large wave length are

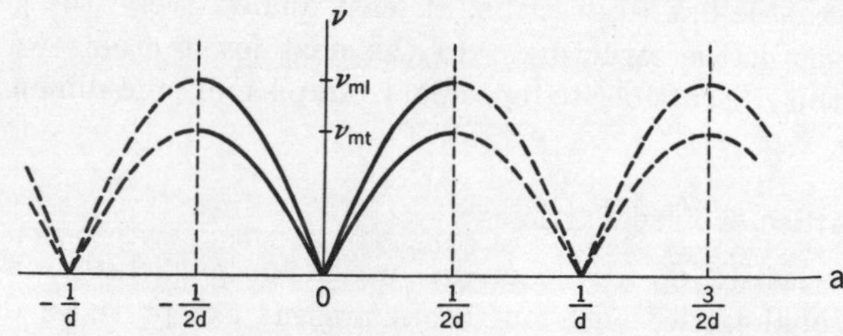

FIG. 5.1.—Longitudinal and transverse vibration along the row of particles shown on Fig. 2.1.

different in the longitudinal and transverse cases, and the maximum frequencies are also different. A typical curve for a one-dimensional lattice with particles with two degrees of freedom is shown in Fig. 5.1. The subscripts t and l on the maximum frequencies refer to transverse and longitudinal vibrations, respectively. The lower curve, representing transverse vibrations, should properly be considered a superposition of two branches of the same frequency, since there are two independent directions perpendicular to the lattice in which the masses might move. If there were an asymmetry in the elastic cord (*e.g.*, if it were of elliptical cross section), the lower branch would split into two distinct branches to give the extra frequencies demanded by the added degree of freedom. The solid curve corresponds to the interval (4.6), and its periodic continuation is shown as a dashed curve.

The transverse branches will usually be below the longitudinal branch in a loaded string, since the force required for a given displacement is smaller in the transverse than in the longitudinal direction. The frequency of displacement is proportional to the square root of the elastic constant, which will be smaller in the case of transverse displacements.

6. Longitudinal Vibration in a Row of Equidistant Coupled Oscillators

A particle attracted to some equilibrium position by an elastic restoring force acts as a harmonic oscillator. It has one proper frequency ν_0 that depends on the elastic restoring force and the mass of the particle. If its elastic restoring force is different in the x, y, and z directions, we have what is called an *anisotropic oscillator*. An anisotropic oscillator has three proper frequencies,

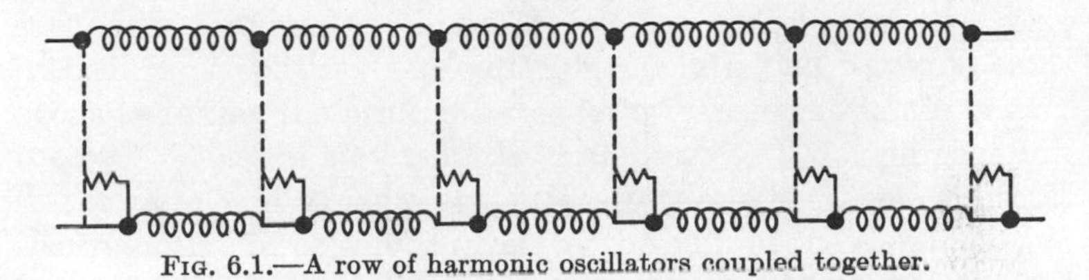

FIG. 6.1.—A row of harmonic oscillators coupled together.

ν_{0x}, ν_{0y}, and ν_{0z}, corresponding to vibrations in the x, y, and z directions, respectively.

Let us consider a row of similar harmonic oscillators (isotropic) spaced at distance d from one another along the x axis and allow interactions between nearest neighbors (Fig. 6.1). We wish to study the longitudinal modes of vibration of this system. For infinite wave length, $a = 0$. Infinite wave length means that all the particles are displaced simultaneously by the same amount. Since the distances between the particles do not change, the forces of interaction do not enter into the problem. Each particle is attracted to its equilibrium position with the same elastic force, and the system will oscillate with frequency ν_0. For a slightly smaller wave length the particles will be displaced relatively to one another, and the forces of interaction will play a part in the motion of the system. The frequency associated with this wave length will be slightly different from ν_0. Whether the frequency increases or decreases will depend on whether the resulting forces (elastic plus interaction) are larger or smaller than the restoring force tending to return each particle to its equilibrium position.

It may be shown that for large wave lengths ν is given by

$$\nu = \nu_0 + ba^2 \tag{6.1}$$

The sign of b depends on the constants of the system and determines whether ν shall increase or decrease as $|a|$ increases. As the wave length becomes comparable with $2d$, the considerations of the previous sections on one-dimensional lattices apply, and ν approaches an extremum. Thus we will have two limiting frequencies, ν_0 and ν_m (where m stands for maximum or minimum as the case may be). Frequencies between ν_0 and ν_m will propagate along the system, and other frequencies will be damped out. The system therefore forms a band-pass filter. The solid curve

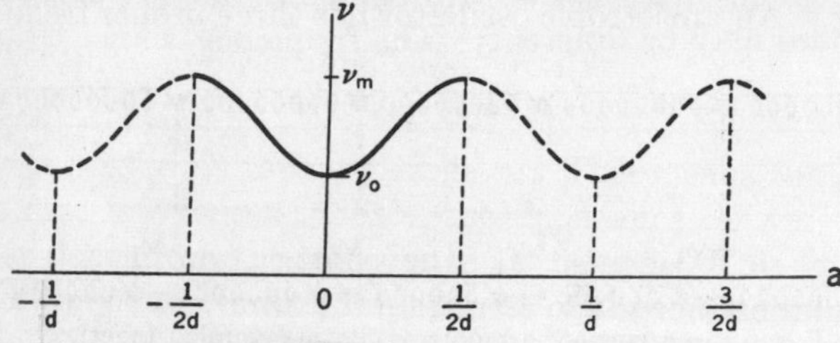

FIG. 6.2.—Frequency ν as a function of $a = 1/\lambda$ for the row of harmonic oscillators.

in Fig. 6.2 shows the curve ν vs. a in the fundamental interval (4.6) for the case $b > 0$. If each particle represented an anisotropic oscillator instead of an isotropic oscillator, there would be three curves, one for longitudinal and two for transverse vibrations. These curves might overlap and would not necessarily all rise as $|a|$ increases from zero.

7. Longitudinal Vibrations in a Row of Diatomic Molecules

The scheme described in the last section is somewhat artificial. It is rather difficult to imagine a particle in nature being tied to an equilibrium position by a little spring. A more realistic picture is obtained by considering diatomic molecules. This is a more complicated problem, since we must introduce a second type of particle that may interact with the first type as well as with its own type.

A lattice of diatomic molecules is shown in Fig. 7.1. The open circles are to have mass M, and the dots are to have mass m. An isolated molecule will have a certain proper frequency of vibration that we call ν_0. This frequency corresponds to an oscillation of the two masses along the x axis in opposite directions in such a way that their center of mass remains at rest.

Let us consider the motion of a row of diatomic molecules spaced at distance d from one another along the x axis. We assume, of course, that the molecules interact, but we limit the interaction to nearest neighbors. There will now be *two* wave functions, both imaginary exponential, one describing the motion of the masses M and the other describing the motion of the masses m. These two functions may be written

$$\psi_M = A_M e^{2\pi i(\nu t - ax)} \qquad \text{and} \qquad \psi_m = A_m e^{2\pi i(\nu t - ax)} \tag{7.1}$$

The frequencies and wave numbers will be the same, but the amplitudes may be different. The frequency ν may be found as

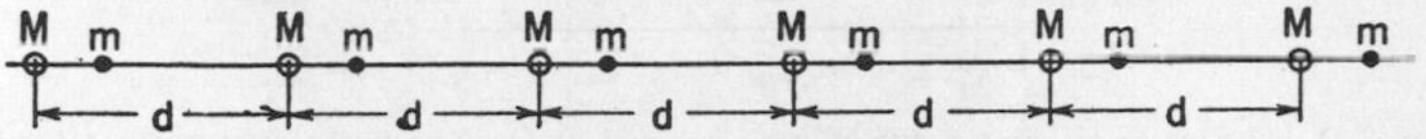

FIG. 7.1.—A row of diatomic molecules.

a function of the constants of the system and of a. It turns out to be double valued in ν, as will be shown in the rigorous theory, corresponding to the doubly infinite set of degrees of freedom of the system.

For infinite wave length, the atoms all oscillate in phase, and we may take

$$A_M = A_m \tag{7.2}$$

This corresponds to a translation of the lattice as a whole without alteration of the distance between particles, and hence the frequency is zero. Another frequency for infinite wave length is obtained if we take the small and large masses moving in opposite directions in such a way that the centers of gravity of the molecules remain at rest. This frequency would be ν_0 if there were no interaction between molecules. The presence of interactions would change this frequency. If the wave length is decreased, the lower branch of the ν vs. a curve will rise. This branch is just what would be obtained if we took each molecule to be a single particle. The upper branch will increase or decrease from its frequency at $a = 0$, depending on the relative values of the constants involved. Figure 7.2 shows the frequency curves. The limit to the frequency of the upper branch is ν'_0 for $a = 0$. Either, but not both, of the two upper branches shown may occur. Figure 3.2 (Vincent) and Fig. 3.9 (Born) represent two typical examples with different upper curves. The size of ν_0 relative to the maximum frequency of the lower branch depends on the constants of the system, as does also the width of the

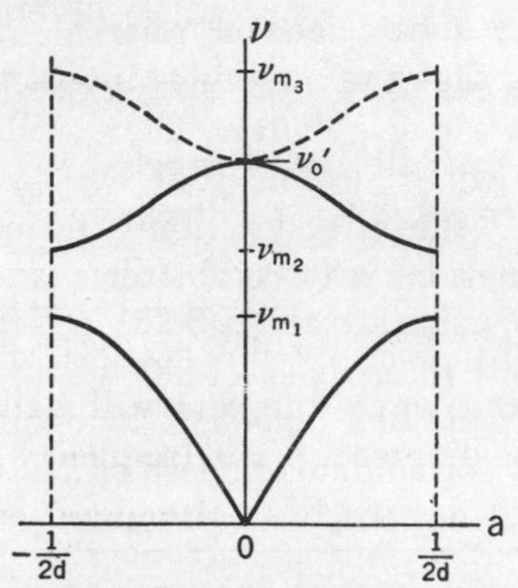

Fig. 7.2.—Frequency ν as a function of $a = 1/\lambda$ for a row of diatomic molecules.

upper branch. Frequencies located in the stopping bands may be shown to decay exponentially, as in the other models we have discussed. The a corresponding to these frequencies are complex with imaginary part β. β is therefore the attenuation constant for a given frequency. The attenuation curves are shown

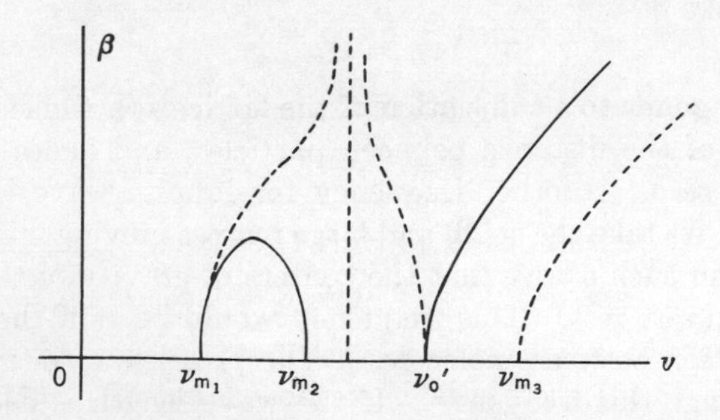

Fig. 7.3.—Attenuation as a function of frequency for a row of diatomic molecules.

in Fig. 7.3. The solid curve is for the solid upper branch and the dashed curve for the dashed upper branch of Fig. 7.2.

In these examples, the following features can be recognized that will be proved in the detailed analysis of later chapters:

1. Periodicity of ν as a function of k or a (4.5).

2. The possibility of a reduction of k or a inside the fundamental interval (4.6).

3. If the elementary cell of the one-dimensional lattice contains a system with N degrees of freedom, there will be N different waves corresponding to each k value, with N different frequencies. Examples with $N = 1, 2, 3$ were given in Secs. 5, 6, and 7.

4. Hence, the number of degrees of freedom inside an elementary cell equals the number of branches in the curve $\nu = F(a)$ and the number of passing bands of the structure (with possible overlapping of the passing bands).

5. Frequencies outside the passing bands are not propagated but decay exponentially along the line.

These are the general properties of one-dimensional periodic structures that will be investigated mathematically in the following sections.

A careful discussion of Vincent's model (p. 12, Fig. 3.3) is recommended as a typical problem, and leads to curves of the type represented on Figs. 7.2 and 7.3 as dashed lines.

CHAPTER III

MATHEMATICAL TREATMENT OF A ONE-DIMENSIONAL LATTICE OF IDENTICAL PARTICLES

8. Equation of Motion of a One-dimensional Lattice of Identical Particles

In this and the following sections we shall derive rigorously the results discussed qualitatively in the first two chapters. We shall assume an infinite lattice of identical particles of mass M. The particles in equilibrium are separated by a distance d along the x axis, and we shall take the oscillations of the particles to be longitudinal. We number the particles by calling the particle at the origin 0, the next particle to the right 1, etc. The displacement of the nth particle is denoted by y_n, so that x_n, the coordinate of particle n, will be given by

$$x_n = nd + y_n \tag{8.1}$$

We shall assume interactions between all particles, and for this we require the expression for the distance between two particles n and $n + m$. This distance is

$$r_{n,n+m} = x_{n+m} - x_n = md + y_{n+m} - y_n \tag{8.2}$$

This expression may be either positive or negative, depending on whether m is positive or negative. The energy of interaction between two particles will be expressed as a potential function that will be assumed to depend only on the distance between the two particles:

$$U(r) = U(|x_{n+m} - x_n|) \tag{8.3}$$

The total potential energy of the lattice will then be given by

$$U = \sum_{n} \sum_{m>0} U(|x_{n+m} - x_n|) \tag{8.4}$$

m must be restricted to positive values so that the interaction between a given pair of particles will be counted only once. We might take the sum over all values of m and divide by two to compensate for counting each pair of particles twice. However, we prefer to restrict m to positive values, since this enables us to drop the absolute-value sign in the argument of U. If we assume that the displacements y_n are small compared with d, we may expand U in a Taylor series. Thus

$$U(x_{n+m} - x_n) = U(md) + (y_{n+m} - y_n)U'(md) + \tfrac{1}{2}(y_{n+m} - y_n)^2U''(md) + \cdots,$$

where $U'(md)$ and $U''(md)$ are the derivatives $\partial U/\partial r$ and $\partial^2 U/\partial r^2$ evaluated at md. Substituting the Taylor expansion in Eq. (8.4), and neglecting powers of $(y_{n+m} - y_n)$ higher than the second, we obtain for the potential energy of the lattice

$$U = \sum_n \sum_{m>0} \left[U(md) + (y_{n+m} - y_n)U'(md) + \frac{1}{2}(y_{n+m} - y_n)^2 U''(md) \right],$$

or

$$U = \text{const.} + \sum_n \sum_{m>0} \left[(y_{n+m} - y_n)U'(md) + \frac{1}{2}(y_{n+m} - y_n)^2 U''(md) \right], \quad (8.5)$$

where the constant is given by

$$\text{Const.} = \sum_n \sum_{m>0} U(md) = n \sum_{m>0} U(md)$$

The force F_p acting on the pth particle is obtained by taking the negative derivative of the potential energy with respect to the displacement of this particle. Before performing the differentiation it should be noted that only two terms from the sum over all values of n will remain, the others dropping out because they do not contain the variable y_p. The two remaining terms will be those for which $n = p$ and $n + m = p$. m is to be positive, so the terms for which $n = p$ will give the force on particle p due to particles to the right, while terms for which $n + m = p$ give the force on particle p due to particles on the left. Therefore,

$$F_p = -\frac{\partial U}{\partial y_p} = -\frac{\partial}{\partial y_p} \sum_n \sum_{m>0} \left[(y_{n+m} - y_n)U'(md) + \frac{1}{2}(y_{n+m} - y_n)^2 U''(md) \right]$$

$$= -\frac{\partial}{\partial y_p} \sum_{m>0} \left[(y_{p+m} - y_p)U'(md) + \frac{1}{2}(y_{p+m} - y_p)^2 U''(md) \right.$$

$$\left. + (y_p - y_{p-m})U'(md) + \frac{1}{2}(y_p - y_{p-m})^2 U''(md) \right]$$

$$= -\sum_{m>0} [-U'(md) - (y_{p+m} - y_p)U''(md)$$

$$+ U'(md) + (y_p - y_{p-m})U''(md)] \quad (8.6a)$$

or, writing U''_m instead of $U''(md)$,

$$F_p = \sum_{m>0} U''_m (y_{p+m} + y_{p-m} - 2y_p) \quad (8.6b)$$

These formulas require some discussion and explanation. In Eq. (8.6*a*), for instance, we find in the first row a term $-U'(md)$ representing the force of atom $(p + m)$ on atom p. In an

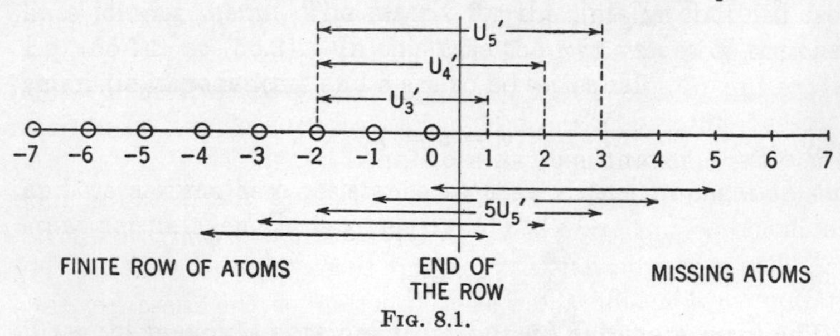

FIG. 8.1.

infinite lattice this term is compensated by an opposite force $+U'(md)$ found in the second row of Eq. (8.6*a*) and representing the force of atom $(p - m)$ on atom p.

The situation is different in a *finite* lattice (Fig. 8.1). Let us assume the row of atoms to extend from $n = -\infty$ to $n = 0$, with all atoms $n = 1, 2, 3, \ldots$ missing, and let us discuss the forces to be added in order to keep the structure undisturbed near the end of the row. External forces that would make up exactly for the forces that the missing atoms would produce on the end of the row must be provided for. For instance, we must add the forces

$$U'_3,\ U'_4,\ U'_5,\ \ldots$$

on atom $n = -2$. This means a very complicated set of forces acting on the last atoms of the row, if the row is to be kept unperturbed with the constant distance d up to the last atom. The *total force* required on all the last atoms of the row is

$$F_t = U'_1 + 2U'_2 + 3U'_3 \cdots = \sum_{m=1}^{\infty} mU'_m \qquad (8.7)$$

since there are m pairs of atoms interacting at distances md across the border. The sketch in Fig. 8.1 visualizes the situation for $m = 5$. In order to obtain a one-dimensional lattice with distance d between neighboring particles, it is *necessary* that the *total force* acting upon the end of the lattice be F_t, but the condition is not sufficient.

If this total force F_t, is differently distributed between the particles at the end of the row, two things may happen:

1. It is possible that a local perturbation of the row is produced near the end, but that at large distances from the end the equidistance d is obtained. This is usually the case, with forces decreasing rapidly when the distance is increased, such as the ones encountered in most physical problems of crystal lattices. If the forces extend only to a distance Ld, the sum in Eq. (8.7) must be taken from $m = 1$ to $m = L$, and the distance upon which the perturbation of the lattice occurs is of the order of Ld.

2. The perturbation may extend throughout the lattice and offer a periodic character as a function of the distance, thus resulting in a sort of superlattice or periodic structure with a distance $D > d$. There may also be different values $d_1, d_2, \ldots$ corresponding to the same total end force F_t.

For instance, a free row of particles is one terminating freely with no external forces added. This means that no perturbation will occur only if all terms $U'_1 = U'_2 = \ldots = U'_L = 0$, and in this case the lattice will keep the interval d up to its end. If all U'_m are not zero, a perturbation appears near the end of the lattice (case 1) or even along the whole lattice (case 2).

This one-dimensional example corresponds to the problem of

surface structure and *surface tension* for solids or liquids. In the three-dimensional problems of physics, the interaction between particles decreases very rapidly for increasing distances, and case 1 above is practically always obtained. The last L atoms of each row build a surface layer Ld deep, which surrounds the solid or liquid structure. The perturbation of the lattice inside this surface layer results in additional forces, the resultant of which is known as surface tension.

The type of perturbation in the lattice and the extent of this perturbation will be discussed later on (see Sec. 10), but we should immediately emphasize the *great complexity of the boundary conditions* for structures including *particles interacting at large distances.* The situation at the boundary cannot be defined by a set of forces acting on the last particles, but the whole distribution of these forces on the different particles at the end of the row must be specified. The usual mathematical statements about forces on the boundary are completely inadequate. A similar situation will be found in connection with problems of wave propagation across the junction of two lattices, or reflection of waves at the boundary of a lattice (see Sec. 24), where a minute description of the type of junction extending all through a boundary layer of order of thickness Ld would be required.

As for Eq. (8.6*b*) and vibrations inside an infinite lattice, the force F_p will be balanced by the inertial force so that the equation of motion for the system will be

$$F_p = M\frac{d^2y_p}{dt^2} = \sum_{m>0} U''_m(y_{p+m} + y_{p-m} - 2y_p) \qquad (8.8)$$

Let us assume a wave solution for Eq. (8.8).

$$y_p = Ae^{2\pi i(\nu t - ax_p)} = Ae^{2\pi i(\nu t - apd)} \qquad a = \frac{1}{\lambda} \qquad (8.9)$$

ν is, of course, the frequency and a the wave number. This gives

$$\begin{aligned} y_{p+m} + y_{p-m} - 2y_p &= Ae^{2\pi i(\nu t - apd)}(e^{-2\pi imda} + e^{2\pi imda} - 2) \\ &= -2y_p(1 - \cos 2\pi amd) = -4y_p \sin^2 \pi amd \end{aligned}$$

Therefore, Eq. (8.9) will be a solution of Eq. (8.8) if the following relation between ν and a is satisfied:

$$\frac{M\omega^2}{4} = M\pi^2\nu^2 = \sum_{m>0} U''_m \sin^2 \pi amd$$

$$= \frac{1}{2}\sum_{m>0} U''_m(1 - \cos 2\pi amd) \qquad (8.10)$$

with $U''_m = U''(md)$. From Eq. (8.10) we may verify at once that ν is a periodic function of a and has period $1/d$, since

$$\nu^2\left(a + \frac{1}{d}\right) = \nu^2(a)$$

and ν must be positive.

9. Rigorous Discussion for the Case of Interactions between Nearest Neighbors Only

If we assume that the interactions among the particles are negligible except for nearest neighbors, Eq. (8.10) reduces to

$$M\pi^2\nu^2 = U'' \sin^2 \pi ad \qquad U'' = U''_1 \qquad (9.1)$$

This is the equation on which the qualitative discussions in the first two chapters were based. We may compute the velocity of propagation of the wave.

$$V = \frac{|\nu|}{a} = \sqrt{\frac{U''}{M}}\,\frac{|\sin \pi ad|}{|\pi a|} = d\sqrt{\frac{U''}{M}}\,\frac{|\sin \pi\, ad|}{|\pi ad|} \qquad (9.2)$$

The velocity for infinite wave length V_∞ is therefore

$$V_\infty = d\sqrt{\frac{U''}{M}} \qquad \lambda \to \infty, \qquad a \to 0 \qquad (9.2a)$$

and Eq. (9.2) checks with Baden-Powell's equation (2.1).

In order to set up the connection between these results and Newton's calculation for the velocity of sound in air, we must define a modulus for our discontinuous system; and this must be done in such a way that in the limit of dense spacing of our particles (*i.e.*, a continuous structure) the modulus will go over into the ordinary extension modulus, defined as tension divided by strain. In our discontinuous structure, we can define the tension between two particles as simply the force between them, and this will be equal, for the pth and $(p + 1)$st particles, to

$$U''(d)(y_{p+1} - y_p)$$

since the resultant force on the pth particle, due to both particles $(p + 1)$ and $(p - 1)$, is

$$U''(d)(y_{p+1} + y_{p-1} - 2y_p)$$

Furthermore, we can define the strain between particles p and $(p + 1)$ as $(y_{p+1} - y_p)/d$. The modulus will, accordingly, be

$$\epsilon = dU''(d) \tag{9.3}$$

and it is evident that in the limiting case of dense spacing all our definitions will go over into the usual definitions.

If we call our modulus ϵ and the average linear density of our system ρ (*i.e.*, $\rho = M/d$), Eq. (9.2*a*) becomes

$$V_\infty = \sqrt{\frac{\epsilon}{\rho}} \tag{9.3a}$$

which is Newton's formula [Eq. (1.1)] with ϵ in place of Newton's bulk modulus ed. We can identify our U'' with Newton's elastic constant e.

For the wave length large compared with d, *i.e.*, if the lattice may be regarded as a continuous medium, the velocity is V_∞ and is independent of the wave length. As the wave length decreases, the velocity decreases and approaches $2V_\infty/\pi$, or 0.635 times V_∞, the value for infinite wave length (see Fig. 2.2). This velocity is reached at the wave length $\lambda = 2d$. For $\lambda = 2d$, there is an ambiguity in the velocity of propagation, as pointed out in an earlier section, since the wave may be propagating in either direction with velocity $0.635V_\infty$ or may be a standing wave. The cutoff frequency ν_m is obtained from Eq. (9.1) by setting $ad = \frac{1}{2}$.

$$\nu_m = \frac{1}{\pi}\sqrt{\frac{U''}{M}} \tag{9.4}$$

For frequencies lower than the limiting frequency ν_m we obtain real solutions for a. For higher frequencies a is complex, since

$$\pi^2\nu^2 M = U'' \sin^2 \pi a d \tag{9.1}$$

If we set

$$\left.\begin{aligned} a = \pm\frac{1}{2d} \pm i\beta, \qquad k = 2\pi a d = \pm\pi \pm i2\pi\beta d \\ \sin \pi a d = \pm \sin\frac{\pi}{2} \cos i\pi\beta d = \pm \cosh \pi\beta d \end{aligned}\right\} \tag{9.5}$$

then

$$\pi^2\nu^2M = U'' \cosh^2 \pi\beta d \tag{9.6}$$

or

$$|\nu| = \frac{1}{\pi}\sqrt{\frac{U''}{M}}\,|\cosh \pi\beta d| \tag{9.7}$$

β is called the *attenuation coefficient*, and in the attenuation curves the magnitude of β is plotted as a function of ν. Curves representing the real and imaginary parts of $a = \alpha + i\beta$ as functions of the frequency ν have been drawn in Fig. 2.7 (Sec. 2). Between 0 and ν_m, a is real, and above ν_m the real part of a keeps a constant value $\pm 1/2d$ while the imaginary part β increases very rapidly. This means that for frequencies above the cutoff ν_m the vibration decays exponentially along the string (β term) while successive atoms oscillate in opposite directions (real part $1/2d$). This is easily seen in Fig. 2.10, which is a reproduction of one of Kelvin's original drawings. It shows that Kelvin had actually grasped all the details of this problem.

10. Discussion of the Distance of Interaction

In the case of interactions between nearest neighbors only, we find that there is a single frequency corresponding to a given wave length and that there is only one wave length larger than $2d$ for each frequency. Now if the interactions extend to the Lth neighbor, *i.e.*, to a distance of Ld, we obtain the following expression relating frequency and wave number [Eq. (8.10)]:

$$\pi^2\nu^2M = \sum_{0<m<L} U''_m \sin^2 \pi amd = \frac{1}{2}\sum_{0<m<L} U''_m(1 - \cos 2\pi amd) \tag{10.1}$$

For very large wave lengths

$$V_\infty{}^2 = \frac{\nu^2}{a^2} = \frac{1}{\pi^2M}\sum_{0<m<L} U''_m \frac{\sin^2 \pi amd}{a^2} = \frac{d^2}{M}\sum_{0<m<L} U''_m m^2 \tag{10.2}$$

Thus V_∞ is still a constant whose value depends on the constants of the system. As the wave length decreases, the velocity of propagation varies. The frequency corresponding to the limiting wave length $\lambda = 2d$, $a = 1/2d$, may be computed.

$$\nu^2 = \frac{1}{\pi^2 M} \sum_{0<m<L} U''_m \sin^2 \frac{\pi m}{2} = \frac{1}{\pi^2 M} \sum_{\substack{0<m<L \\ m \text{ odd}}} U''(md) \qquad (10.3)$$

since

$$\sin \frac{\pi m}{2} = \begin{Bmatrix} 0 & m \text{ even} \\ \pm 1 & m \text{ odd} \end{Bmatrix} \qquad (10.4)$$

so that the even terms in the sum drop out.

Returning to the general equation for ν [Eq. (10.1)], we note that to each value of a there will correspond a single frequency regardless of the extent of the interactions. Now $\cos 2\pi amd$ may be expanded as a polynomial of degree m in $\cos 2\pi ad$. Thus the frequency will be expressed as a polynomial of degree L in $\cos 2\pi ad$. This means that for a given frequency there will be L solutions for $\cos 2\pi ad$ and hence L solutions for a in the interval $-1/2d$ to $+1/2d$. The result of these remarks is that ν is a single-valued function of a, but a is not a single-valued function of ν, as shown in Fig. 10.1. It is not necessary in this case that the maximum value of the frequency appear at the ends of the interval $-1/2d \leqq a \leqq +1/2d$, but the curve must end with a horizontal tangent in any case.

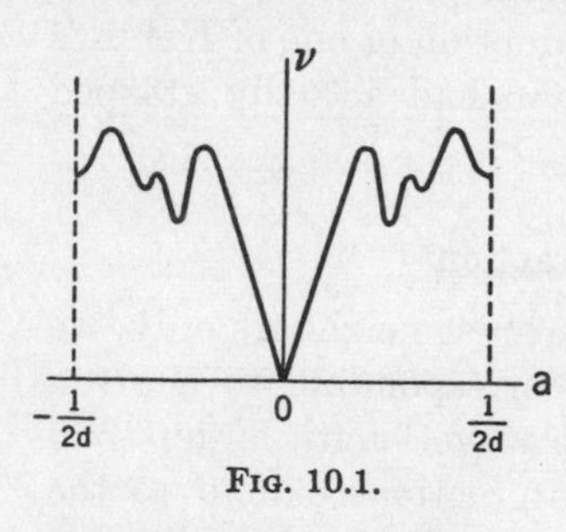

FIG. 10.1.

The L solutions for a for a given frequency need not all be real; some may be imaginary or complex. Such solutions are to be interpreted as meaning that the wave decays exponentially along the lattice. This is of special importance in the case of a finite lattice such as the one already discussed in Sec. 8 with Fig. 8.1. If we assume a sinusoidal motion of frequency ν imposed on the last particle of the lattice, the different waves corresponding to this frequency will be excited in various proportions. Those for which a is real will propagate along the lattice, and those for which a is imaginary or complex will decay exponentially from the point of excitation. If we wish to excite only one of the waves on a semiinfinite row of particles, we must impose on the first L particles the motion characteristic of this special wave. In the case of interactions between nearest neighbors only, the boundary conditions were simple: we had only to specify the motion of the first particle. However, added interactions complicate the procedure, and the boundary conditions must be specified over a length Ld of the lattice.

The problem of the lattice at rest corresponds to the case $\nu = 0$. In drawing the curve in Fig. 10.1, it was assumed that the forces between the particles were such as to give only one real solution a for low ν values. The remaining $(L - 1)$ solutions must then be complex and result in a perturbation of the lattice that would decay exponentially from the border. The whole distance over which these exponential perturbations extend (at the limit $\nu = 0$) represents the thickness of the border in the one-dimensional case or of the surface layer in the three-dimensional problem. This assumption corresponds to case 1 discussed in Sec. 8 after Eq. (8.7). Another possibility would correspond to a curve going down to $\nu = 0$ for some $\pm a_1$ value of a, such as the curve of Fig. 10.2. Under such circumstances a steady periodic perturbation of wave length $\lambda_1 = 1/a_1$ may obtain throughout the lattice and realize a superlattice structure of period

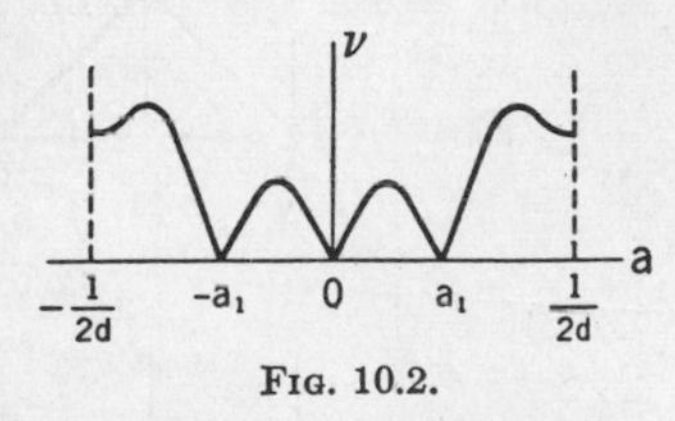

FIG. 10.2.

$$\lambda_1/d = 1/a_1d_1$$

as anticipated in Sec. 8, case 2.

Equation (10.1) gives ν^2 as a finite Fourier expansion in a. We may use Fourier's theorem to obtain the interactions among the various particles if we assume $\nu = F(a)$ is a known function.

$$U''(md) = -4\pi^2 Md \int_{-1/2d}^{1/2d} F^2(a) \, (\cos 2\pi amd) da \quad (10.5)$$

As an example, let us seek the interactions that would give a constant velocity of propagation W throughout the passing band. Then

$$\nu = W|a|, \qquad \nu^2 = F^2(a) = W^2a^2$$

a is, of course, to be taken in the usual interval. Curves corresponding to this problem are shown in Fig. (10.3). Then

$$U''_m = -4\pi^2 MdW^2 \int_{-1/2d}^{1/2d} a^2(\cos 2\pi amd)da$$

$$= (-1)^{m-1} 2M \frac{W^2}{m^2d^2} \quad (10.6)$$

Now U''_m is the second derivative of the interaction energy of the two particles separated by md and appears as a function defined at discrete points at intervals of d along the x axis. We may take the continuous function

$$U''(x) = -2\frac{MW^2}{x^2} \cos \frac{\pi x}{d} \quad (10.7)$$

to represent the discontinuous function. The function (10.7) has the same values as $U''(md)$ at the points where $U''(md)$ is

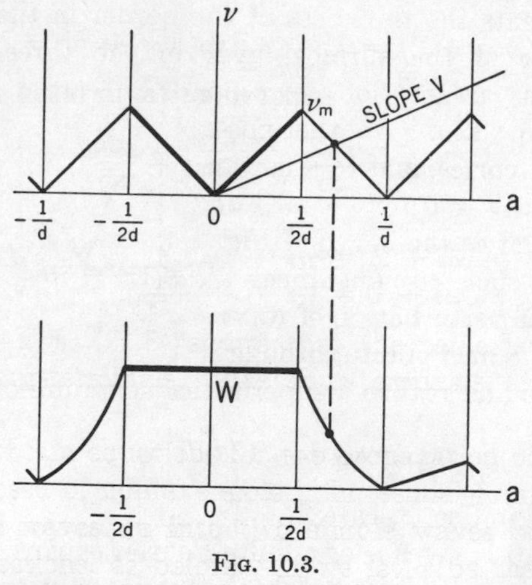

FIG. 10.3.

defined, but it is continuous, and hence we may integrate twice to find the interaction energy. The integration must be done by tables in this case. Once the function $U''(x)$ is known, however, one may construct a discontinuous line with the proper elastic forces between the elements to obtain a low-pass mechanical filter having a constant velocity of propagation for all frequencies in the passing band. The same method may be applied to a high-pass filter or to more complicated filters having one or more passing bands. For this simple example we may easily obtain ω^2, where ω is the angular frequency, 2π times the frequency ν, as a Fourier series.

$$\omega^2 = 4\pi^2\nu^2 = 4 \sum_m \frac{U''_m}{2M} (1 - \cos 2\pi amd)$$

$$= \sum_m \frac{4(-1)^{m-1}W^2}{m^2d^2} (1 - \cos 2\pi amd)$$

$$= \frac{4W^2}{d^2}\Big[(1 - \cos 2\pi ad) - \frac{1}{4}(1 - \cos 4\pi ad) + \frac{1}{9}(1 - \cos 6\pi ad) - \frac{1}{16}(1 - \cos 8\pi ad) + \cdots\Big]$$

$$= \frac{4W^2}{d^2}\Big[\Big(1 - \frac{1}{4} + \frac{1}{9} - \frac{1}{16} + \cdots\Big) - \cos 2\pi ad + \frac{1}{4}\cos 4\pi ad - \frac{1}{9}\cos 6\pi ad + \frac{1}{16}\cos 8\pi ad - \cdots\Big]$$

$$= \frac{4W^2}{d^2}\Big[\frac{\pi^2}{12} - \cos 2\pi ad + \frac{1}{4}\cos 4\pi ad - \frac{1}{9}\cos 6\pi ad + \frac{1}{16}\cos 8\pi ad \cdots\Big] \quad (10.8)$$

since

$$\frac{\pi^2}{12} = 1 - \frac{1}{4} + \frac{1}{9} - \frac{1}{16} + \cdots \quad (10.9)$$

Let us replace $2\pi ad$ by k and recall that $a = \nu/W$ to obtain

$$k^2 = 4\pi^2a^2d^2 = \frac{4\pi^2\nu^2d^2}{W^2}$$

$$= 4\Big(\frac{\pi^2}{12} - \cos k + \frac{1}{4}\cos 2k - \frac{1}{9}\cos 3k + \cdots\Big) \quad (10.10)$$

Thus we have k^2 as a well-known Fourier expansion in k in the interval $-\pi$, $+\pi$.

11. The Low-pass Electric Filter

The electric filter shown in Fig. 11.1 is a low-pass electric filter. The equal self-inductances L alternate with equal capacities C. The capacities shunt out the high frequencies, and the low frequencies are allowed to pass. To obtain the equations of this line, we call Q_n and V_n the charge and potential, respectively, on condenser n, while i_n will be the current flowing between condensers $(n - 1)$ and n. Then

$$L\frac{di_n}{dt} = V_{n-1} - V_n = \frac{Q_{n-1}}{C} - \frac{Q_n}{C}$$

and

$$i_n - i_{n+1} = \frac{dQ_n}{dt} \tag{11.1}$$

since

$$V_n = \frac{Q_n}{C} \tag{11.2}$$

Differentiating Eq. (11.1), we obtain

$$L\frac{d^2 i_n}{dt^2} = \frac{1}{C}\left(\frac{dQ_{n-1}}{dt} - \frac{dQ_n}{dt}\right) = \frac{1}{C}(i_{n-1} + i_{n+1} - 2i_n) \tag{11.3}$$

The solution of Eq. (11.3) gives the flow of current in the line, and from this the potential differences and charges on the condenser plates may be found. Equation (11.3) is identical with

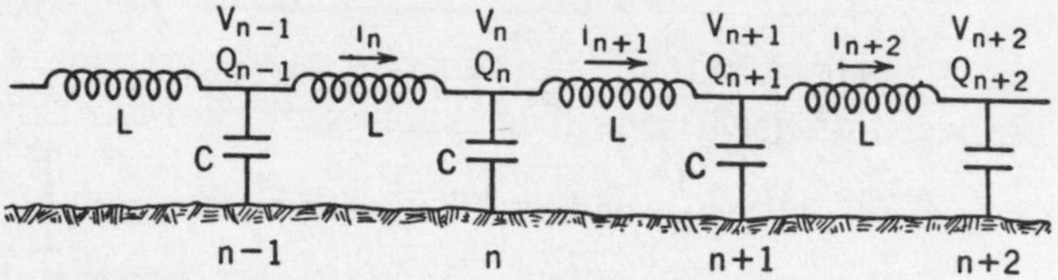

Fig. 11.1.

the equation of motion of a one-dimensional mechanical lattice [Eq. (8.8)] with interaction between nearest neighbors only (Chap. I, Sec. 2, or Chap. III, Sec. 9).

$$M\frac{d^2 y_n}{dt^2} = U''_1(y_{n-1} + y_{n+1} - 2y_n) \tag{11.4}$$

U''/M is replaced by $1/LC$, and y_n is replaced by i_n. Thus all the results obtained for the low-pass mechanical filter apply automatically. The velocity of propagation for very long waves is $d/\sqrt{LC}$ where d is the distance between condensers; there is a cutoff frequency ν_m, and all frequencies higher than ν_m decay exponentially; ν is a periodic function of the wave number. From Eq. (9.4) we may compute the cutoff frequency.

$$\nu_m = \frac{1}{\pi\sqrt{LC}} \tag{11.5}$$

The low-pass electric filter shown in Fig. 11.1, to which Eq. (11.3) applies, contains no resistance. Introduction of resistance changes the properties of the line slightly. There will be a slight attenuation of frequencies in the passing band due to energy losses in the resistance, and the cutoff frequency will be less abrupt; *i.e.*, there will be a region of rapidly increasing attenuation for increasing frequency near ν_m. This problem will be discussed in detail in Chap IX. The curves in Fig. 2.7 will be changed into those in Fig. 11.2.

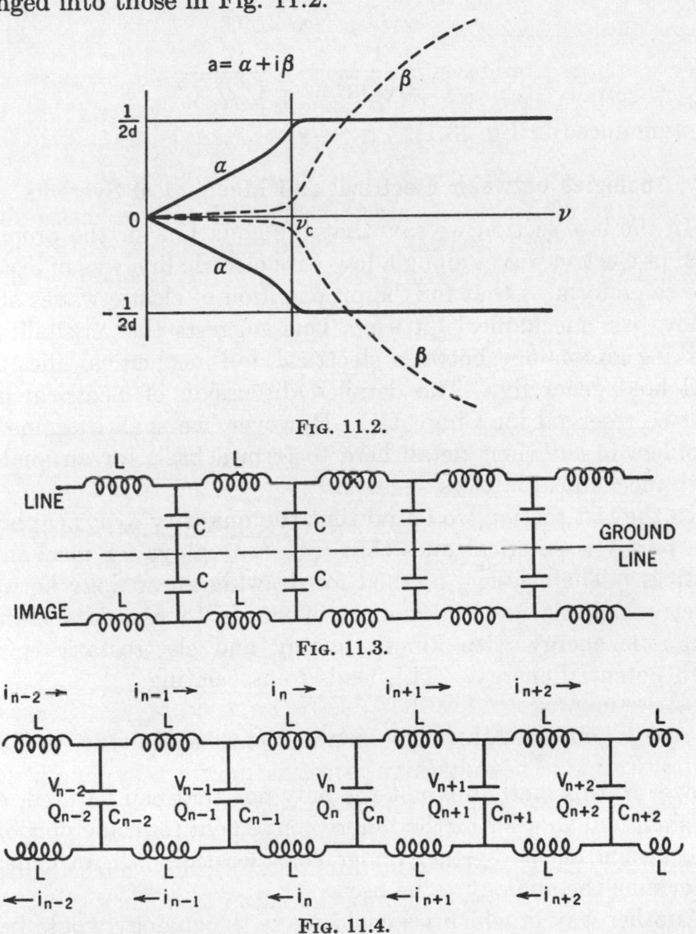

FIG. 11.2.

FIG. 11.3.

FIG. 11.4.

The single-line structure of Fig. 11.1 is equivalent to a double line (Fig. 11.3) constructed from the original line of Fig. 11.1 and its image. This can be simplified in the scheme of Fig. 11.4 with the same L values as in the single line but with capacities $\frac{1}{2}C$.

$$L' = L, \qquad C' = \frac{C}{2} \tag{11.6}$$

Hence, the double line of Fig. 11.4 has exactly the same properties as the single line, with the values

$$V_\infty = \frac{d}{\sqrt{LC}} = \frac{d}{\sqrt{2L'C'}} \tag{11.7}$$

$$\nu_m = \frac{1}{\pi\sqrt{LC}} = \frac{1}{\pi\sqrt{2L'C'}}$$

as announced in Eq. (3.1).

12. Analogies between Electrical and Mechanical Systems

In the last section we saw that the equation for the propagation of electric waves along a low-pass electric line was of exactly the same form as that for the propagation of elastic waves along a low-pass mechanical lattice. This suggests the possibility of making an analogy between electrical and mechanical lines that will hold generally. The detailed discussion of electrical lines will be reserved for Chap. IX. However, we shall examine the problem in sufficient detail here to form a basis for an analogy with mechanical lattices.

In the last section we found that the quantity $\sqrt{1/LC}$ played the part for electrical lines that $\sqrt{U''/M}$ plays for mechanical lattices. The classical method for drawing an analogy between electromagnetic and mechanical effects is to associate electromagnetic energy with kinetic energy and electrostatic energy with potential energy. This leads to associating

$$\frac{1}{C} \text{ with } U'' \qquad \text{and} \qquad L \text{ with } M \tag{12.1}$$

However, this method is not the only one that can be used, and we shall find another method more convenient for some purposes. The design of the system under consideration will, in general, determine the analogy to be used.

Another way in which we could make the analogy would be to take

$$U''_p \sim \frac{1}{L_p} \qquad \text{and} \qquad M \sim C \tag{12.2}$$

For instance, this is the proper analogy to use if we wish to construct an electrical line with the same propagation properties as a lattice with equally spaced particles of equal mass and interactions between all particles. This can best be shown by constructing such a line according to Eq. (12.2) and verifying that the line equations of the two systems are exactly the same. The line is shown in Fig. 12.1. Each condenser has capacity C and is connected to its nearest neighbors through an inductance L_1. The condensers are connected to next nearest neighbors by inductances L_2 and to the pth neighbors by inductances L_p. Only L_1 and L_2 are shown in the diagram in order not to complicate it too much. The condensers are numbered as before. The current flowing through L_1 will be $i_{n-1,n}$, $i_{n,n+1}$, $i_{n+1,n+2}$, and, in general, that flowing through L_p will be $i_{n-p,n}$, $i_{n-p+1,n+1}$, . . . ,

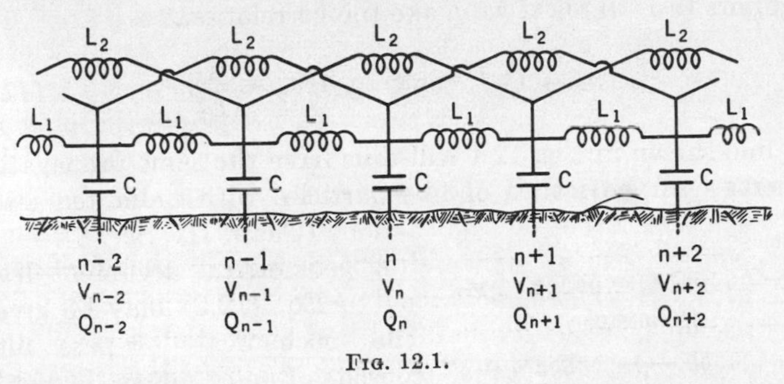

FIG. 12.1.

$i_{n-1,n+p-1}$, $i_{n,n+p}$. The second subscript on the current indicates the condenser into which the current flows, and the first subscript indicates the condenser from which the current started. The charge Q_n on condenser n will be given by

$$\begin{aligned}\frac{dQ_n}{dt} &= i_{n-p,n} + i_{n-p+1,n} + \cdots + i_{n-1,n} \\ &\qquad - (i_{n,n+1} + i_{n,n+2} + \cdots + i_{n,n+p}) \\ &= \sum_p (i_{n-p,n} - i_{n,n+p})\end{aligned} \tag{12.3}$$

We have the following equations for the current in the various branches of the circuit denoted by L_p, if we take the potential of condenser n to be V_n:

$$\left.\begin{aligned}L_1 \frac{d}{dt} i_{n-1,n} &= V_{n-1} - V_n = \frac{Q_{n-1} - Q_n}{C} \\ L_2 \frac{d}{dt} i_{n-2,n} &= V_{n-2} - V_n = \frac{Q_{n-2} - Q_n}{C} \\ L_p \frac{d}{dt} i_{n-p,n} &= V_{n-p} - V_n = \frac{Q_{n-p} - Q_n}{C}\end{aligned}\right\} \tag{12.4}$$

Differentiating Eq. (12.3) and combining with Eq. (12.4), we obtain

$$C\frac{d^2Q_n}{dt^2} = C\sum_p\left(\frac{di_{n-p,n}}{dt} - \frac{di_{n,n+p}}{dt}\right) = \sum_p \frac{Q_{n-p} + Q_{n+p} - 2Q_n}{L_p} \quad (12.5)$$

Equation (12.5) is indeed identical with that for a row of particles, each having mass M, with interactions allowed among all neighbors [Eq. (8.8)], if we make the correlation.

$$M \sim C \quad \text{and} \quad U''_p \sim \frac{1}{L_p} \quad (12.2)$$

The line shown in Fig. 12.1 will thus have the same propagation properties as the lattice of like particles with unlimited interactions (Chap. III, Sec. 8).

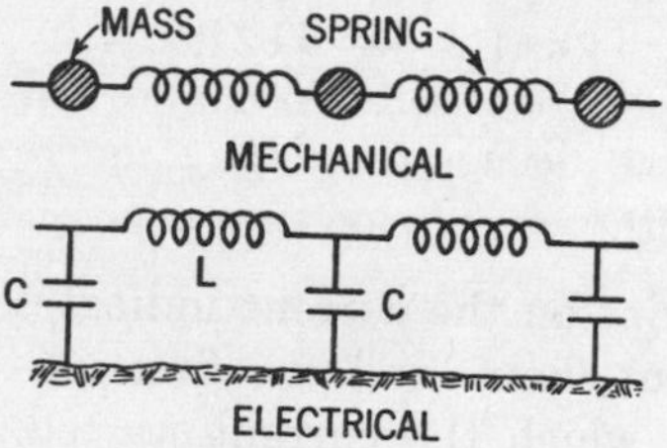

FIG. 12.2.

A geometrical argument leading to Eq. (12.2) may be given. The mechanical low-pass filter consists of point masses joined by elastic elements that we might visualize as springs. The elastic elements (Fig. 12.2) each have two ends, one connected to one mass and one to another mass, while the masses are represented by single points. An electric line having all its condensers shunting the high frequencies may be regarded as a single line with the condensers connected between the line and ground at regular intervals. Then the inductances appear as having two ends connected to different condensers, and the condensers are essentially points in the structure. Another way of looking at the problem is to regard the elastic forces as coupling forces in the lattice and the inductances as coupling forces in the electric line, while the masses and condensers are thought of as supplying inertial forces to their respective systems.

In the case of a high-pass filter, the electric circuit would have inductances leading to ground with condensers incorporated in the line and separating the inductances. In this case the inductances would have to be regarded as the points of the system and the condensers as the parts having two ends, so that the classical analogy [Eq. (12.1)] would again hold. For a band-pass filter with a low-pass band and higher bands in addition, the inductances would have to be shunted by condensers that would be regarded as masses, since one plate of each condenser could still be taken as grounded. However, a closer analysis of the system would be necessary to decide which analogy to use, since there might be condensers elsewhere in the circuit.

There is a limit to which these analogies may be carried. It is not possible, for instance, to construct an electrical line by Eq. (12.5), giving an arbitrary relation between a and ν, as it is for a mechanical lattice (discussed in Sec. 10). The reason is that it is sometimes necessary to allow U''_p to take on negative values. This is easy to realize mechanically, but it would not be possible to obtain a negative self-inductance for the analogous electrical line.

The electrical problem offers different possibilities, if mutual inductances between the coils are used. This was first discussed by G. W. Pierce and carefully investigated by L. Brillouin (Proc. of a Symposium on Large-Scale Digital Calculating Machinery, Harvard Univ. Press, 1948, p. 110) with a discussion of the possibility of obtaining a constant velocity of propagation, as plotted on Fig. 10.3.

CHAPTER IV

MATHEMATICAL TREATMENT OF MORE COMPLICATED ONE-DIMENSIONAL LATTICES

13. Equations of Motion for the One-dimensional NaCl Lattice

The one-dimensional NaCl lattice is a special case of the one-dimensional diatomic lattice that was discussed qualitatively in Secs. 3 and 7. The general lattice is shown in Fig. 13.1. There are two masses M_1 and M_2 alternating. A given mass M_1 will have its right-hand neighbor a distance d_1 away and its left-hand

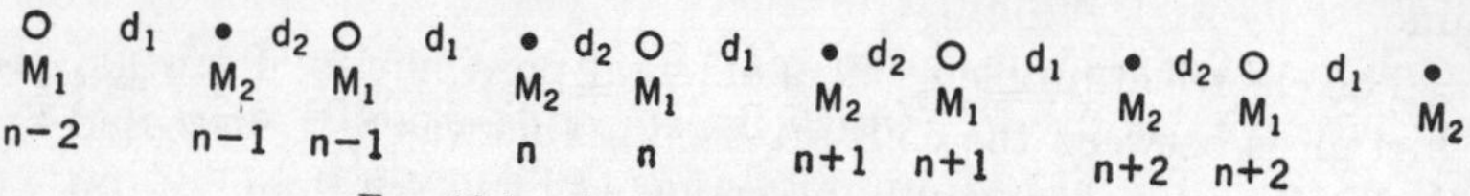

○ d_1 • d_2 ○ d_1 • d_2 ○ d_1 • d_2 ○ d_1 • d_2 ○ d_1 •
M_1 M_2 M_1 M_2 M_1 M_2 M_1 M_2 M_1 M_2
$n-2$ $n-1$ $n-1$ n n $n+1$ $n+1$ $n+2$ $n+2$

FIG. 13.1.—A row of diatomic molecules.

neighbor a distance d_2 on the other side. The period of the lattice is then

$$d = d_1 + d_2 \tag{13.1}$$

In Sec. 7 we assumed one mass, say M_2, much smaller than the other. Then M_1 was supposed to interact with the small mass nearest to it and with each of the two large masses nearest to it. The small masses were supposed to interact only with the nearest large mass. In other words, we allowed molecules as a whole to interact and then included the internal degree of freedom in our discussion.

In this section we shall discuss a slightly different lattice. The two will have the same type of curve, however, since we shall change only the rules of interaction. The *interactions* shall take place *between nearest neighbors only*, without reference to the size of the masses. This implies, of course, that we are dealing with particles that are comparable. If we limit the problem to one in which the distances are equal and the interactions of a particle with its two nearest neighbors are equal, we obtain the one-dimensional analogue of the NaCl lattice used by Born in his theory of specific heats. The lattice is shown in Fig. 13.2. The solid dots represent particles of mass M_2 and the open circles those of mass M_1. The particles can be numbered in two different ways as shown in Figs. 13.1 and 13.2. We use the second one, where we have assigned even numbers to solid dots and odd numbers to the open circles. This means that the equilibrium coordinates of the particles with mass M_1 are $(2n + 1)d/2$, while the equilibrium coordinates of particles with mass M_2 are $2nd/2 = nd$.

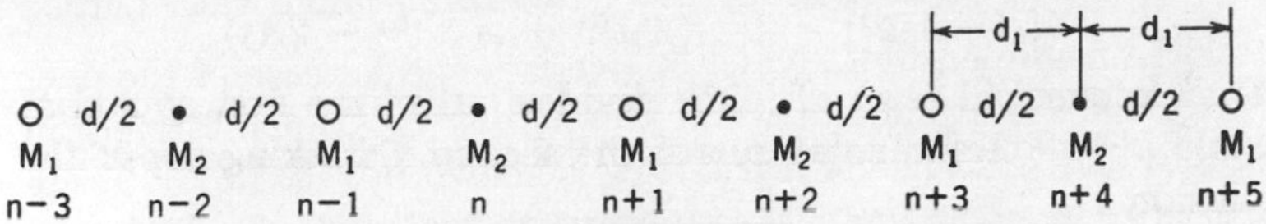

○	d/2	•	d/2	○	d/2	•	d/2	○	d/2	•	d/2	○	d/2	•	d/2	○
M_1		M_2		M_1		M_2		M_1		M_2		M_1		M_2		M_1
n−3		n−2		n−1		n		n+1		n+2		n+3		n+4		n+5

(Above the last three particles: ←d₁→ ←d₁→)

FIG. 13.2.—M. Born's model for sodium chloride.

The equations of motion of the two types of particles are different because of their different masses. If we denote the force on the mth particle by F_m, which is computed exactly as in Sec. 8, Eq. (8.6) or Eq. (11.4), we obtain for the equations of motion

$$\left.\begin{aligned} F_{2n} &= U''_1(y_{2n-1} + y_{2n+1} - 2y_{2n}) = M_2 \frac{d^2 y_{2n}}{dt^2} \\ F_{2n+1} &= U''_1(y_{2n} + y_{2n+2} - 2y_{2n+1}) = M_1 \frac{d^2 y_{2n+1}}{dt^2} \end{aligned}\right\} \quad (13.2)$$

where y_k is the displacement of the kth particle from its equilibrium position. Let us assume a wave solution to these equations of the following form:

$$\left.\begin{aligned} y_{2n} &= A_2 e^{i(\omega t - 2nk_1)} \\ y_{2n+1} &= A_1 e^{i(\omega t - (2n+1)k_1)} \end{aligned}\right\} \quad (13.3)$$

where

$$k = 2\pi a d$$

$$k_1 = 2\pi a \frac{d}{2} = \pi a d = \frac{1}{2} k$$

$$\omega = 2\pi\nu$$

$$a = \frac{1}{\lambda}$$

It should be noted that the first of Eqs. (13.3) represents a wave propagating only through the particles of mass M_2, while the second represents a wave propagating only through those of mass M_1. The wave lengths and frequencies for a given disturbance must be equal. The amplitudes of the two waves, on the other hand, are not necessarily equal. They may differ in magnitude as well as in phase.

In order that Eq. (13.3) may satisfy Eq. (13.2), certain relations must be imposed on the constants in the solution. These relations are obtained by substituting the assumed solution (13.3) in Eq. (13.2). The substitution yields

$$M_2(-A_2\omega^2) = U''_1(A_1e^{ik_1} + A_1e^{-ik_1} - 2A_2)$$
$$M_1(-A_1\omega^2) = U''_1(A_2e^{ik_1} + A_2e^{-ik_1} - 2A_1)$$

The exponential term $e^{i(\omega t - 2nk_1)}$ divides out of the first equation, while $e^{i[\omega t - (2n+1)k_1]}$ divides out of the second. Making use of the relation

$$e^{ik_1} + e^{-ik_1} = 2 \cos k_1$$

and rearranging terms, we obtain two linear equations in A_1 and A_2.

$$\left.\begin{aligned} A_2(M_2\omega^2 - 2U''_1) + 2A_1U''_1 \cos k_1 = 0 \\ A_1(M_1\omega^2 - 2U''_1) + 2A_2U''_1 \cos k_1 = 0 \end{aligned}\right\} \quad (13.4)$$

The condition that these equations give nontrivial solutions for A_1 and A_2 is that the determinant of the coefficients of A_1 and A_2 shall vanish. This condition gives us a relation between ω and k_1 in terms of the constants of the lattice: M_1, M_2, and U''_1. Thus

$$(M_1\omega^2 - 2U''_1)(M_2\omega^2 - 2U''_1) = 4U''^2_1 \cos^2 k_1$$

or, expanding,

$$\omega^4 - 2U''_1\left(\frac{1}{M_1} + \frac{1}{M_2}\right)\omega^2 + 4\frac{U''^2_1}{M_1M_2}\sin^2 k_1 = 0 \quad (13.5)$$

This equation possesses two solutions for ω^2 and hence two solutions for ω, since the frequency is always taken to be positive; *i.e.*, for each value of k_1 there will be two values of the frequency, so that the ω vs. k_1 curve will have two branches.

$$\omega^2 = U''_1\left[\left(\frac{1}{M_1} + \frac{1}{M_2}\right) \pm \sqrt{\left(\frac{1}{M_1} + \frac{1}{M_2}\right)^2 - 4\frac{\sin^2 k_1}{M_1M_2}}\right] \quad (13.6)$$

Substitution of Eq. (13.6) into Eq. (13.4) yields two equations for A_1 and A_2. These two equations are, however, not linearly independent and hence may be used only to determine the ratio A_1/A_2, which is real. The magnitudes and actual phases of the amplitudes for the two waves will depend on the initial conditions.

14. Electrical Analogue of the One-dimensional Diatomic Lattice

To construct the electrical line analogous to the one-dimensional diatomic lattice, we must use the classical method of association [Eq. (12.1)]. This means that since we have two masses in the mechanical model, we must have two inductances in the electrical model. We could generalize the problem treated in the preceding section and allow different coupling between the two masses or, what amounts to the same thing, allow the distance between M_1 and M_2 to be different on the two sides of the particle.

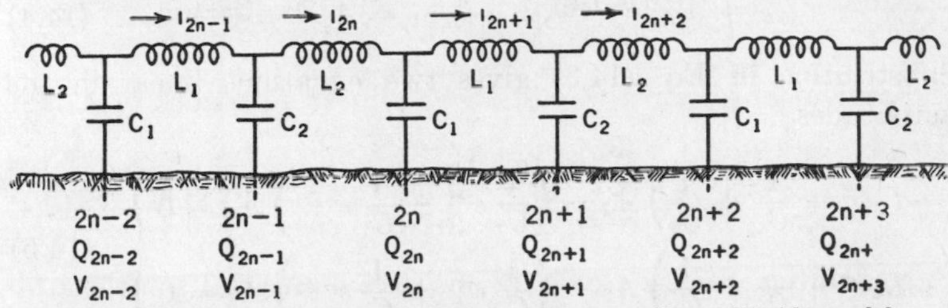

FIG. 14.1.—Electric line corresponding to the sodium-chloride model.

This would give an electric line with condensers C_1 and C_2 alternating. The condenser C_1 to the right of a given condenser C_2 would be joined to it by an inductance L_2, while the condenser C_1 to the left would be joined by an inductance L_1. This arrangement would, in general, be analogous to the mechanical model described in Sec. 7.

The electric line is shown in Fig. 14.1. As before, i_m represents current flowing from condenser $(m - 1)$ to condenser m as in the case of Fig. 11.3. The fundamental equations are

$$i_{2n} - i_{2n+1} = \frac{dQ_{2n}}{dt}; \qquad i_{2n+1} - i_{2n+2} = \frac{dQ_{2n+1}}{dt} \tag{14.1}$$

$$\left.\begin{aligned} L_1 \frac{di_{2n+1}}{dt} &= V_{2n} - V_{2n+1} = \frac{Q_{2n}}{C_1} - \frac{Q_{2n+1}}{C_2} \\ L_2 \frac{di_{2n}}{dt} &= V_{2n-1} - V_{2n} = \frac{Q_{2n-1}}{C_2} - \frac{Q_{2n}}{C_1} \end{aligned}\right\} \tag{14.2}$$

Differentiating Eq. (14.2) and combining with Eq. (14.1) will yield

$$\left.\begin{aligned} L_1 \frac{d^2 i_{2n+1}}{dt^2} &= \frac{i_{2n} - i_{2n+1}}{C_1} - \frac{i_{2n+1} - i_{2n+2}}{C_2} \\ L_2 \frac{d^2 i_{2n}}{dt^2} &= \frac{i_{2n-1} - i_{2n}}{C_2} - \frac{i_{2n} - i_{2n+1}}{C_1} \end{aligned}\right\} \qquad (14.3)$$

These two equations would be identical with Eq. (13.2) for the diatomic lattice treated in the last section if $C_1 = C_2$ and we replaced capacitance by the elastic constant and inductance by mass.

The solution of Eq. (14.3) is carried out in exactly the same way as that of Eq. (13.2). We assume wave solutions for i_{2n} and i_{2n+1} with the same frequency and wave number but with different amplitudes, as in Eq. (13.3).

$$i_{2n} = A_2 e^{i(\omega t - 2nk_1)}, \qquad i_{2n+1} = A_1 e^{i[\omega t - (2n+1)k_1]} \qquad (14.4)$$

Substitution in Eq. (14.3) gives two equations linear in the amplitudes

$$\left.\begin{aligned} \left(-L_1\omega^2 + \frac{1}{C_1} + \frac{1}{C_2}\right) A_1 - \left(\frac{1}{C_1} e^{ik_1} + \frac{1}{C_2} e^{-ik_1}\right) A_2 = 0 \\ \left(-L_2\omega^2 + \frac{1}{C_1} + \frac{1}{C_2}\right) A_2 - \left(\frac{1}{C_2} e^{ik_1} + \frac{1}{C_1} e^{-ik_1}\right) A_1 = 0 \end{aligned}\right\} \qquad (14.5)$$

These simultaneous linear equations in A_1 and A_2 have a nontrivial solution if their determinant vanishes.

$$\left(-L_1\omega^2 + \frac{1}{C_1} + \frac{1}{C_2}\right)\left(-L_2\omega^2 + \frac{1}{C_1} + \frac{1}{C_2}\right) \\ - \left(\frac{1}{C_1} e^{ik_1} + \frac{1}{C_2} e^{-ik_1}\right)\left(\frac{1}{C_2} e^{ik_1} + \frac{1}{C_1} e^{-ik_1}\right) = 0 \qquad (14.6)$$

which reduces to

$$\omega^4 - \omega^2 \left(\frac{1}{L_1} + \frac{1}{L_2}\right)\left(\frac{1}{C_1} + \frac{1}{C_2}\right) + 4 \frac{\sin^2 k_1}{L_1 L_2 C_1 C_2} = 0 \qquad (14.7)$$

the solution of which is

$$\omega^2 = \frac{1}{2}\left(\frac{1}{L_1} + \frac{1}{L_2}\right)\left(\frac{1}{C_1} + \frac{1}{C_2}\right) \\ \pm \sqrt{\frac{1}{4}\left(\frac{1}{L_1} + \frac{1}{L_2}\right)^2 \left(\frac{1}{C_1} + \frac{1}{C_2}\right)^2 - \frac{4 \sin^2 k_1}{L_1 L_2 C_1 C_2}} \qquad (14.8)$$

This reduces to the expression (13.6) obtained for the mechanical case if $L_1 = M_2$, $L_2 = M_1$, and $1/U''_1 = C_1 = C_2$. There will be two branches to the ω vs. k_1 curve whether $L_1 \neq L_2$ or not, but taking $C_1 \neq C_2$ would distort the shape of the curves.

This problem was discussed by electrical engineers[1] who did not notice the similarity with the one-dimensional NaCl lattice discussed by Born. The problem originated from an attempt to join an aerial telephonic line with a city cable, as shown in

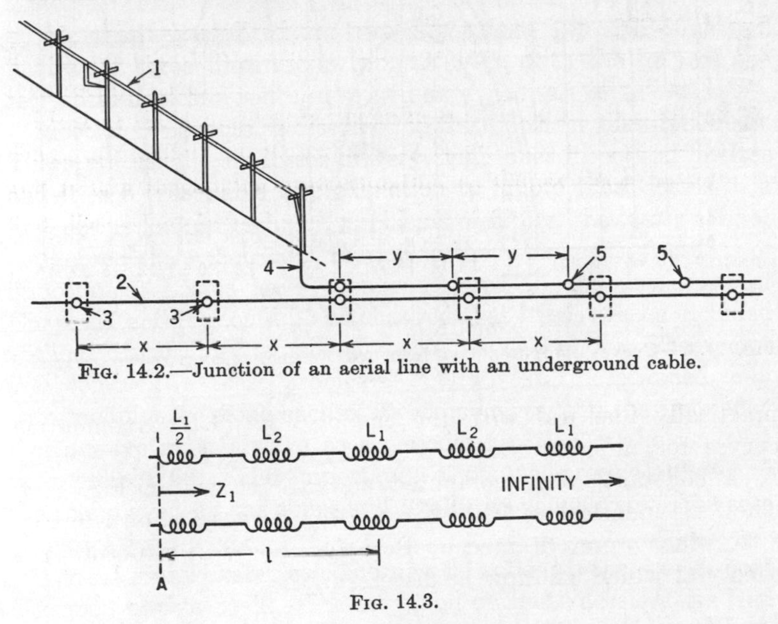

FIG. 14.2.—Junction of an aerial line with an underground cable.

FIG. 14.3.

Fig. 14.2. In order to obtain a correct junction at 4, where the line is connected with the cable, it would be necessary to load the cable with equal coils at a distance $y, y, \ldots$. This results from two conditions that must be satisfied in order to match the line and the cable at their junction: (1) to have the same passing bands, and (2) to have the same characteristic impedances (see Chap. V). The difficulty was that the underground city cable was already built to receive its loading coils at given distances $x, x, \ldots$. The solution proposed consists in using alternately two types of coils L_1 and L_2 (Fig. 14.3), resulting in a structure

[1] FRENCH, N. R., U.S. patent 1,741,926, Dec. 31, 1929; S. P. MEAD and N. R. FRENCH, U.S. patent 1,769,959, July 8, 1930.

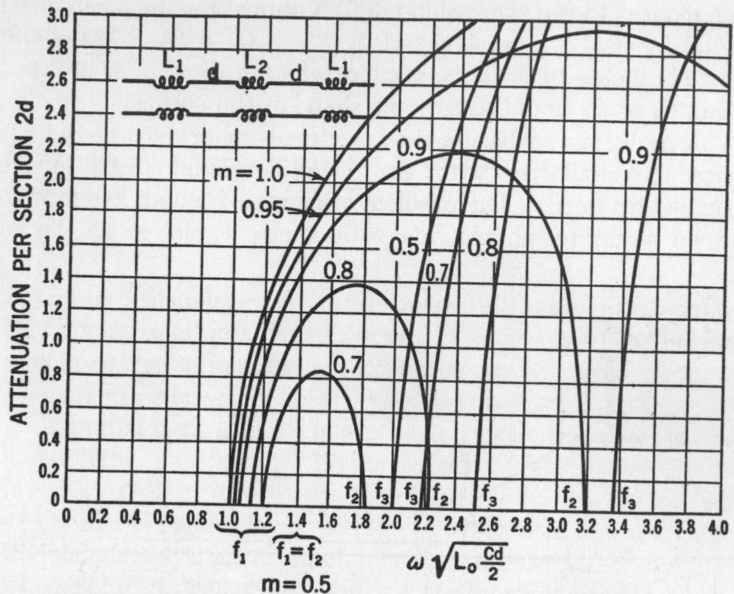

FIG. 14.4.—Curves computed by Mead and French. Compare with Fig. 7.3 or 3.9*b*.

practically identical with the one of Fig. 14.1. Attenuation curves for different values of m [$L_1 = mL_0$, $L_2 = (1 - m)L_0$, L_0 a constant] were computed and are shown in Fig. 14.4. They are identical with the attenuation curves β shown in Fig. 3.9*b*, which were obtained by Born for the NaCl structure, the theory of which will now be discussed.

15. Discussion of the One-dimensional NaCl Lattice

In this section we shall discuss the motion given by the two branches of the ω vs. $k_1 = k/2$ curve with particular attention to the case $k_1 = 0$ and $k_1 = \pm\pi/2$. The relation between ω and k_1 is given by Eq. (13.6).

$$\omega^2 = U''_1 \left[\left(\frac{1}{M_1} + \frac{1}{M_2} \right) \pm \sqrt{\left(\frac{1}{M_1} + \frac{1}{M_2} \right)^2 - \frac{4 \sin^2 k_1}{M_1 M_2}} \right] \quad (13.6)$$

or, rearranging terms,

$$\omega^2 = \frac{U''_1}{M_1 M_2} (M_1 + M_2 \pm \sqrt{M_1^2 + M_2^2 + 2M_1M_2 \cos 2k_1}) \quad (15.1)$$

Equation (15.1) is completely symmetrical in M_1 and M_2, and we may therefore assume M_1 the larger of the two masses without loss of generality.

$$M_1 > M_2$$

The ratio of the amplitudes of the waves may be obtained from either of Eqs. (13.4). Both give the same result in terms of k_1. Using the first,

$$\frac{A_1}{A_2} = \frac{2U''_1 - M_2\omega^2}{2U''_1 \cos k_1} \tag{15.2}$$

and, substituting Eq. (15.1) for ω^2, we obtain

$$\frac{A_1}{A_2} = \frac{M_1 - M_2 \mp \sqrt{M_1^2 + M_2^2 + 2M_1M_2 \cos 2k_1}}{2M_1 \cos k_1} \tag{15.3}$$

The minus sign in Eq. (15.3) corresponds to the plus sign in Eq. (15.1) or the upper branch of the ω vs. k_1 curve, while the plus sign of Eq. (15.3) corresponds to the minus sign of Eq. (15.1) or the lower branch. It should be noted that the amplitude ratio is always real; therefore, the waves may have only two phase relations: phase difference zero if $A_1/A_2 > 0$, and phase difference π if $A_1/A_2 < 0$. This is typical of a system without any resistance and with no damping.

For large wave lengths λ, $k_1 \to 0$ as does k. For this case we may set

$$\cos 2k_1 \approx 1 - 2k_1^2 = 1 - \tfrac{1}{2}k^2 \approx \cos k$$

where

$$k_1 = 2\pi a d_1 = \pi a d = \tfrac{1}{2}k$$

and the radical in Eq. (15.1) becomes

$$\begin{aligned}\sqrt{M_1^2 + M_2^2 + 2M_1M_2\left(1 - \frac{k^2}{2}\right)} &= (M_1 + M_2)\sqrt{1 - \frac{k^2M_1M_2}{(M_1 + M_2)^2}} \\ &\approx (M_1 + M_2)\left(1 - \frac{1}{2}\frac{k^2M_1M_2}{(M_1 + M_2)^2}\right)\end{aligned} \tag{15.4}$$

and Eq. (15.1) reduces to

$$\left.\begin{aligned}\omega_-^2 &= \frac{k^2U''_1}{2(M_1 + M_2)} && \text{lower branch} \\ \omega_+^2 &= 2U''_1\left[\frac{1}{M_1} + \frac{1}{M_2} - \frac{k^2}{4(M_1 + M_2)}\right] && \text{upper branch}\end{aligned}\right\} \tag{15.5}$$

The subscripts + and − denote the sign used before the radical. Thus ω_- is linear in k near the origin as in the case of like particles; ω_+ has a maximum at the origin and decreases parabolically as $|k|$ increases.

To interpret properly the meaning of a second frequency for infinite wave length, we must compute the amplitude ratio for small k_1. Substitution of Eq. (15.4) into Eq. (15.3) yields the following relations for small k (powers of k higher than the second are neglected):

$$\left.\begin{aligned} \left(\frac{A_1}{A_2}\right)_+ &= 1 + \frac{k^2}{8}\frac{M_1 - M_2}{M_1 + M_2} & \text{lower branch} \\ \left(\frac{A_1}{A_2}\right)_- &= -\frac{M_2}{M_1}\left(1 - \frac{k^2}{8}\frac{M_1 - M_2}{M_1 + M_2}\right) & \text{upper branch} \end{aligned}\right\} \qquad (15.6)$$

Thus the lower branch increases parabolically at the origin as $|k|$ increases from zero. At $k = 0$

$$\left(\frac{A_1}{A_2}\right)_+ = 1, \qquad \left(\frac{A_1}{A_2}\right)_- = -\frac{M_2}{M_1}; \qquad |k| << 1 \qquad (15.7)$$

The waves corresponding to the lower branch have equal amplitudes and phase difference zero; thus all the particles are displaced by the same amount and in the same direction. The wave length of each of the waves is infinite, and the lattice is displaced as a whole. There is thus no restoring force, and the frequency is zero. On the other hand, the waves for the upper branch are exactly out of phase; *i.e.*, the displacement of particles of mass M_1 is opposite to that of the neighboring particles M_2. Evidently the center of mass of two neighboring particles is stationary, but restoring forces enter in so that the frequencies of the waves are no longer zero. The lengths of the waves are still infinite since each wave is regarded as propagating through just one type of particle.

The values for k on the limits of the interval to which k is restricted are $\pm\pi$. The two limits will be symmetrical, and we consider only the case

$$k = \pi - \epsilon = 2k_1 \qquad \epsilon \text{ small}$$

Then

$$\cos k = \cos(\pi - \epsilon) = -\cos\epsilon \approx -1 + \frac{\epsilon^2}{2}$$

and the radical in Eq. (15.1) becomes

$$\sqrt{\cdots} = (M_1 - M_2)\left[1 + \frac{\epsilon^2 M_1 M_2}{2(M_1 - M_2)^2}\right]$$

if $(M_1 - M_2)$ is not too small. Substitution in Eq. (15.1) yields

$$\left.\begin{aligned} \omega_+^2 &= \frac{2U''_1}{M_2} + \frac{U''_1\epsilon^2}{2(M_1 - M_2)} \\ \omega_-^2 &= \frac{2U''_1}{M_1} - \frac{U''_1\,\epsilon^2}{2(M_1 - M_2)} \end{aligned}\right\} \tag{15.8}$$

so that the upper branch increases parabolically from

$$\omega = \sqrt{\frac{2U''_1}{M_2}}$$

while the lower branch decreases parabolically from

$$\omega = \sqrt{\frac{2U''_1}{M_1}}$$

as $|\epsilon|$ increases from zero. It should be noted that $\omega_+ > \omega_-$ at the limits of the interval since $M_1 > M_2$, and between these limiting values of ω we have a stopping band to be discussed later.

The amplitude ratio at the ends of the interval is easily obtained. We have

$$\cos k_1 = \cos\left(\frac{\pi}{2} - \frac{\epsilon}{2}\right) \approx \frac{\epsilon}{2}$$

(since $k = 2k_1$), and therefore from Eq. (15.3)

$$\left(\frac{A_1}{A_2}\right)_- = \frac{M_1 - M_2 - (M_1 - M_2)\left[1 + \epsilon^2\frac{M_1 M_2}{2(M_1 - M_2)^2}\right]}{\epsilon M_1}$$

$$= \frac{-\epsilon M_1 M_2}{2M_1(M_1 - M_2)} \rightarrow 0 \tag{15.9a}$$

$$\left(\frac{A_1}{A_2}\right)_+ = \frac{M_1 - M_2 + (M_1 - M_2)\left[1 + \frac{\epsilon^2 M_1 M_2}{2(M_1 - M_2)^2}\right]}{\epsilon M_1}$$

$$= \frac{2(M_1 - M_2) + \frac{\epsilon^2 M_1 M_2}{2(M_1 - M_2)}}{\epsilon M_1} \rightarrow \infty \tag{15.9b}$$

as $\epsilon \rightarrow 0$. The interpretation of these ratios is not very difficult. We have already seen that for the upper branch $[(A_1/A_2)_-, \omega_+]$

the amplitude ratio is negative and different from zero at and near the origin. Equation (15.9*a*) shows that it is negative near the ends of the interval $|k| \leqq \pi$ and zero at the ends. Then for infinite wave length the particles oscillate in opposite directions, the lighter particles with larger amplitude. As the wave length decreases, the amplitude of the heavy particles decreases, and for the limiting wave length the light particles oscillate while the heavy particles remain at rest.

For the lower branch $[(A_1/A_2)_+, \omega_-]$, on the other hand, the particles start out all in phase and with equal amplitudes for infinite wave length. As the wave length decreases, the amplitude of the light particles decreases, and they remain at rest for

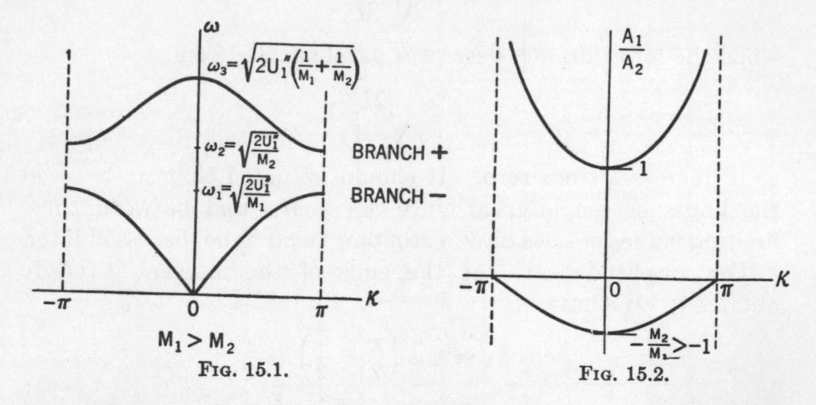

FIG. 15.1. FIG. 15.2.

the limiting wave length while the heavy particles are still oscillating.

These results are summarized in Figs. 15.1 through 15.3. Figure 15.1 shows ω as a function of k for $M_1 > M_2$. Figure 15.2 shows the variation of the amplitude ratio for the two branches, and Fig. 15.3 gives the motion of the particles for the various cases discussed. The arrows in Fig. 15.3 indicate the amplitudes with which the two types of particles oscillate. Figure 15.3 shows clearly that the motions obtained for ν_1 and ν_2 are very similar: for ν_1 the particles M_2 are all at rest, and particles M_1 move in alternate directions. For ν_2, M_1 is at rest and M_2 moving. The forces involved are the same in both cases, since changes in the distances between particles are the same; hence, the frequency ratio must be proportional to the square root of the inverse ratio of the masses.

$$\frac{\nu_1}{\nu_2} = \sqrt{\frac{M_2}{M_1}}$$

as is actually obtained.

The lower branch is frequently called the *acoustical* branch. This name comes from the fact that the frequencies in it are of the same order of magnitude as acoustical or supersonic vibrations. The upper branch is frequently called the *optical* branch, because of the fact that its frequencies are of the order of magnitude of infrared frequencies. Further, if we think of the lattice

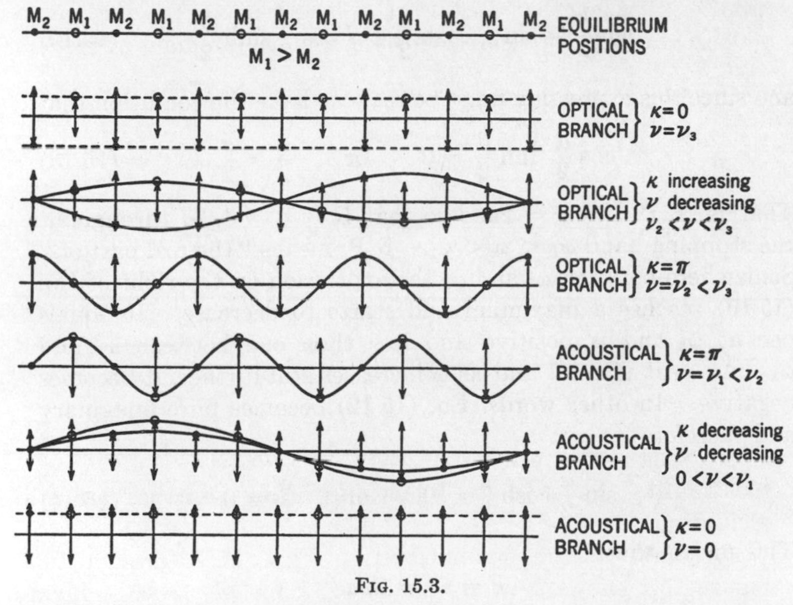

FIG. 15.3.

as being composed of ions having alternate signs, *e.g.*, Na^+ ions alternating with Cl^- ions, an alternating electric field could not excite the acoustical type of wave in which two neighboring particles are in phase, but it could excite the optical type and displace neighboring particles in opposite directions.

So far we have discussed only the passing bands of our lattice. We now consider the stopping bands. These occur for frequencies between ω_1 and ω_2 and for frequencies above ω_3. We return to Eq. (13.5).

$$-\left(\frac{\omega^2}{2U''_1}\right)^2 M_1M_2 + \frac{\omega^2}{2U''_1}(M_1 + M_2) = \sin^2 k_1 = \sin^2 \frac{k}{2}$$

We may rewrite this in the form

$$\omega^2\left(\frac{M_1 + M_2}{2U''_1} - \frac{\omega^2 M_1 M_2}{4U''^2_1}\right) = \sin^2\frac{k}{2} \tag{15.10}$$

We have seen that as ω increases from zero to $\omega_1 = 2\pi\nu_1$, the expression on the right increases from zero to one. If ω increases still further, the expression on the right becomes greater than one, and $k/2$ must become complex. Let

$$k = \alpha + i\beta \tag{15.11}$$

Then

$$\sin\frac{k}{2} = \sin\frac{\alpha}{2}\cosh\frac{\beta}{2} + i\cos\frac{\alpha}{2}\sinh\frac{\beta}{2} \tag{15.12}$$

and since this expression must be real, we have the condition that

$$\cos\frac{\alpha}{2}\sinh\frac{\beta}{2} = 0 \qquad \text{or} \qquad \frac{\alpha}{2} = \frac{\pi}{2} \tag{15.13}$$

That is, R.P. $k = \pi = 2\pi ad$ so that R.P. $a = 1/2d$ throughout the stopping band $\omega_1 < \omega < \omega_2$. R.P. means "the real part of." Somewhere between ω_1 and ω_2 the expression on the right of Eq. (15.10) reaches a maximum and starts to decrease. It equals one at ω_2 and is positive and less than one between ω_2 and ω_3. At ω_3 it is zero, and as ω increases still further, it becomes negative. In other words, Eq. (15.12) becomes pure imaginary and therefore

$$\sin\frac{\alpha}{2}\cosh\frac{\beta}{2} = 0 \qquad \text{or} \qquad \frac{\alpha}{2} = 0 \tag{15.14}$$

This means that

$$k = i\beta = 2\pi ad$$

Hence

$$\text{R.P. } a = 0 \qquad\qquad \omega > \omega_3$$

Since the real part of k is constant throughout both stopping bands and only the imaginary part varies, we have attenuation of the waves. In the first case $\omega_1 < \omega < \omega_2$ at the low frequency end ω_1 of the stopping band, the light particles are at rest and the heavy particles are in motion, neighboring heavy particles being just out of phase; and at the other end ω_2 the heavy particles are at rest with the light particles vibrating out of phase. The motion is attenuated along the lattice (*i.e.*, the amplitude of the vibrations decreases from particle to particle) with an attenuation constant that first increases with the frequency. Somewhere in the stopping band the motion changes from acoustical type to optical type, and as ω increases the attenuation decreases until $\omega = \omega_2$, where it becomes zero.

In the other stopping band $\omega > \omega_3$ the particles are vibrating in opposite phase with the limiting wave length. This motion is attenuated with an attenuation coefficient that increases as ω increases.

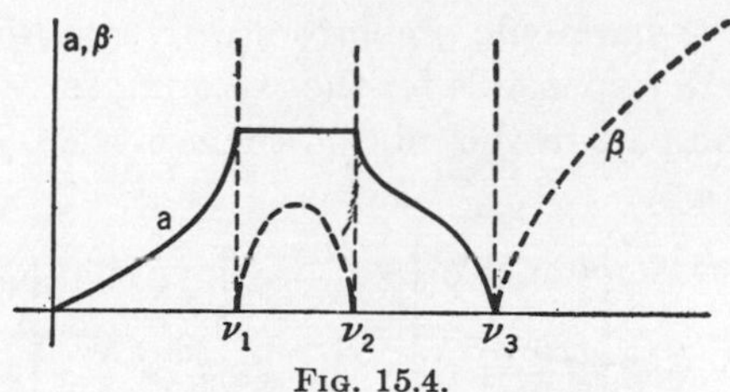

FIG. 15.4.

Curves of wave number a and of attenuation coefficient β against frequency are shown in Fig. 15.4. (Compare with Fig. 14.4.)

16. Transition from a Diatomic to a Monatomic Lattice

The diatomic lattice discussed in the last section is exactly like the monatomic lattice discussed previously except that two masses appear instead of only one; *i.e.*, the distances between neighboring particles are all the same and the interactions are restricted to nearest neighbors. The diatomic lattice may be reduced to a monatomic lattice in three ways:

1. Let $M_2 \to 0$.
2. Let $M_1 \to \infty$.
3. Let $M_1 \to M_2$.

The first two methods leave the period d of the lattice unchanged, while the last halves the period and results in a lattice $d/2 = d_1$. We shall discuss the three methods in the order given above.

1. *Let* $M_2 \to 0$.—In this case $\omega_1 = \sqrt{2U''_1/M_1}$ is unchanged, while $\omega_2 = \sqrt{2U''_1/M_2}$ and $\omega_3 = \sqrt{\omega_1^2 + \omega_2^2}$ both go to infinity. The width of the upper passing band goes to zero; for

$$\omega_3 - \omega_2 = \sqrt{\omega_1^2 + \omega_2^2} - \omega_2 = \omega_2\left(\sqrt{\frac{\omega_1^2}{\omega_2^2} + 1} - 1\right)$$
$$\to \omega_2 \frac{1}{2}\left(\frac{\omega_1}{\omega_2}\right)^2 \to 0 \quad (16.1)$$

Thus the upper band rises and becomes narrower, finally disappearing entirely. The lower branch remains, and we have a low-pass filter with period $d = 2d_1$ left.

2. *Let* $M_1 \to \infty$.—Here $\omega_1 = \sqrt{2U''_1/M_1}$ goes to zero. ω_2 remains unchanged and $\omega_3 \to \omega_2$. Thus in the limiting case there is only a single frequency $\omega_2 = \sqrt{2U''_1/M_2}$, and this frequency does not really propagate. Each of the light particles oscillates separately with frequency ω_2. This corresponds to the case of a row of harmonic oscillators with no interaction. The heavy masses are responsible for the restoring force on the oscillators but take no part in the motion themselves. The amplitude

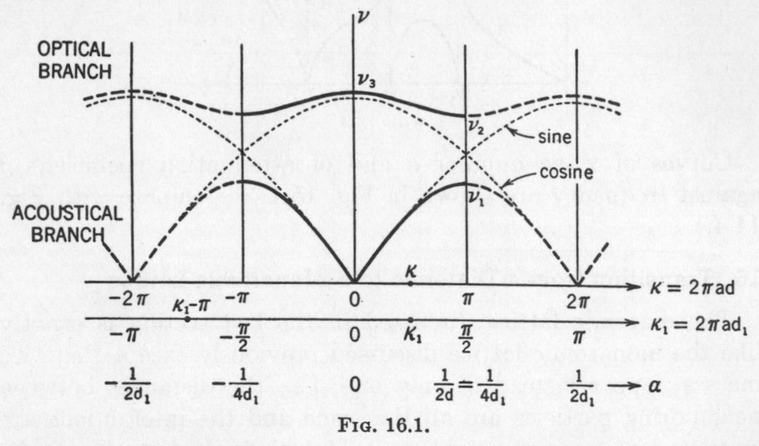

FIG. 16.1.

of the vibration is, of course, restricted to values less than d_1; the light particles must not go through the heavy particles.

Had we allowed interactions between second neighbors as well as nearest neighbors, we would have obtained in the limiting case a lattice of coupled harmonic oscillators that would lead to a band-pass filter. The single frequency present for independent oscillators would spread out into a band; the lower branch present in the diatomic lattice would still be missing.

3. *Let* $M_1 \to M_2$.—This process is considerably more complicated than the previous two because a sudden change in the periodicity of the lattice is involved. The original structure, with $M_1 > M_2$, repeats itself after a distance d, but when $M_1 = M_2$, the period suddenly drops to $d_1 = d/2$. Let us first discuss the relation between frequency and wave number $a = 1/\lambda$. This relation was shown in Fig. 15.1, which must be

understood as representing only one section of a periodic curve, as drawn in Fig. 16.1. The central section (Fig. 15.1) corresponds to $-\pi < k < \pi$ where $k = 2\pi ad$ as usual, and the complete curve is obtained when k takes any arbitrary value.

When $M_1 = M_2$, two changes must be made:

a. The change in periodicity results in a sudden extension of the fundamental interval. For a lattice with period d, the wave number a has period $1/d$, and its fundamental interval extends from $-1/2d$ to $+1/2d$. When the lattice period changes to $d_1 = d/2$, the wave-number period becomes $1/d_1 = 2/d$, and the fundamental interval is $\pm 1/2d_1 = \pm 1/d$.

The following table summarizes the changes in a, k, and k_1:

	Period for				Fundamental interval	
	Lattice	a	k	k_1	k	k_1
$M_1 > M_2$	d	$\frac{1}{d}$	2π	π	$\pm\pi$	$\pm\frac{\pi}{2}$
$M_1 = M_2$	$d_1 = \frac{d}{2}$	$\frac{1}{d_1} = \frac{2}{d}$	4π	2π	$\pm 2\pi$	$\pm\pi$

(16.2)

where $k = 2\pi ad$ and $k_1 = 2\pi ad_1 = k/2$.

b. Another change in the curve is that it must become a single curve as in Fig. 2.4 instead of the double curve of Fig. 15.1. The single curve is drawn as a dotted line in Fig. 16.1, assuming that $M_1, M_2 \rightarrow M = 2\sqrt{M_1M_2/(M_1 + M_2)}$ simultaneously.

All this can be obtained from Eq. (13.6), giving the frequency as a function of k_1. If we take $M_1 = M_2 = M$, the formula reduces to

$$\frac{M\omega_2}{2U''_1} = 1 \pm \sqrt{1 - \sin^2 k_1} = 1 \pm \cos k_1 = \begin{cases} 2\sin^2 \frac{k_1}{2} \\ 2\cos^2 \frac{k_1}{2} \end{cases} \tag{16.3}$$

Selecting the sine function, we obtain

$$\omega = 2\sqrt{\frac{U''_1}{M}}\left|\sin\frac{k_1}{2}\right| \tag{16.4}$$

which is identical with Eq. (9.1) for the monatomic structure (Fig. 2.4). The cosine curve duplicates the results and in its middle part represents the upper curve of Fig. 16.1. The sine and cosine curves intersect at a point that is the common limit of ω_1 and ω_2.

$$\omega_1 \rightarrow \omega_2 \rightarrow \sqrt{\frac{2U''_1}{M}} \qquad M_1 \rightarrow M_2 \rightarrow M$$

and the stopping band disappears.

Another aspect of this transformation refers to the description of the wave and of the motion of the particles of the lattice. Referring to Eq. (13.3),

$$\left.\begin{aligned} y_{2n} &= A_2 e^{i(\omega t - 2nk_1)} \\ y_{2n+1} &= A_1 e^{i[\omega t - (2n+1)k_1]} \end{aligned}\right\} \tag{13.3}$$

we see that the solution for the lattice (with $M_1 > M_2$) is represented as two waves, one propagating along particles of mass M_2 and the other propagating along particles of mass M_1. The wave number k_1 is therefore to be restricted to values between $-\pi/2$ and $+\pi/2$. For the discussion of this section, it will be convenient to *change* our conventions and obtain the solution (13.3) as a *wave propagating through all of the particles.* This means that we must allow k_1 to take on values in the larger interval from $-\pi$ to π. To achieve this we introduce two new quantities C and D, defined by

$$\left.\begin{aligned} A_1 &= C - D = C + De^{i(2n+1)\pi} \\ A_2 &= C + D = C + De^{i(2n\pi)} \end{aligned}\right\} \tag{16.5}$$

From Eq. (16.5) it follows that

$$\frac{D}{C} = \frac{A_2 - A_1}{A_2 + A_1}$$

Equation (13.3) may now be written

$$\begin{aligned} y_{2n} &= Ce^{i(\omega t - 2nk_1)} + De^{i[\omega t - 2n(k_1 - \pi)]} \\ y_{2n+1} &= Ce^{i[\omega t - (2n+1)k_1]} + De^{i[\omega t - (2n+1)(k_1 - \pi)]} \end{aligned}$$

and the sum of the two waves

$$y_m = Ce^{i(\omega t - mk_1)} + De^{i[\omega t - m(k_1 - \pi)]} \tag{16.6}$$

gives a single wave propagating through all (both M_1 and M_2) particles. The two methods of representing the wave are shown in Figs. 16.2*a* to 16.3*b*. Figure 16.2 shows the representation with two waves, one passing through each set of particles. The a part is for the acoustical and the b part for the optical branch. Figure 16.3 shows the k_1 and $k_1 - \pi$ waves and their sums for the acoustical and optical branches in a and b, respectively. It

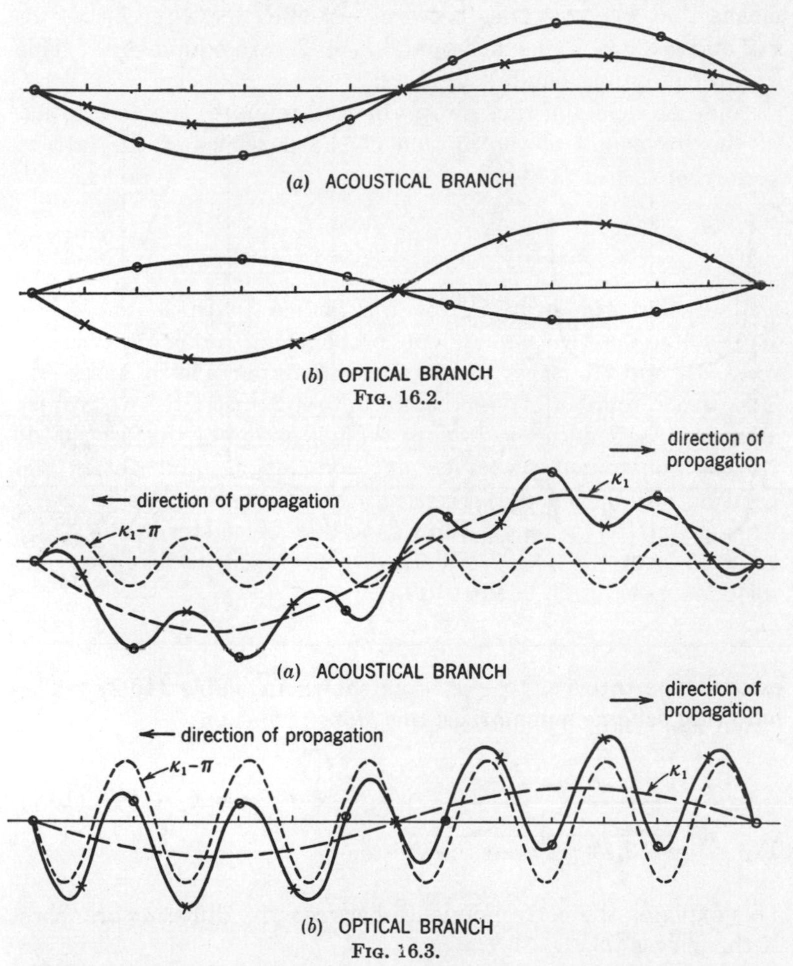

(a) ACOUSTICAL BRANCH

(b) OPTICAL BRANCH

FIG. 16.2.

(a) ACOUSTICAL BRANCH

(b) OPTICAL BRANCH

FIG. 16.3.

should be noted that the k_1 and k_1-π waves propagate in opposite directions, so that one may think of the wave propagating to the right as being partially reflected as it traverses each particle, thus giving rise to a disturbance that consists of a transmitted and a reflected wave.

In order to see clearly how the transition from the diatomic to the monatomic lattice takes place, we must refer to Table (16.2), which shows the interval of variation for k_1 in both cases. The original k_1 was restricted to values between $-\pi/2$ and $\pi/2$, which means that $k_1 - \pi$ varies between $-\pi$ and $-\pi/2$ for $k_1 > 0$ or $\pi/2$ and π for $k_1 < 0$, since k_1 and $k_1 + 2\pi$ are equivalent. This

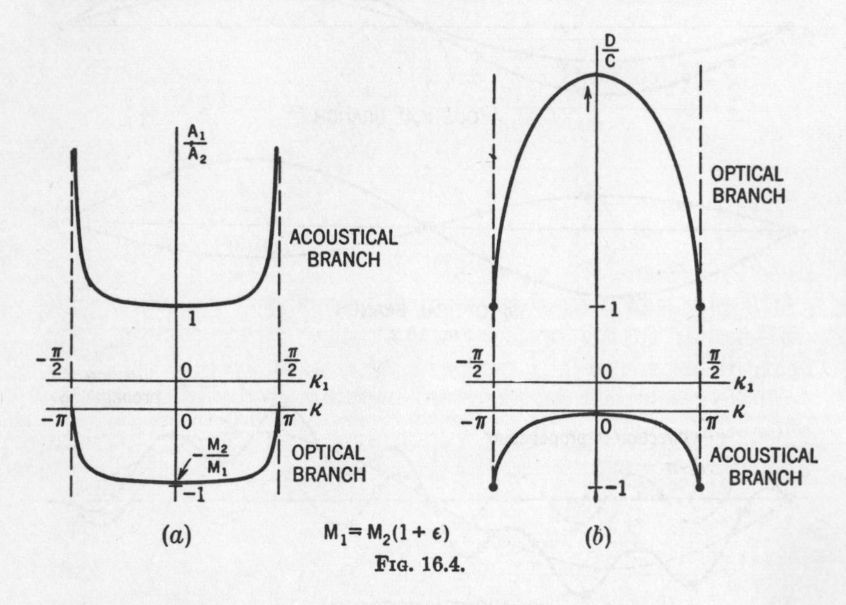

FIG. 16.4.

extends the interval to $-\pi$, π as shown in Table (16.2). The following scheme summarizes this transformation:

k_1: $-\pi/2$ ... 0 ... $\pi/2$

$k_1 - \pi$: $-\pi$ ... $-\pi/2$ ... $\pi/2$ ... π

$$(k_1 - \pi + 2\pi = k_1 + \pi) \qquad (16.7)$$

This explains the correspondence between the different branches of the curves in Fig. 16.1.

We have previously discussed the variation of the ratio A_1/A_2 for the different types of waves [Eq. (15.3) and Fig. 15.2]. These same curves were drawn again in Fig. 16.4a under the assumption of a very small difference between the masses.

$$M_2 = M_1(1 - \epsilon) \qquad \epsilon << 1$$

In this case Eq. (15.3) reduces to

$$\frac{A_1}{A_2} = \frac{1 - \dfrac{M_2}{M_1} \mp \sqrt{1 + \left(\dfrac{M_2}{M_1}\right)^2 + 2\dfrac{M_2}{M_1}\cos 2k_1}}{2\cos k_1}$$

$$= \frac{\epsilon \mp \sqrt{2 + 2(1-\epsilon)\cos 2k_1 - 2\epsilon + \epsilon^2}}{2\cos k_1}$$

$$= \frac{\dfrac{\epsilon}{2} \mp \sqrt{\cos^2 k_1(1-\epsilon) + \left(\dfrac{\epsilon}{2}\right)^2}}{\cos k_1} \approx \frac{\epsilon}{2\cos k_1} \mp \left(1 - \frac{\epsilon}{2}\right) \qquad \cos k_1 >> \epsilon \quad (16.8)$$

$$-\frac{\pi}{2} \leqq k_1 \leqq \frac{\pi}{2}$$

since $\frac{1}{2}(1 + \cos 2k_1) = \cos^2 k_1$.

The plus sign gives the acoustical branch, and the minus sign corresponds to the optical branch. The curves remain very near the horizontals ± 1 except at the ends of the interval.

These results can be expressed in terms of the ratio D/C of our new waves [Eq. (16.5)].

Acoustical branch:

$$\frac{D}{C} = \frac{1 - \dfrac{A_1}{A_2}}{1 + \dfrac{A_1}{A_2}} = \frac{-\dfrac{\epsilon}{2\cos k_1} + \dfrac{\epsilon}{2}}{2 + \dfrac{\epsilon}{2\cos k_1} - \dfrac{\epsilon}{2}} \approx \frac{\epsilon}{4}\left(1 - \frac{1}{\cos k_1}\right) \qquad (16.9)$$

The C wave is dominant with a very small D wave.

Optical branch:

$$\frac{D}{C} = \frac{2 - \dfrac{\epsilon}{2\cos k_1} - \dfrac{\epsilon}{2}}{\dfrac{\epsilon}{2\cos k_1} + \dfrac{\epsilon}{2}} \approx \frac{4}{\epsilon\left(1 + \dfrac{1}{\cos k_1}\right)} \qquad (16.10)$$

The D wave is dominant with a small C wave.

Here we see that in the limit $M_1 = M_2$ the description of the wave motion is much simpler with the C, D waves of Eq. (16.6) than with the A_1, A_2 waves previously used.

Let us allow k_1 to run from $-\pi$ to $+\pi$ as shown in the diagram 16.7. For the *acoustical branch*

$$-\frac{\pi}{2} < k_1 < \frac{\pi}{2} \qquad D \to 0 \qquad C \neq 0 \tag{16.11}$$

while for the *optical branch* we obtain

$$\left.\begin{array}{c} -\pi < k_1 < -\dfrac{\pi}{2} \\ \hline \dfrac{\pi}{2} < k_1 < \pi \end{array}\right\} \qquad C \to 0 \qquad D \neq 0 \tag{16.12}$$

There is only one wave left (either C or D) almost everywhere except in the immediate neighborhood of $k_1 = \pm\pi/2$, which are the branching points where the curves separate in case $M_1 > M_2$ and give place to a stopping band.

The example just discussed is very important, since it represents the first instance of a general type of problem very often

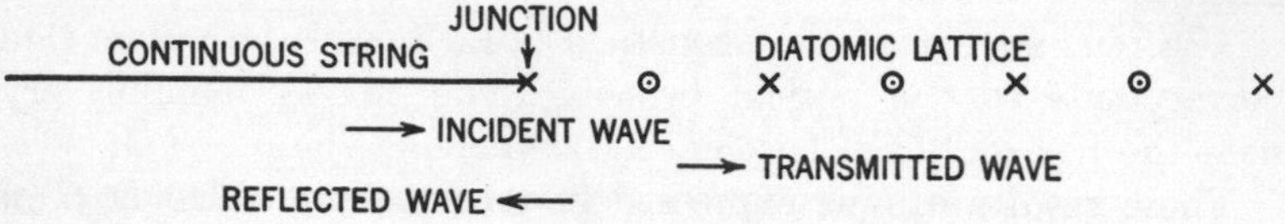

JUNCTION
CONTINUOUS STRING
DIATOMIC LATTICE
INCIDENT WAVE
TRANSMITTED WAVE
REFLECTED WAVE

FIG. 16.5.

encountered on other occasions. Here it was possible to follow the transformation from the unperturbed case $M_1 = M_2 = M$ to the perturbed problem $M_1 \neq M_2$ in all details. This is not always possible, and the method followed in more complicated problems will be to start from the unperturbed C, D plane waves and to make linear combinations of them [as in Eq. (16.6)] before discussing the perturbation near the branching points. Such examples may be found in connection with electromagnetic waves (X rays) or with electronic De Broglie waves in crystals, when the periodic distribution of atoms in the crystal lattice can be treated as a small perturbation.

One more remark should be added to show the *connection* between *passing or stopping bands* and *reflection of waves*. If a continuous line capable of transmitting all frequencies is joined to the diatomic lattice (see Fig. 16.5), the coefficient of reflection at the junction will depend on the frequency incident from the continuous line. If the frequency is in one of the stopping bands of the lattice, total reflection will occur; *i.e.*,

$$R = \text{coefficient of reflection} = 1$$

while for a frequency in a passing band both a reflected and a transmitted wave will be excited. The coefficient of reflection will be less than one, and the actual value will depend on the characteristics of the lattice in this case.

17. The One-dimensional Lattice of Polyatomic Molecules

To treat a lattice of polyatomic molecules, we divide the lattice into cells. A cell contains one period of the lattice; *i.e.*, if we start out with atom 1, then the first cell consists of atom 1 to N, where atom $N + 1$ has the same relation to atom $N + 1 + m$ as atom 1 has to atom $1 + m$. Having defined what we mean by *cell* (in general, the same as molecule, unless the molecule itself possesses a periodic structure that is a period of the lattice), we

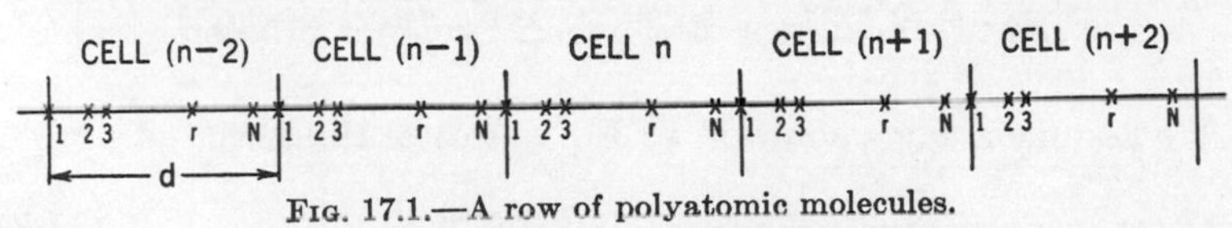

FIG. 17.1.—A row of polyatomic molecules.

change our notation slightly. We number the atoms in a given cell from 1 to N. The cells are also numbered, n being used to denote an arbitrary cell and $n + p$ being the number of the pth cell to the right of cell n. The notation is illustrated in Fig. 17.1. The crosses indicate the equilibrium positions of the atoms, and the vertical lines the positions of the first atom in each cell, *i.e.*, the boundaries of the cells. We take the length of a cell to be d.

We shall assume small displacements of the atoms when a wave propagates along the lattice and also shall assume that all interactions are elastic. We shall not limit the distance at which interactions occur. The force on atom r in cell n due to atom s in cell $n + p$ is therefore

$$f_{n,r;n+p,s} = C_{prs}(y_{n+p,s} - y_{n,r}) \tag{17.1}$$

where C_{prs} is the interaction constant and is independent of n.

It follows that the force on particle s in cell $n + p$ due to particle r in cell n is

$$f_{n+p,s;n,r} = C_{-psr}(y_{n,r} - y_{n+p,s}) \tag{17.2}$$

According to Newton's third law

$$f_{n,r;n+p,s} = -f_{n+p,s;n,r} \tag{17.3}$$

and substituting Eqs. (17.1) and (17.2) into Eq. (17.3), we obtain

$$C_{prs}(y_{n+p,s} - y_{n,r}) = -C_{-psr}(y_{n,r} - y_{n+p,s})$$

or

$$C_{prs} = C_{-psr} \tag{17.4}$$

We take

$$C_{0rr} = 0 \tag{17.5}$$

since the term

$$C_{0rr}(y_{n,r} - y_{n,r}) = 0$$

and does not enter any of the calculations.

The total force acting on particle r in cell n will be given by

$$f_{n,r} = \sum_p \sum_s f_{n,r,n+p,s} = \sum_p \sum_s C_{prs}(y_{n+p,s} - y_{n,r}) \tag{17.6}$$

We assume a wave solution to Eq. (17.6) of the form

$$y_{n,r} = A_r e^{2\pi i(\nu t - ax)} \tag{17.7}$$

A_r is to be complex so as to contain the phase difference of particle r with particle 0, *while x is the distance of the origin of the cell from the origin of the lattice.*

$$x = nd$$

We may thus write Eq. (17.7) in the form

$$y_{n,r} = A_r e^{i(\omega t - kn)} \qquad \left\{ \begin{aligned} \omega &= 2\pi\nu \\ k &= 2\pi ad \end{aligned} \right\} \tag{17.8}$$

$y_{n,r}$ therefore has period $1/d$ in a and 2π in k as in Sec. 4. This means that k may be replaced by $k' = k + 2\pi p$ without affecting the solution. Substitution of Eq. (17.8) into Eq. (17.6) gives

$$\begin{aligned} f_{n,r} &= e^{i(\omega t - kn)} \sum_{p,s} C_{prs}(A_s e^{-ikp} - A_r) \\ &= M_r \frac{d^2 y_{n,r}}{dt^2} = -\omega^2 M_r A_r e^{i(\omega t - kn)} \end{aligned} \tag{17.9}$$

from which we obtain the following relation between ω and k:

$$\sum_s D_{r,s}(k) A_s = -\omega^2 M_r A_r \tag{17.10}$$

where the function $D_{r,s}(k$ is defined by

$$\left.\begin{aligned} D_{r,s}(k) &= \sum_p C_{prs}e^{-ikp} \qquad r \neq s \\ D_{r,r}(k) &= -\sum_{ps} C_{prs} + \sum_p C_{prr}e^{-ikp} \end{aligned}\right\} \tag{7.11}$$

The sum over s is to be taken over all atoms in a given cell and the sum over p is to be taken over all the cells.

The acoustical branch gives $A_r = A_s$ at $k = 0$, and hence

$$\begin{aligned} \omega^2 M_r &= \sum_s D_{r,s}(0) = \sum_{s\neq r} D_{r,s}(0) + D_{r,r}(0) \\ &= \sum_{s\neq r}\sum_p C_{prs} - \sum_{ps} C_{prs} + \sum_p C_{prr} \\ &= \sum_{s\neq r}\sum_p C_{prs} - \sum_{p,s\neq r} C_{prs} = 0 \\ \omega &= 0 \end{aligned}$$

For other values of k we write Eq. (17.10) as

$$\sum_s [D_{r,s}(k) + \omega^2 M_r \delta_{rs}]A_s = 0 \tag{17.12}$$

where δ is the Kronecker δ, defined by

$$\delta_{rs} = \begin{cases} 0 & r \neq s \\ 1 & r = s \end{cases}$$

Equation (17.12) gives N linear homogeneous equations for A_s, and the condition that they be consistent is that the determinant of the coefficients vanish; *i.e.*,

$$|D_{r,s}(k) + \omega^2 M_r \delta_{rs}| = 0 \tag{17.13}$$

Equation (17.13) is an equation of degree N in ω^2, and hence there will be N values of ω^2 for a given k, *i.e.*, there will be N branches in the ω vs. k curve or the ν vs. a curve. One of these branches will be the acoustical branch, and the remaining $(N - 1)$ will be optical branches. ω^2 will be a periodic function of k since $D_{rs}(k)$ is a periodic function of k.

If we let $N \to \infty$, the number of optical branches becomes infinite, since we must have the total number of branches equal to the number of degrees of freedom of the system. The lattice will become a continuous string with some sort of periodic structure. We shall discuss the problem of the continuous periodic string in a later chapter. If the string is continuous and uniform, ω is a linear function of k. Figure 17.2 shows the general appearance of the ω vs. k curves. The dotted curves are ω vs. k for a uniform continuous string.

The transition from the uniform continuous string to the continuous string with periodic structure (a loaded string, for

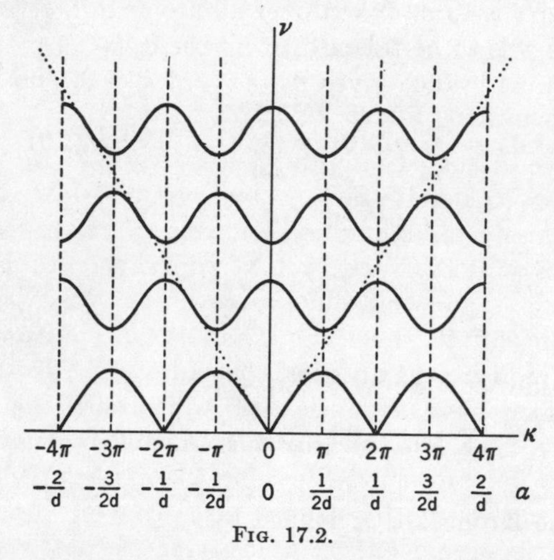

FIG. 17.2.

instance) is one of the problems of periodic perturbation sketched at the end of Sec. 16, and for the discussion of which the example of Sec. 16 will be used as a model. The change from the V-shaped dotted curve in Fig. 17.2 to the wavy curves occurs in a way similar to the change from the single dotted sine curve to the two solid curves in Fig. 16.1.

CHAPTER V

ENERGY VELOCITY, ENERGY FLOW, AND CHARACTERISTIC IMPEDANCE

18. General Discussion; Phase Velocity

So far we have discussed infinite lattices only. If we wish to apply our results to a finite lattice, we must add forces at the ends that will satisfy the boundary conditions. At the left end we must have a source of energy that will supply to the first particle the power that would have come to it if the lattice had extended indefinitely to the left. Then the propagation will depend on the frequency as noted at the end of Sec. 16. On the right end we must have a device that will absorb the energy that would have been absorbed by the omitted portion of the lattice extending indefinitely to the right. To set up the boundary conditions rigorously requires a discussion of the energy density, energy flow, and energy velocity in the lattice. This discussion will be carried on in the next few sections.

The one-dimensional mechanical lattice is an academic rather than a practical problem, and the only important instance of one-dimensional structures is found in electric lines, a discussion of which will be given in detail in the last chapters. It is, however, very useful to know how to set up the boundary conditions for the applications of the theory to two- and three-dimensional lattices. The method developed in this chapter is general and will be extended later to these problems, but it is easier to understand in the one-dimensional case.

The problems discussed are closely connected with the property of the structures of exhibiting *dispersion*. The wave velocity defined in the preceding chapters is known as *phase velocity*, since it is obtained from a comparison of the relative phase of the oscillations of two neighboring atoms. This phase velocity is the one to be used in formulas like

$$\lambda = V\tau, \qquad V = \frac{\nu}{a}, \qquad \nu = \frac{1}{\tau}, \qquad a = \frac{1}{\lambda} \tag{18.1}$$

where τ is the period, ν the frequency, λ the wave length, and a the wave number. A *dispersive medium* is one for which the phase velocity V depends upon the frequency ν of oscillations. Many classical problems of wave propagation do not exhibit any such variation. Maxwell's equations of electromagnetism in vacuum lead to the equations of propagation of light and yield a constant velocity of propagation. Such is also the case for the standard equations for the propagation of sound waves, which result from a number of simplifications practically eliminating any frequency dependence of V. In such cases there is no difficulty in defining the velocity with which energy is transmitted through the medium by the wave motion. This velocity is simply equal to V. When, however, the transmitting medium is dispersive, the definition of energy velocity requires special attention and will be found to differ from phase velocity. This results from the fact that sine waves extending from $-\infty$ to $+\infty$ are the only waves to be transmitted without a change in their shape. Short signals or short impulses are distorted while they travel through the medium, and this distortion makes it difficult to define their average velocity. This is where the concept of *group velocity* comes in. A *group of waves*, or a *wave packet* (in the language of wave mechanics), is a signal of finite length, comprising only a limited number of wave lengths. We shall discuss the properties of such groups and the way in which they propagate through the medium and then compare the average velocity of the group with the energy velocity obtained from other definitions.

19. A Theorem from the Theory of Complex Variables

Following a method very commonly used, complex exponentials were introduced to represent waves or oscillations. For instance, the displacement and velocity of a particle in a wave were written

$$y = Ae^{2\pi i(\nu t - ax)}, \qquad \dot{y} = \frac{dy}{dt} = 2\pi i \nu A e^{2\pi i(\nu t - ax)}$$

respectively. Time derivatives are indicated by dots over the function. The order of the derivative is given by the number of dots.

$$\frac{dy}{dt} = \dot{y}, \qquad \frac{d^2y}{dt^2} = \ddot{y}, \text{ etc.}$$

It must be recalled that such expressions should always be preceded by the sign R.P., meaning that only the *real part* of the quantity is taken into consideration, *viz.*,

$$y = A \cos 2\pi(\nu t - ax), \qquad \dot{y} = -2\pi\nu A \sin 2\pi(\nu t - ax)$$

As long as we were working with equations linear in $y, \dot{y}, \ddot{y}, \ldots$, we could drop the R.P. sign. But this is no longer allowed when double products or powers are encountered, since $y\dot{y}$, for instance, means

$$y\dot{y} = -2\pi\nu A^2 \cos 2\pi(\nu t - ax) \sin 2\pi(\nu t - ax) \neq 2\pi i\nu A^2 e^{4\pi i(\nu t - ax)}$$

This question will now be discussed.

We shall require the time average of the product of the real parts of complex functions on numerous occasions. There is a simple way of doing this by the following equation:

$$\overline{\text{R.P.} f \times \text{R.P.} F} = \tfrac{1}{2}\text{R.P.}\ (fF^*) \tag{19.1}$$

where f and F are complex functions of time of the form

$$f = f_0 e^{i(\omega t - \varphi)}, \qquad F = F_0 e^{i(\omega t - \phi)} \tag{19.2}$$

The star means "complex conjugate of." Note that the time dependence of the two functions is the same.

We now prove that Eq. (19.1) is an identity.

$$\begin{aligned}\overline{\text{R.P.} f \times \text{R.P.} F} &= f_0 F_0\, \overline{\cos(\omega t - \varphi)\cos(\omega t - \phi)} \\ &= f_0 F_0 \frac{1}{\tau}\int_0^\tau \cos(\omega t - \varphi)\cos(\omega t - \phi)\,dt, \end{aligned} \tag{19.3}$$

where τ is the period of f and F and is equal to $2\pi/\omega$. We may expand the integrand in Eq. (19.3) and obtain

$$\begin{aligned}\overline{\text{R.P.} f \times \text{R.P.} F} &= \frac{f_0 F_0}{\tau}\int_0^\tau \cos(\omega t - \varphi)\cos(\omega t - \varphi + \varphi - \phi)\,dt \\ &= \frac{f_0 F_0}{\tau}\int_0^\tau \cos(\omega t - \varphi) \\ &\qquad [\cos(\omega t - \varphi)\cos(\varphi - \phi) - \sin(\omega t - \varphi)\sin(\varphi - \phi)]\,dt\end{aligned}$$

We replace $(\varphi - \phi)$ by ψ in the above so that

$$\overline{\text{R.P.}\, f \times \text{R.P.}\, F} = \frac{f_0 F_0}{\tau} \int_0^\tau$$
$$[\cos\psi \cos^2(\omega t - \varphi) - \sin\psi \sin(\omega t - \varphi)\cos(\omega t - \varphi)]dt$$

The second term in the integrand becomes zero on integration, while the first term gives $\frac{\tau}{2}\cos\psi$. Therefore,

$$\overline{\text{R.P.}\, f \times \text{R.P.}\, F} = \frac{1}{\tau} f_0 F_0 \frac{\tau}{2}\cos\psi = \frac{1}{2} f_0 F_0 \cos\psi = \frac{1}{2}\text{R.P.}\,(fF^*)$$

since

$$fF^* = f_0 F_0 e^{i(\omega t - \varphi)} e^{-i(\omega t - \phi)} = f_0 F_0 e^{i(\phi - \varphi)} = f_0 F_0 e^{-i\psi}$$

which proves the theorem.

20. Energy Density, Energy Flow, and Energy Velocity

First, we discuss the energy density and derive a mathematical expression for it. For the moment we shall confine ourselves to the *monatomic lattice* with *interactions between nearest neighbors only*. The theory of wave propagation in such a medium was discussed in Chap. III, Secs. 8 and 9.

We shall require the following relations, already derived in Eqs. (8.8), (8.10), and (9.2), for the discussion:

$$\left.\begin{aligned} y_n &= A e^{i(\omega t - kn)} \qquad\qquad k = 2\pi a d \\ \omega^2 &= \frac{2U''}{m}(1 - \cos k) = \frac{4U''}{m}\sin^2\frac{k}{2} \\ W &= \text{phase velocity} = \frac{\nu}{a} = \frac{\omega d}{k} = W_\infty \left|\frac{\sin k/2}{k/2}\right| \end{aligned}\right\} \qquad (20.1)$$

We shall temporarily drop the subscript on U''_1.

The average energy density of the lattice will be the sum of the average potential-energy density and the average kinetic-energy density. The average potential-energy density is the average potential energy per cell divided by d, the length of the cell. Thus

$$\overline{E_{\text{pot}}} = \frac{1}{d}\,\text{R.P.}\,\frac{1}{2} U''\, \overline{(y_n - y_{n-1})^2} \qquad (20.2)$$

and since

$$y_n - y_{n-1} = \text{R.P.}\, A e^{i(\omega t - kn)}(1 - e^{ik})$$

it follows that

$$\overline{E_{\text{pot}}} = \frac{U''}{2d}\frac{1}{2}\,\text{R.P.}\,(y_n - y_{n-1})(y_n - y_{n-1})^*$$
$$= \frac{A^2U''}{4d}(1 - e^{ik})(1 - e^{-ik}) = \frac{A^2U''}{4d}(2 - e^{ik} - e^{-ik})$$
$$= \frac{A^2U''}{4d}\,2(1 - \cos k) = \frac{A^2U''}{d}\sin^2\frac{k}{2} \tag{20.3}$$

The average kinetic-energy density is obtained in a similar manner; it is the average kinetic energy per cell divided by d, the length of the cell.

$$\overline{E_{\text{kin}}} = \text{R.P.}\,\frac{1}{d}\frac{1}{2}\,m\overline{(\dot{y}_n)^2} \tag{20.4}$$

and since

$$\dot{y}_n = \text{R.P.}\,\frac{dy_n}{dt} = \text{R.P.}\,A\,\frac{d}{dt}\,e^{i(\omega t - kn)} = \text{R.P.}\,i\omega y_n$$

we have

$$\overline{E_{\text{kin}}} = \text{R.P.}\,\frac{m}{2d}\,\overline{(i\omega y_n)^2} = \frac{\omega^2}{2d}\frac{m}{2}\,\text{R.P.}\,(iy_n)(iy_n)^* = \frac{m\omega^2A^2}{4d} \tag{20.5}$$

Making use of the equation for ω^2 as a function of k in Eq. (20.1), we find that Eq. (20.5) reduces to

$$\overline{E_{\text{kin}}} = \frac{mA^2}{4d}\frac{4U''}{m}\sin^2\frac{k}{2} = \frac{U''A^2}{d}\sin^2\frac{k}{2} = \overline{E_{\text{pot}}} \tag{20.6}$$

The total energy density therefore is

$$\overline{E} = \frac{2U''A^2}{d}\sin^2\frac{k}{2} \tag{20.7}$$

We shall need this relation later when we discuss the energy velocity.

The *energy flow* from one cell to the next will be the average power absorbed by the second cell from the first. With the first cell as cell n, this will be given by the negative product of the real part of the force $f_{n,n+1}$ on cell n due to cell $n + 1$ and the real part of the velocity of the particle in cell n (for the case of the monatomic lattice). The negative product must be taken since $f_{n,n+1}$ is a force acting on particle n; and hence the positive product would be the power furnished while the negative product would be the power absorbed by particle $n + 1$. We have

$$\left.\begin{aligned} f_{n,n+1} &= U''(y_{n+1} - y_n) \\ y_n &= Ae^{i(\omega t - kn)} \\ \dot{y}_n &= i\omega A e^{i(\omega t - kn)} = i\omega y_n \end{aligned}\right\} \tag{20.8}$$

The average power Φ (time average) absorbed by cell $n + 1$ is thus

$$\Phi = -\overline{\text{R.P.}\, f_{n,n+1} \times \text{R.P.}\, \dot{y}_n} = -\frac{1}{2}\text{R.P.}\,(f_{n,n+1}\dot{y}_n{}^*)$$

$$= -\frac{U''A^2}{2}\text{R.P.}\,(e^{-ik} - 1)(i\omega)^*$$

$$= \frac{U''A^2\omega}{2}\text{R.P.}\,[\sin k - i(1 - \cos k)] = \frac{U''A^2\omega}{2}\sin k \tag{20.9}$$

Substituting the value for ω given in Eq. (20.1),

$$\Phi = U''A^2\sqrt{\frac{U''}{m}}\sin\frac{k}{2}\sin k \tag{20.10}$$

The energy flow gives us the energy passing from cell n to cell $(n + 1)$ per unit time. A quantity closely connected with this is the *energy velocity*. It is defined as the energy flow divided by the energy density and gives the rate at which energy flows along the lattice. We denote the energy velocity by U_e.

$$U_e = \frac{\Phi}{E} = \frac{U''A^2\sqrt{\dfrac{U''}{m}}\sin k \sin\dfrac{k}{2}}{2\dfrac{U''}{d}A^2\sin^2\dfrac{k}{2}} = d\sqrt{\frac{U''}{m}}\cos\frac{k}{2} \tag{20.11}$$

The energy velocity can always be defined, even if absorption is present. The meaning of Eq. (20.11) will appear clearly if it is compared with the formula giving the flow of matter in a fluid: let ρ be the density of the fluid and v its velocity. The flow of matter is $\Phi = \rho v$; hence the ratio Φ/ρ is the velocity of the fluid. In a similar way the ratio Φ/E of energy flow to energy density obviously yields a velocity that is the velocity with which energy is flowing through the system. More detailed explanations and examples can be found in a report by the author.[1]

21. Group Velocity and Propagation of a Signal

Having explained in Sec. 18 the meaning attached to the expression "group" or "wave packet," we may immediately

[1] "Congrès international d'électricité," Paris, 1932, vol. II, p. 739.

proceed to the discussion of the simplest example, obtained by considering the wave motion due to the superposition of two sine waves of frequencies $\nu_0 \pm \Delta\nu$ and equal amplitudes A. The wave $\nu_0 + \Delta\nu$ has wave number $a_0 + \Delta a$, while $\nu_0 - \Delta\nu$ has wave number $a_0 - \Delta a$. Thus the wave $\nu_0 - \Delta\nu$ has the equation of motion

$$y_- = A \cos 2\pi[(\nu_0 - \Delta\nu)t - (a_0 - \Delta a)x]$$

while the equation for the wave $\nu_0 + \Delta\nu$ is

$$y_+ = A \cos 2\pi[(\nu_0 + \Delta\nu)t - (a_0 + \Delta a)x]$$

To obtain the resultant motion, we add the two disturbances algebraically.

$$\begin{aligned} y = y_- + y_+ = A \ \{&\cos 2\pi[(\nu_0 - \Delta\nu)t - (a_0 - \Delta a)x] \\ &+ \cos 2\pi[(\nu_0 + \Delta\nu)t - (a_0 + \Delta a)x]\} \\ = 2A \cos 2\pi&(\nu_0 t - a_0 x) \cos 2\pi(\Delta\nu \cdot t - \Delta a \cdot x) \end{aligned} \quad (21.1)$$

This represents a *modulated wave* with an average frequency ν_0 in the *carrier wave*

$$\cos 2\pi(\nu_0 t - a_0 x) \quad (21.2)$$

and a slowly variable amplitude considered as the *modulation*

$$A \cos 2\pi(\Delta\nu \cdot t - \Delta a \cdot x) \quad (21.3)$$

The *phase velocity* of the carrier wave is

$$V = \frac{\nu_0}{a_0} \quad (21.4)$$

In the same way the modulation is seen to move with a velocity given by $\Delta\nu/\Delta a$. In the limit when the two frequencies become equal,

$$U_g = \textit{group velocity} = \frac{\partial \nu}{\partial a} \quad (21.5)$$

There is no difficulty in defining U_g as long as the medium is purely dispersive, *i.e.*, $\nu = \nu(a)$; but if absorption also occurs, a becomes complex or imaginary and the group velocity ceases to have a clear physical meaning.

So far we have assumed zero coefficient of absorption in the monatomic lattice. Therefore,

$$U_g = \frac{\partial \nu}{\partial a} = d\frac{\partial \omega}{\partial k} = d\frac{\partial}{\partial k}\left(2\sqrt{\frac{U''}{m}}\sin\frac{k}{2}\right)$$
$$= 2d\sqrt{\frac{U''}{m}}\frac{1}{2}\cos\frac{k}{2} = d\sqrt{\frac{U''}{m}}\cos\frac{k}{2} = U_e \qquad (21.6)$$

Thus if no absorption is present, the group velocity and the energy velocity are the same. However, the group velocity breaks down for cases with absorption, while the energy velocity can always be defined.

The motion represented by Eq. (21.1) is best described in the following way: It consists of a succession of wavelets (21.2) of frequency ν_0 and wave length $1/\lambda_0$. At a certain instant of time the average amplitude of these wavelets is given by the modulation (21.3). If we do not pay attention to the detailed motion of

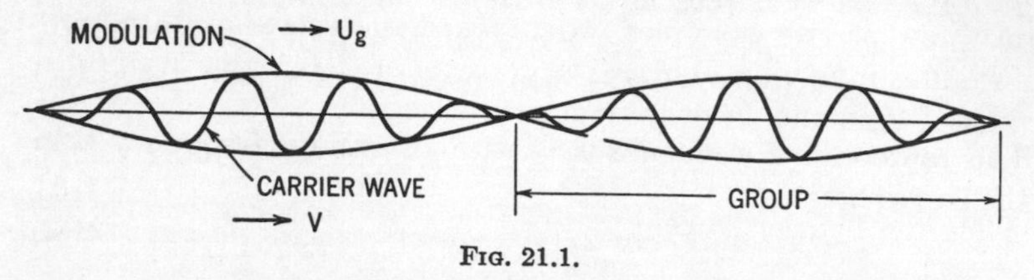

FIG. 21.1.

the wavelets and look only at the average amplitude distribution, we see this amplitude curve (21.3) move forward with the group velocity U_G. But if we look at the phenomenon more carefully, we notice the wavelets moving inside the envelope (21.3) with their own phase velocity V (Fig. 21.1). A well-known example of such an appearance is found when surface waves are created by throwing a stone into a pond. The preceding example is just one among many similar ones, and the results obtained are to a large extent independent of the shape of the group or of the type of the modulation curve. It is characterized by the following feature: The modulation curve propagates without distortion and exhibits a well-defined velocity. The absence of distortion is obviously connected with the *absence of attenuation.* In an absorbing medium with attenuation the definition of a group velocity loses its accuracy.

Furthermore, the absence of distortion can be obtained only if the wave packet results from the superposition of elementary waves whose frequencies lie within a small interval. In the preceding example we had just two frequencies $\nu_0 + \Delta\nu$ and

$\nu_0 - \Delta\nu$ within a finite interval $2\Delta\nu$. We should find similar results with wave groups obtained by superposition of any number of waves with frequencies within a given interval $\Delta\nu$. In other words, the Fourier analysis of the group must yield a spectrum of finite length, which in the limit can be made infinitely small and can allow for the transition from $\Delta\nu/\Delta a$ to the derivative $\partial\nu/\partial a$ of Eq. (21.5).

There are other types of groups or signals whose Fourier spectra extend from $-\infty$ to $+\infty$ in the frequency range. For such signals it is impossible to go to the limit $\Delta\nu \to 0$, and the definition of a group velocity again loses its accuracy. This results in the fact that the modulation curve progressively changes its shape in the course of propagation and is more and more distorted as time goes on. These general remarks will be illustrated in a few precise examples, where we shall use some well-known formulas involving Fourier integrals. Let $C(t)$ be an even function of time and $B(\nu)$ its frequency spectrum.

$$C(t) = C(-t)$$

Then the Fourier transformation reads

$$\left.\begin{aligned} C(t) &= \int_{-\infty}^{\infty} B(\nu) \cos 2\pi\nu t \, d\nu \\ B(\nu) &= \int_{-\infty}^{\infty} C(t) \cos 2\pi\nu t \, dt \end{aligned}\right\} \tag{21.7}$$

The last formula obviously yields B as an even function.

$$B(\nu) = B(-\nu)$$

and the reciprocity between C and B results in the following statement: If a signal $C(t)$ has a spectrum $B(\nu)$, then a reciprocal signal $B(t)$ will be represented by a spectrum $C(\nu)$. We may use the signal $C(t)$ as a modulation curve on a carrier oscillation of frequency ν_0, and we obtain a new even function

$$C_1(t) = C(t) \cos 2\pi\nu_0 t \tag{21.8}$$

The frequency spectrum of C_1 is easily obtained.

$$\begin{aligned} B_1(\nu) &= \int_{-\infty}^{\infty} C_1(t) \cos 2\pi\nu t \, dt = \int_{-\infty}^{\infty} C(t) \cos 2\pi\nu t \cos 2\pi\nu_0 t \, dt \\ &= \frac{1}{2}\int_{-\infty}^{\infty} C(t)[\cos 2\pi(\nu_0 + \nu)t + \cos 2\pi(\nu_0 - \nu)t]dt \\ &= \frac{1}{2}[B(\nu_0 + \nu) + B(\nu_0 - \nu)] = \frac{1}{2}[B(\nu + \nu_0) + B(\nu - \nu_0)]. \end{aligned} \tag{21.9}$$

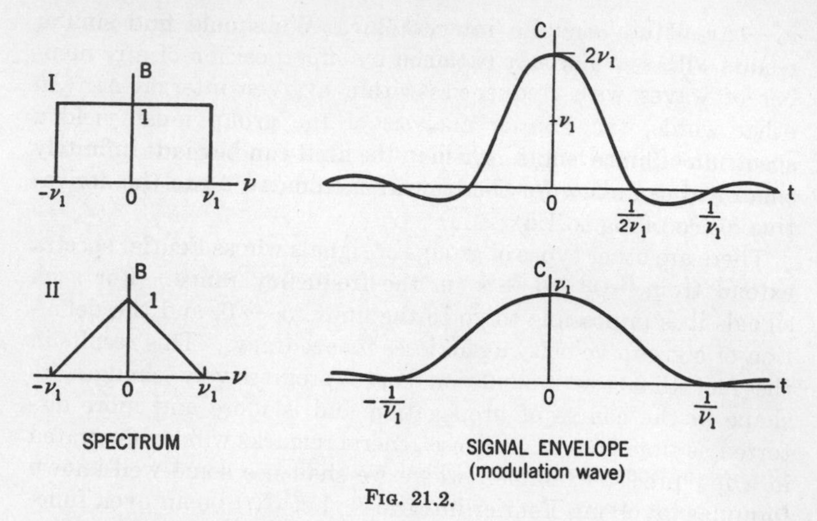

FIG. 21.2.

$B_1(\nu)$ is again an even function of ν. The spectrum $B(\nu)$ of the original signal is centered on the origin O. The new spectrum is obtained by the average of two such curves, translated by $\pm\nu_0$.

Let us give a few examples of Fourier transformations, corresponding to the reciprocal curves of Fig. 21.2.

Spectrum $B(\nu)$ *Signal* $C(t)$

I. Rectangular

$$B(\nu) = \begin{cases} 1 & |\nu| < \nu_1 \\ 0 & |\nu| > \nu_1 \end{cases} \qquad C(t) = 2\nu_1 \frac{\sin 2\pi\nu_1 t}{2\pi\nu_1 t} \tag{21.10}$$

II. Triangular

$$B(\nu) = \begin{cases} 1 - \dfrac{|\nu|}{\nu_1} & |\nu| < \nu_1 \\ 0 & |\nu| > \nu_1 \end{cases} \qquad C(t) = \nu_1 \left(\frac{\sin \pi\nu_1 t}{\pi\nu_1 t}\right)^2 \tag{21.11}$$

Both signals exhibit a finite spectrum, while the signals themselves extend from $t = -\infty$ to $t = \infty$ with a strong maximum at $t = 0$. The reciprocal signals would be finite signals (rectangular or triangular) $B(t)$ with infinite spectra $C(\nu)$.

We now want to prove that a signal with a finite spectrum propagates in a way similar to the beats of Eq. (21.1). Let us take a $C(t)$ modulation impressed upon a ν_0 carrier, as in Eq. (21.8). We assume this motion to be impressed on the atom at

$x = 0$, and we compute the motion at a distance x from the origin. This means only replacing

$$\nu t \qquad \text{by} \qquad \nu t - a(\nu)x$$

where $a(\nu)$ is the wave number $1/\lambda$ as a function of ν for the transmitting medium. Taking our modulated signal (21.8), we obtain according to Eq. (21.9)

$$\begin{aligned} C_1(t) &= \int_{-\infty}^{\infty} B_1(\nu) \cos 2\pi\nu t \, d\nu = 2 \int_0^{\infty} B_1 \cos 2\pi\nu t \, d\nu \\ &= \int_0^{\infty} [B(\nu + \nu_0) + B(\nu - \nu_0)] \cos 2\pi\nu t \, d\nu \end{aligned} \tag{21.12}$$

Let us write

$$\nu = \nu_0 + \mu \qquad\qquad \nu_0 > \nu_1$$

Then, for both examples (21.10) and (21.11), the first term in $B(\nu + \nu_0)$ is always zero, and we find

$$C_1(t) = \int_{\mu=-\nu_1}^{\mu=+\nu_1} B(\mu) \cos 2\pi(\nu_0 + \mu)t \, d\mu \tag{21.13}$$

This is the motion of the point at the origin $x = 0$. For a point at distance x we obtain

$$C_1(t,x) = \int_{-\nu_1}^{\nu_1} B(\mu) \cos 2\pi[(\nu_0 + \mu)t - a(\nu_0 + \mu)x] d\mu \tag{21.14}$$

But ν_1 is supposed to be small enough to allow for an expansion.

$$a(\nu_0 + \mu) = a(\nu_0) + \mu \left(\frac{\partial a}{\partial \nu}\right)_0 \qquad |\mu| < \nu_1 \tag{21.15}$$

Hence

$$(\nu_0 + \mu)t - ax = \nu_0 t - a_0 x + \mu \left(t - \frac{\partial a}{\partial \nu_0} x\right)$$

Expanding the cosine in Eq. (21.14) and recalling that B is even, we obtain

$$\begin{aligned} C_1(t,x) &= \cos 2\pi(\nu_0 t - a_0 x) \int_{-\nu_1}^{\nu_1} B(\mu) \cos \mu \left(t - \frac{\partial a}{\partial \nu_0} x\right) d\mu \\ &= \cos 2\pi(\nu_0 t - a_0 x) C\left(t - \frac{\partial a}{\partial \nu_0} x\right) \end{aligned} \tag{21.16}$$

This is the result announced: Individual wavelets propagate with their own phase velocity as shown by the cosine term. The modulation curve $C\left(t - \frac{\partial a}{\partial \nu_0} x\right)$ moves along without distortion with *group velocity* (21.5).

The proof rests upon the assumption of a finite spectrum whose limit ν_1 can be taken small enough to use Eq. (21.15). Signals with an infinite spectrum are always more or less distorted.

The results are plotted on the curves of Fig. 21.3. The upper curve is the familiar one of ν against a, as in Fig. 2.4, for the monatomic lattice with interactions between nearest neighbors only.

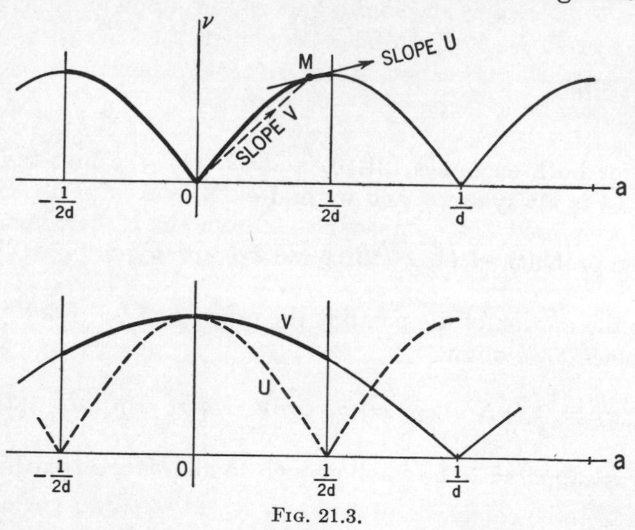

FIG. 21.3.

If a point M is taken on the curve, the absolute value of the slope of a chord OM gives the phase velocity $V = \nu/a$, while the tangent at M yields the group velocity $U = \partial\nu/\partial a$. Curves for V and U as functions of a are given at the bottom. The V curve does not exhibit any singularity at $a = 1/2d$ (cf. discussion of Fig. 2.2), but the group velocity U drops to zero on the limit $\pm 1/2d$ of the interval, a feature that checks very well with our description of these limit waves as standing waves (Secs. 2, 4, and 9).

22. Preliminary Definition of Characteristic Impedance

Impedance for a mechanical system is defined as the ratio of force exerted to velocity. In discussing periodic lines, *i.e.*, lattice structures with cells that repeat themselves periodically or a continuous line with a periodic structure, we mean by *characteristic impedance* the ratio between force and velocity for a single sine wave at the entrances or exits of the cells. For an infinite line, along which a single wave is propagated, this should be the same for all cells. The same is true if the line is finite but has been provided with suitable forces for absorbing and furnishing energy, so that, except at the ends, the line behaves as though it were infinite. Obviously, a determination of characteristic impedance gives us the impedances that must terminate a finite line if it is to behave as an infinite line exhibiting no reflection.

In this section we shall consider only the lattice consisting of like particles with interactions between nearest neighbors only. Then the characteristic impedance is given by

$$f_{n,n+1} = -Z\dot{y}_n \tag{22.1}$$

where $f_{n,n+1}$ is the force exerted by particle $n + 1$ on particle n, $\dot{y}_n$ its velocity, and Z the impedance. From the earlier discussion of the problem [cf. Eqs. (20.1) and (20.8)]

$$\begin{aligned} y_n &= Ae^{i(\omega t - kn)} \\ f_{n,n+1} &= U''(y_{n+1} - y_n) = U''y_n(e^{-ik} - 1) \\ \dot{y}_n &= i\omega y_n \end{aligned}$$

and therefore

$$Zi\omega = U''(1 - e^{-ik}) = U''(1 - \cos k + i \sin k) \tag{22.2}$$

We allow Z to be complex and set

$$Z = Z_r + iZ_i \tag{22.3}$$

Equating real and imaginary parts in Eq. (22.2), we obtain

$$\left.\begin{aligned} Z_i &= \frac{U''}{\omega}(\cos k - 1) = -\frac{2U''}{\omega}\sin^2\frac{k}{2} \\ &= -\sqrt{U''m}\sin\frac{k}{2} \\ Z_r &= \frac{U''}{\omega}\sin k = \frac{2U''}{\omega}\sin\frac{k}{2}\cos\frac{k}{2} = \sqrt{U''m}\cos\frac{k}{2} \end{aligned}\right\} \tag{22.4}$$

on making use of $\omega = 2\sqrt{U''/m}\sin k/2$. With the results of the last section,

$$Z_r = \frac{m}{d}U_e \qquad U_e, \text{ energy velocity} \tag{22.5}$$

We can interpret Z_r and Z_i completely by replacing

$$U''(1 - \cos k)$$

by C and noting that C is always positive. Further, Z_r is positive for the fundamental interval $-\pi < k < \pi$, since $\cos k/2$ is positive in this region.

$$f_{n,n+1} = -Z\dot{y}_n = -Z_r\dot{y}_n - iZ_i\dot{y}_n = -Z_r\dot{y}_n + i\frac{C}{\omega}\dot{y}_n$$

$$= -Z_r\dot{y}_n - \frac{C}{i\omega}\dot{y}_n = -Z_r\dot{y}_n - Cy_n \quad (22.6)$$

We have now split the force acting on mass n into two parts: the first term gives a viscous force and the second an elastic force.

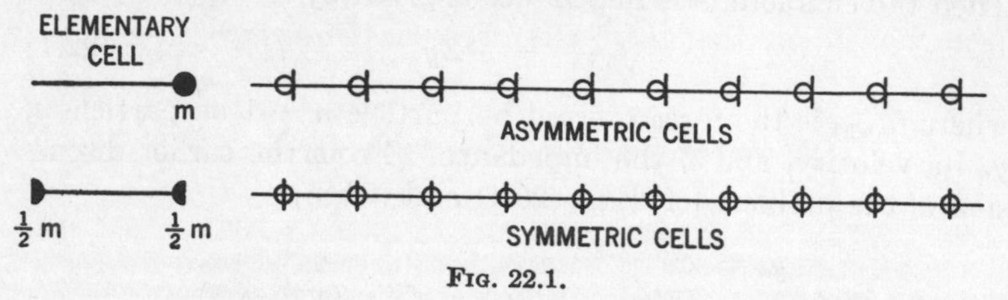

FIG. 22.1.

There is a disadvantage to the treatment we have just given; we have taken the cells to contain a whole particle at one end. If we try to find the impedance at the other end of the cell, we run into a difficulty because there is nothing there to exert a force or to have a velocity, since the cell must contain exactly one period of the lattice. The cells, as we have chosen them, are asymmetric and do not lend themselves conveniently to impedance considerations.

The difficulty may be obviated by defining the cells differently and making them symmetric. We take the cells to be of length d (where d is the distance between the particles) as before, but we associate with the cell half of each of the masses at the ends. This makes the cell symmetric. The symmetric and asymmetric cells are shown in Fig. 22.1, where the vertical lines denote the boundaries of the cells in the two cases. Figure 22.2 shows a line composed of symmetric cells and terminating on an impedance Z_s.

Let us find this impedance Z_s at the right end of the cell containing half of mass $n - 1$ at the left and half of mass n at the right end. The force on mass n due to mass $n - 1$ is given by

$U''(y_{n-1} - y_n)$, and the impedance term is $-Z_s\dot{y}_n$. Therefore, the equation of motion at the right end $\frac{1}{2}m$ of the cell will be

$$U''(y_{n-1} - y_n) - Z_s\dot{y}_n = \tfrac{1}{2}m\ddot{y}_n \tag{22.7}$$

The force due to mass $n + 1$ is thought of as acting on the half of mass n in the next cell to the right. If that force were added to this, we would find exactly the equation of motion obtained before; the impedance would have opposite signs for the two halves of mass n and would cancel, so that the solution for y_n would be the same as before. Substituting the solution in Eq. (22.7) gives an equation for Z_s.

$$U''(e^{ik} - 1) - i\omega Z_s = \tfrac{1}{2}m(i\omega)^2 = -\tfrac{1}{2}m\omega^2 \tag{22.8}$$

We want to show that Z_s gives rise only to a viscous force in this model, and that the elastic force has already been explicitly

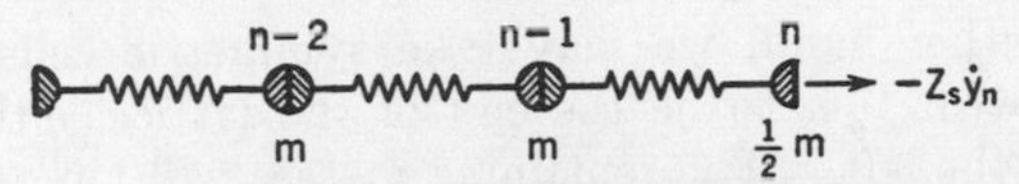

A LINE WITH SYMMETRIC CELLS AND TERMINATION ON A CHARACTERISTIC IMPEDANCE Z_s

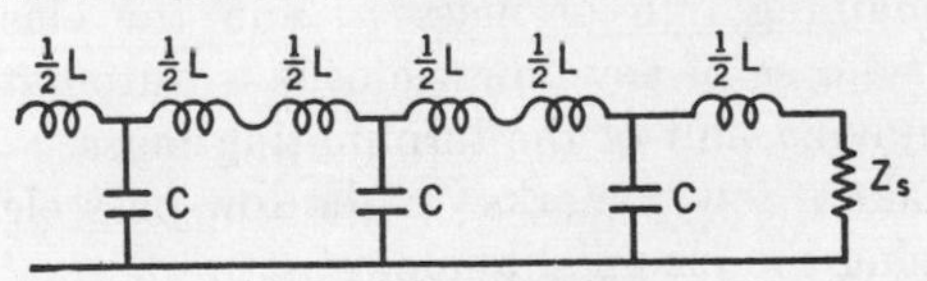

ELECTRICAL ANALOGUE

FIG. 22.2.

included; *i.e.*, we now have Z_s real. Equating the real and imaginary parts of Eq. (22.8), we obtain

$$\left.\begin{aligned} Z_s = \frac{U''}{\omega}\sin k = \sqrt{U''m}\cos\frac{k}{2} = Z_r \\ 2\frac{U''}{m}(1 - \cos k) = 4\frac{U''}{m}\sin^2\frac{k}{2} = \omega^2 \end{aligned}\right\} \tag{22.9}$$

The impedance at the other end of the cell is easily obtained in exactly the same manner. The equation of motion will be

$$U''(y_n - y_{n-1}) + Z_s\dot{y}_{n-1} = \tfrac{1}{2}m\ddot{y}_{n-1}$$

and Eq. (22.8) will be replaced by

$$U''(e^{-ik} - 1) + i\omega Z_s = -\tfrac{1}{2}m\omega^2$$

from which we obtain

$$\left.\begin{aligned} Z_s &= \frac{U''}{\omega} \sin k = Z_r \\ \omega^2 &= 4 \frac{U''}{m} \sin^2 \frac{k}{2} \end{aligned}\right\} \tag{22.10}$$

Summarizing the whole discussion, we have found that if we wish to end the line with particle n (mass m) on the right we must use asymmetric cells and apply an impedance $Z_r + iZ_i$ where Z_r is the viscous force and Z_i is an elastic force. If such an impedance is applied, the remaining masses will vibrate exactly as if the lattice were infinite. If we wished to make mass n the last mass on the left, we should have to take asymmetric cells with masses on the left instead of on the right end of the cells.

On the other hand, we may take symmetric cells and take particle n with $\frac{1}{2}m$ to be the end of the lattice, either on the right or on the left. The remaining masses will vibrate as if the line were infinite if we apply only a viscous force with impedance Z_s to the remaining half of mass n; and the elastic force Z_i occurring in the case of asymmetric cells is automatically taken care of by removing half of the terminating mass.

We may make a few remarks on the low-pass electric line of Fig. 22.2. Using the classical analogy

$$M \sim L, \qquad C \sim \frac{1}{U''}$$

we obtain

$$Z_s = \sqrt{\frac{L}{C}} \cos \frac{k}{2} \tag{22.11}$$

or, for infinite wave length,

$$Z_s = \sqrt{\frac{L}{C}}$$

L and C are, of course, to be taken as inductance and capacity per cell, respectively, though inductance and capacity per unit length of line give the same result since the ratio is the quantity occurring. The impedance of electric lines will be discussed in detail later.

The *energy flow* through the lattice was defined in Sec. 20, Eq. (20.9), by the formula

$$\Phi = -\overline{\text{R.P.}\, f_{n,n+1} \times \text{R.P.}\, \dot{y}_n}^t = -\tfrac{1}{2}\, \text{R.P.}\, (f_{n,n+1}\dot{y}_n{}^*)$$

and now we obtain the characteristic impedance from Eq. (22.1).

$$f_{n,n+1} = -Z\dot{y}_n$$

Comparing these formulas, we find

$$\Phi = \tfrac{1}{2}\, \text{R.P.}\, (Z\dot{y}_n\dot{y}_n{}^*) = \tfrac{1}{2}Z_r|\dot{y}_n|^2 \tag{22.12}$$

This yields a *relation* between *energy flow* and the *real part* of the *characteristic impedance*, and it must be emphasized here that this real part Z_r is the one upon which all our different definitions agree simultaneously.

At the limit of indefinitely long wave lengths, our formulas will reduce to the well-known ones for a continuous structure. We have already discussed this transition in Sec. 9 and obtained

$$\epsilon = dU''_1 \qquad \text{elasticity modulus} \tag{9.3}$$

$$\rho = \frac{m}{d} \qquad \text{density}$$

$$V_\infty = d\sqrt{\frac{U''_1}{m}} = \sqrt{\frac{\epsilon}{\rho}} \qquad \text{phase velocity} \tag{9.3a}$$

In the same way we find now

$$\left.\begin{aligned} U_\infty &= V_\infty \\ Z_r &= \sqrt{mU''_1} = \sqrt{\epsilon\rho} \end{aligned}\right\} \tag{22.13}$$

When there is no dispersion and V is a constant, then, of course,

$$U = \frac{\partial \nu}{\partial a} = \frac{\nu}{a} = V$$

The group velocity is equal to the phase velocity. The formula (22.13) for the characteristic impedance is the usual one.

23. Junction of Two Lattices

We are now in a position to discuss the behavior of waves at the junction of two monatomic lattices with the particles spaced at distance d from one another and with interactions between nearest neighbors only. Let us suppose that we have two such lattices with phase velocities W_1 and W_2, group velocities U_1 and

U_2, energy flows Φ_1 and Φ_2, impedances Z_1 and Z_2, and amplitudes A_1 and A_2 at the ends to be joined. We shall call the ratio of the amplitudes the transformer ratio T.

$$T = \frac{A_2}{A_1} \quad \text{or} \quad A_2 = TA_1 \tag{23.1}$$

We have obtained a relation between energy flow and characteristic impedance for any lattice [Eq. (22.12)]. If we substitute the value of $\dot{y}_n$ and take the time average in the usual fashion, Eq. (22.12) becomes

$$\Phi = \tfrac{1}{2} Z_r \omega^2 A^2 \tag{23.2}$$

Later we shall find it convenient to use Eq. (23.2) as the defining equation for the characteristic impedance.

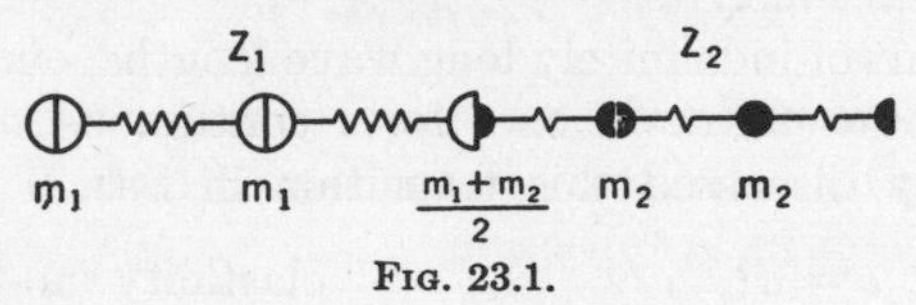

FIG. 23.1.

If we now join the two lines described above and require that the ends to be joined be the ends of cells in the two lattices, we obtain

$$\Phi_1 = \tfrac{1}{2} Z_{r_1} \omega_1^2 A_1^2 \tag{23.3}$$
$$\Phi_2 = \tfrac{1}{2} Z_{r_2} \omega_2^2 A_2^2 \tag{23.4}$$

In general, we shall take $\omega_1 = \omega_2$ and the condition that there be no energy loss and no reflected wave is

$$\Phi_1 = \Phi_2 \quad \text{or} \quad Z_{r_1} A_1^2 = Z_{r_2} A_2^2 \quad \text{or} \quad \frac{Z_{r_1}}{Z_{r_2}} = T^2 \tag{23.5}$$

T may be easily computed for two monatomic lattices when the conditions at the junction are specified. Let us take, for instance, the lattices as divided into symmetrical cells; then Z_1 and Z_2 are real. At the junction in this structure we have a particle, one half of which belongs to one lattice and the other half of which belongs to the other lattice (see Fig. 23.1). Since the two halves must move together, we have the condition

$$A_1 = A_2 \quad \text{or} \quad T = 1 \tag{23.6}$$

Hence, the condition for zero energy loss and no reflection at the junction is

$$Z_1 = Z_2 \tag{23.7}$$

We obtained the expression for the characteristic impedance in the last section. If the masses in the two lattices are different, it follows that the elastic coefficients must also be different.

In general, *reflection* occurs *at the junction* of two lattices, and the coefficient of reflection may be obtained in terms of the constants of the lattices. If reflection occurs, we have three waves at the junction: the incident wave with amplitude A_1, the transmitted wave with amplitude A_2, and the reflected wave with amplitude A_3. The energy flows associated with these waves are given by

$$\left.\begin{aligned}\Phi_1 &= \tfrac{1}{2}Z_{r_1}\omega^2 A_1^2\\ \Phi_2 &= \tfrac{1}{2}Z_{r_2}\omega^2 A_2^2\\ \Phi_3 &= \tfrac{1}{2}Z_{r_1}\omega^2 A_3^2\end{aligned}\right\} \qquad (23.8)$$

since the incident and reflected waves propagate in the first lattice and the transmitted wave in the second lattice. We wish to obtain the coefficient of reflection

$$R = \frac{A_3}{A_1} \qquad (23.9)$$

To do this, we note that we have two conditions for the expressions in Eq. (23.8). Conservation of energy requires that

$$\Phi_1 = \Phi_2 + \Phi_3 \qquad (23.10)$$

and the condition that the two halves of the particle at the junction move together is

$$A_2 = A_1 + A_3 \qquad (23.11)$$

since the resultant of the motion due to the incident and reflected waves is an algebraic sum of these waves.

From Eq. (23.10) we obtain

$$Z_{r_1}A_1^2 = Z_{r_2}A_2^2 + Z_{r_1}A_3^2$$

or

$$\frac{Z_{r_2}}{Z_{r_1}}\left(\frac{A_2}{A_1}\right)^2 = 1 - \left(\frac{A_3}{A_1}\right)^2$$

or

$$\left(\frac{A_2}{A_1}\right)^2 = \frac{Z_{r_1}}{Z_{r_2}}\left[1 - \left(\frac{A_3}{A_1}\right)^2\right] \qquad (23.12)$$

and from Eq. (23.11)

$$\left(\frac{A_2}{A_1}\right)^2 = 1 + 2\frac{A_3}{A_1} + \left(\frac{A_3}{A_1}\right)^2 \tag{23.13}$$

Combining Eq. (23.12) with Eq. (23.13), we obtain a quadratic equation in $(A_3/A_1) = R$.

$$\left(\frac{A_3}{A_1}\right)^2\left(1 + \frac{Z_{r_1}}{Z_{r_2}}\right) + 2\left(\frac{A_3}{A_1}\right) + 1 - \frac{Z_{r_1}}{Z_{r_2}} = 0$$

or

$$R^2\left(1 + \frac{Z_{r_1}}{Z_{r_2}}\right) + 2R + 1 - \frac{Z_{r_1}}{Z_{r_2}} = 0 \tag{23.14}$$

$$(R + 1)^2 + \frac{Z_{r_1}}{Z_{r_2}}(R^2 - 1) = 0$$

$$(R + 1)\left[R + 1 + \frac{Z_{r_1}}{Z_{r_2}}(R - 1)\right] = 0 \tag{23.15}$$

The solution

$$R = -1 \tag{23.16}$$

is trivial. The incident and reflected waves are just out of phase, and the particle at the junction is at rest. The transmitted wave has amplitude zero, as may be seen by substitution of Eq. (23.16) in Eqs. (23.11) to (23.13). The other solution is

$$R = \frac{Z_{r_1} - Z_{r_2}}{Z_{r_1} + Z_{r_2}} \tag{23.17}$$

which gives the coefficient of reflection for amplitudes. The coefficient of reflection for intensities is

$$R' = |R|^2$$

The coefficient of transmission T' for intensities and the transformation ratio T are given by

$$T = \frac{A_2}{A_1} = \text{transformation ratio} = 1 + R = \frac{2Z_{r_1}}{Z_{r_1} + Z_{r_2}}$$

$$T' = \text{coefficient of transmission} = |T|^2 = \frac{Z_{r_1}}{Z_{r_2}}(1 - R^2)$$

$$= \frac{4Z_{r_1}{}^2}{(Z_{r_1} + Z_{r_2})^2}$$

24. General Definitions of Characteristic Impedance

So far we have discussed the monatomic lattice with interactions between nearest neighbors only. We may extend the treatment to the case of a monatomic lattice with the range of interaction unlimited and use the definitions and formulas of Secs. 8 and 10. The potential energy was obtained in Eq. (8.5).

$$U = U_0 + \sum_n \sum_{p>0} \left[(y_{n+p} - y_n)U'_p + \frac{1}{2}(y_{n+p} - y_n)^2 U''_p \right] \qquad (8.5)$$

The *potential-energy density* is the energy per cell divided by d. In a single wave, each particle has a sinusoidal motion and $\overline{(y_{n+p} - y_n)}^t$ is zero; hence

$$\overline{E_{\text{pot}}}^t = \frac{1}{2d} \sum_{p>0} \overline{U''_p(y_n - y_{n+p})^2}^t \qquad (24.1)$$

A single wave $y_n = Ae^{i(\omega t - kn)}$ propagating to the right gives

$$\begin{aligned} \overline{(y_n - y_{n+p})^2}^t &= \tfrac{1}{2}\,\text{R.P.}\,(y_n - y_{n+p})(y_n - y_{n+p})^* \\ &= \tfrac{1}{2}A^2\,\text{R.P.}\,(1 - e^{-ikp})(1 - e^{ikp}) \\ &= A^2(1 - \cos kp) \end{aligned} \qquad (24.2)$$

and hence

$$\overline{E_{\text{pot}}}^t = \frac{A^2}{2d} \sum_{p>0} U''_p(1 - \cos kp) \qquad (24.3)$$

The *average kinetic-energy density* is the same as before [Eq. (20.5)]:

$$\overline{E_{\text{kin}}}^t = \frac{m}{4d} A^2\omega^2 = \frac{A^2}{2d} \sum_{p>0} U''_p(1 - \cos kp) \qquad (24.4)$$

on substitution for ω^2 [Eq. (10.1)]. Thus

$$\overline{E_{\text{kin}}}^t = \overline{E_{\text{pot}}}^t = \frac{1}{2}\overline{E}^t = \frac{A^2}{2d} \sum_{p>0} U''_p(1 - \cos kp) \qquad (24.5)$$

The larger range of interaction complicates the problem of finding the *energy flow*. Let us compute the flow of energy to the right from all of the cells to the left of a certain particle that can be taken at the origin ($n = 0$). To do this, we must compute the force exerted by a particle $n < 0$ on all particles interacting with it on the right. The force on particle n due to particle $n + p$ is $f_{n,n+p}$ in the previous notation. The subscripts denoting particle numbers have been omitted since each cell contains essentially only one particle.

$$f_{n,n+p} = U''_p(y_{n+p} - y_n)$$

and the average energy flow due to this force will be given by

$$\overline{-f_{n,n+p}\dot{y}_n}^t = -\tfrac{1}{2}\ \text{R.P.}\ (f_{n,n+p}\dot{y}_n{}^*) \tag{24.6}$$

Again the minus sign occurs since $f_{n,n+p}$ is the force acting on particle n due to particle $n + p$ rather than the force exerted by particle n on particle $n + p$. The latter is, of course, the negative of the former. The right-hand side of Eq. (24.6) may be

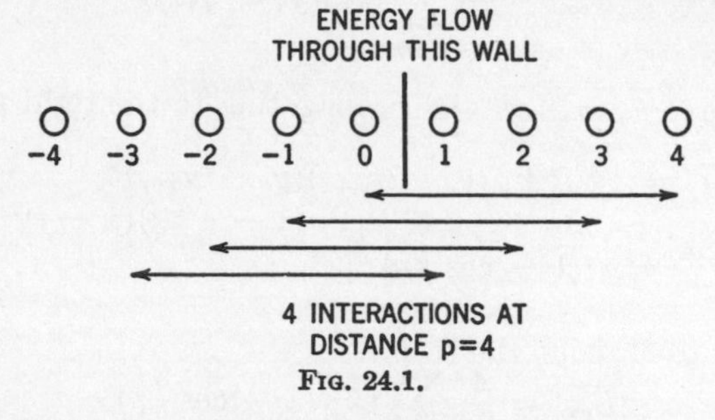

FIG. 24.1.

given explicitly by substituting the well-known exponential expressions for y_n and y_{n+p}.

$$\frac{1}{2}\ \text{R.P.}\ (f_{n,n+p}\dot{y}_n{}^*) = \frac{A^2U''_p}{2}\ \text{R.P.}\ (e^{-ikp} - 1)(i\omega)^*$$

$$= -\frac{1}{2}U''_pA^2\omega \sin kp$$

which gives for Eq. (24.6)

$$-\overline{f_{n,n+p}\dot{y}_n}^t = \tfrac{1}{2}U''_pA^2\omega \sin kp \tag{24.7}$$

There will be p terms of the type (24.7) contributing to the energy flow across particle $n = 0$, since each of the particles $n = 0, -1, -2, \ldots, -p + 1$ will furnish this amount of power to the first p particles to the right of particle 0 (see Fig. 24.1). Thus the total *energy flow* will be given by the following sum over p:

$$\Phi = \sum_p \frac{1}{2}\ U''_pA^2\omega p \sin kp \tag{24.8}$$

The *energy velocity* is defined as in Eq. (20.11) and accordingly is

$$U_e = \frac{\Phi}{\bar{E}} = \frac{\sum_p \frac{1}{2} U''_p A^2 \omega p \sin kp}{\frac{m}{2d} A^2\omega^2} = \frac{d}{m\omega} \sum_p U''_p p \sin kp \quad (24.9)$$

It is easy to verify that this is the *same as* the *group velocity*, for

$$U_g = \frac{\partial \nu}{\partial |a|} = d\,\frac{\partial \omega}{\partial k} = \frac{d}{2\omega}\frac{\partial \omega^2}{\partial k} \qquad \text{since} \qquad \begin{aligned} \omega &= 2\pi\nu \\ k &= 2\pi a d \end{aligned}$$

We have already shown [Eq. (10.1)] that

$$\omega^2 = \frac{2}{m} \sum_p U''_p (1 - \cos kp)$$

and hence

$$\frac{\partial \dot{\omega}^2}{\partial k} = \frac{2}{m} \sum_p U''_p p \sin kp$$

and substitution yields the equation

$$U_g = \frac{d}{m\omega} \sum_p U''_p p \sin kp = U_e \quad (24.10)$$

In the previous section we defined the *characteristic impedance* by

$$f_n = -Z\dot{y}_n \quad (24.11)$$

where f_n is the force acting on particle n and $\dot{y}_n$ its velocity. Here, however, we have more than one particle affected by the particles to the right of particle n, and thus the characteristic impedance cannot be defined by Eq. (24.11) since it is not the impedance that would be required to terminate the lattice at particle n in such a way that no reflection occurs. It would be necessary to combine the impedances due to the different L particles near the end of the line. A convenient way of doing this is offered by Eq. (23.2). According to this equation

$$\Phi = \tfrac{1}{2} Z A^2 \omega^2 \quad (24.12)$$

where Z is the characteristic impedance and always remains real. The combination of the impedances offered by the different particles is implicit in the equation since the contribution of each particle to the total energy flow has been taken into consideration. We note that Eq. (24.12) is equivalent to

$$\Phi = \tfrac{1}{2}\overline{Z|y_n|^2}^t \tag{24.13}$$

and we use Eq. (24.13) as the general definition of the characteristic impedance of a one-dimensional lattice. This definition introduces no inconsistencies, and once we have computed Φ, we need consider only the particle terminating the lattice in problems of finite lattices and the junction of lattices. Z is to be real and the cells so chosen that any imaginary part of Z that might arise is taken care of by the interactions of the particles in the lattice. This definition of the *characteristic impedance* enables one to state the *necessary* condition for *no reflection* at the end of the lattice: that the lattice be terminated on a system of impedances resulting in a total impedance equal to the characteristic impedance. This condition is *necessary but not sufficient,* and the general situation near the boundary is very similar to the one obtained in Secs. 8 and 10, where the problem of steady-state equilibrium was discussed.

For cases where the cells contain particles of various masses the problem is more complicated, but the same general methods are applicable. To obtain the average potential and kinetic energies, the average contributions of each particle in the cell to the energy are summed and divided by the length of the cell. The energy flow Φ is obtained by summing the contributions of all particles through a junction between cells. Once the flux Φ and the energy density $\bar{E}$ are obtained, the energy velocity U_e is defined by Eq. (20.11) and found equal to the group velocity [Eq. (21.5)] for all structures exhibiting no absorption.

The curve $\nu(a)$ always has a horizontal tangent on the limits of the interval $a = \pm 1/2d$. This means $\partial\nu/\partial a = 0$ and zero group velocity and checks very well with the fact that these special waves behave practically like standing waves. This was observed, for instance, in the NaCl problem discussed in Chap. IV, for the waves corresponding to ω_1 and ω_2, the limits of the passing bands.

The *characteristic impedance* becomes increasingly difficult to define and loses more and more of its practical significance. Different values would be found for Z according to the assumptions made about the distribution of Z between the particles of the last cell, and, furthermore, the Z value gives a necessary but not a sufficient condition for no reflection.

To conclude, let us emphasize the importance of quantities such as energy flow, energy density, energy velocity, and group velocity, in addition to the usual phase velocity. These definitions were introduced long ago by theoretical physicists. They can be extended from one to two or three dimensions. For electromagnetic waves, for instance, a most general definition of the energy flow leads to Poynting's vector.

The characteristic or surge impedance, familiar to electrical engineers, is very useful for one-dimensional structures with interactions between nearest neighbors only. This includes practically all problems of filters, lines, and cables for electrical communications. We have just found how delicate is the extension to one-dimensional structures with interactions at large distances. Despite many interesting attempts, the extension to two or three dimensions remains rather artificial.[1]

[1] See SCHELKUNOFF, S. A., "Electromagnetic Waves," Chap. XII, Van Nostrand, New York, 1943.

CHAPTER VI

TWO-DIMENSIONAL LATTICES

25. Direct and Reciprocal Lattices in Two Dimensions

Lattices in two dimensions offer much the same sort of difficulties as those in three dimensions, but they are easier to discuss since drawings are simpler and clearer to understand. This is

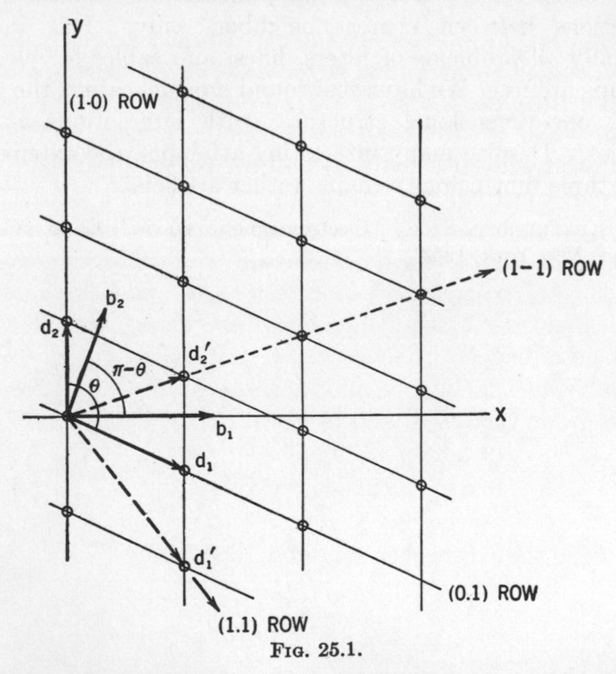

FIG. 25.1.

the reason why a whole chapter is devoted to the two-dimensional problem.

We shall start with a two-dimensional lattice composed of particles all having the same mass and spaced at equal distances from one another along two lines intersecting at an arbitrary angle θ. Later we shall find the generalization to more complicated lattices easy to make. This lattice is shown in Fig. 25.1.

The dots represent the masses. The distance between particles in direction $\mathbf{d}_1$ is not necessarily the same as in direction $\mathbf{d}_2$.

We take $\mathbf{d}_1$ and $\mathbf{d}_2$ as basis vectors drawn from the particle chosen as the origin of the lattice. The vector coordinate of any point in the lattice is then given by

$$\mathbf{r}_{l_1 l_2} = l_1\mathbf{d}_1 + l_2\mathbf{d}_2 \tag{25.1}$$

where l_1 and l_2 are integers. The basis system is not, of course, unique. $\mathbf{d}_1$ and $\mathbf{d}'_2$ would serve just as well and, in fact, any two linearly independent vectors $\mathbf{d}''_1$ and $\mathbf{d}''_2$ given by

$$\left.\begin{aligned} \mathbf{d}''_1 &= m_1\mathbf{d}_1 + n_1\mathbf{d}_2 \\ \mathbf{d}''_2 &= m_2\mathbf{d}_1 + n_2\mathbf{d}_2 \end{aligned}\right\} \qquad \frac{m_1}{m_2} \neq \frac{n_1}{n_2} \tag{25.2}$$

where m_1, m_2, n_1, and n_2 are integers,[1] would give a satisfactory basis. The $\mathbf{d}''$'s correspond to nd in the one-dimensional system, and there we used $n = 1$, *i.e.*, the vector with the smallest absolute value greater than zero. Similarly, here we shall more or less arbitrarily designate $\mathbf{d}_1$ and $\mathbf{d}_2$, the smallest pair of basis vectors greater than zero, as the basis vectors of the lattice.

When we assume two basis vectors $\mathbf{d}_1$ and $\mathbf{d}_2$ for a lattice, then the lattice is completely determined if we restrict ourselves to a single type of particle and require that the particles be equally spaced along the two independent directions. We refer to the lattice described by the vectors $\mathbf{d}_1$ and $\mathbf{d}_2$ as the *direct lattice.* For each direct lattice we may define a reciprocal lattice that is to have basis vectors $\mathbf{b}_1$ and $\mathbf{b}_2$ given by the equation

$$(\mathbf{b}_i \cdot \mathbf{d}_k) = \delta_{ik} \qquad \left\{\begin{aligned} i &= 1, 2 \\ k &= 1, 2 \end{aligned}\right\} \tag{25.3}$$

where δ_{ik} is the Kronecker δ symbol, defined by

$$\delta_{ik} = \left\{\begin{matrix} 1 \; i = k \\ 0 \; i \neq k \end{matrix}\right\} \tag{25.4}$$

The reasons for the term *reciprocal lattice* become apparent with a little calculation. For, if we take the origin of a pair of orthogonal axes x and y at the origin of the basis system, the vectors $\mathbf{d}_1$ and $\mathbf{d}_2$ may be written in terms of their Cartesian components as follows:

[1] The area of the new cell $\mathbf{d}''_1\ \mathbf{d}''_2$ should equal that of $\mathbf{d}_1\ \mathbf{d}_2$; otherwise the simple lattice is changed into a lattice with basis (see p. 128).

$$\left.\begin{aligned} \mathbf{d}_1 &= (d_{1x} \quad d_{1y}) \\ \mathbf{d}_2 &= (d_{2x} \quad d_{2y}) \end{aligned}\right\} \tag{25.5}$$

or, in terms of the matrix notation, the matrix

$$D = \begin{pmatrix} d_{1x} & d_{1y} \\ d_{2x} & d_{2y} \end{pmatrix} \tag{25.6}$$

represents the basis system. Similarly, the reciprocal basis system has the matrix

$$B = \begin{pmatrix} b_{1x} & b_{2x} \\ b_{1y} & b_{2y} \end{pmatrix} \tag{25.7}$$

The subscripts on the elements of the matrix D must be transposed for the matrix B since, if $\mathbf{d}_1$ and $\mathbf{d}_2$ are thought of as *row* vectors, $\mathbf{b}_1$ and $\mathbf{b}_2$ must be *column* vectors because the latter are defined by taking a scalar product with the former [Eq. (25.3)]. It is readily verified that D and B are *reciprocal matrices.* Let us form the matrix product.

$$\begin{aligned} D \cdot B &= \begin{pmatrix} d_{1x} & d_{1y} \\ d_{2x} & d_{2y} \end{pmatrix} \begin{pmatrix} b_{1x} & b_{2x} \\ b_{1y} & b_{2y} \end{pmatrix} \\ &= \begin{pmatrix} d_{1x}b_{1x} + d_{1y}b_{1y} & d_{1x}b_{2x} + d_{1y}b_{2y} \\ d_{2x}b_{1x} + d_{2y}b_{1y} & d_{2x}b_{2x} + d_{2y}b_{2y} \end{pmatrix} \\ &= \begin{pmatrix} (\mathbf{d}_1 \cdot \mathbf{b}_1) & (\mathbf{d}_1 \cdot \mathbf{b}_2) \\ (\mathbf{d}_2 \cdot \mathbf{b}_1) & (\mathbf{d}_2 \cdot \mathbf{b}_2) \end{pmatrix} = \begin{pmatrix} 1 & 0 \\ 0 & 1 \end{pmatrix} = \delta \end{aligned} \tag{25.8}$$

wnere δ is the unit matrix. From this it follows that

$$B = D^{-1} \tag{25.9}$$

From Eq. (25.3) we see that

$$\left.\begin{aligned} &\mathbf{b}_1 \text{ is perpendicular to } \mathbf{d}_2 \\ &\mathbf{b}_2 \text{ is perpendicular to } \mathbf{d}_1 \end{aligned}\right\} \tag{25.10}$$

and therefore

$$\left.\begin{aligned} (\mathbf{b}_1 \cdot \mathbf{d}_1) &= 1 = |\mathbf{b}_1||\mathbf{d}_1| \cos\left(\frac{\pi}{2} - \theta\right) = |\mathbf{b}_1||\mathbf{d}_1| \sin\theta \\ (\mathbf{b}_2 \cdot \mathbf{d}_2) &= 1 = |\mathbf{b}_2||\mathbf{d}_2| \cos\left(\frac{\pi}{2} - \theta\right) = |\mathbf{b}_2||\mathbf{d}_2| \sin\theta \end{aligned}\right\} \tag{25.11}$$

where θ is the angle between $\mathbf{d}_1$ and $\mathbf{d}_2$. This is easily seen by inspection of Fig. 25.1. Now the area of the elementary cell in the direct lattice (*i.e.*, the parallelogram with $\mathbf{d}_1$ and $\mathbf{d}_2$ for two of its sides) is given by

$$S_d = |\mathbf{d}_1 \times \mathbf{d}_2| = |\mathbf{d}_1||\mathbf{d}_2| \sin \theta \tag{25.12}$$

from elementary vector analysis, while that of the elementary cell in the reciprocal lattice is

$$S_b = |\mathbf{b}_1||\mathbf{b}_2| \sin \theta \tag{25.13}$$

The product of these areas is

$$\begin{aligned} S_d \cdot S_b &= |\mathbf{d}_1||\mathbf{d}_2| \sin \theta |\mathbf{b}_1||\mathbf{b}_2| \sin \theta \\ &= |\mathbf{d}_1||\mathbf{d}_2| \sin \theta \frac{\sin \theta}{|\mathbf{d}_1| \sin \theta |\mathbf{d}_2| \sin \theta} = 1 \end{aligned} \tag{25.14}$$

from Eq. (25.11). In other words, the *areas* of the direct and reciprocal cells are reciprocals.

In the one-dimensional lattice the length of the cell in the direct lattice was d. The length of the cell in the frequency vs. wave-number space was $1/d$, and this was, therefore, the reciprocal cell of the lattice. Thus the direct lattice gave the periodicity of the medium, and the reciprocal lattice gave that of the frequency of the waves propagating through the medium. Similar results will be obtained for two dimensions.

For readers accustomed to the definitions of tensor analysis, the following comment may be added. The $\mathbf{d}_1$ and $\mathbf{d}_2$ basis vectors of the direct lattice play essentially the role of the covariant unit vectors, while $\mathbf{b}_1$ and $\mathbf{b}_2$ represent the contravariant unit vectors in an oblique coordinate system.[1]

As a matter of fact, many discussions are simplified if the $\mathbf{d}_1$ and $\mathbf{d}_2$ vectors are used as unit vectors defining an oblique axis system, and any arbitrary vector $\mathbf{r}$ is given by its ξ_1 and ξ_2 components along the $\mathbf{d}$ vectors.

$$\mathbf{r} = \xi_1 \mathbf{d}_1 + \xi_2 \mathbf{d}_2 \tag{25.15}$$

The oblique $(\mathbf{d}_1, \mathbf{d}_2)$ cell in the xy space is thus reduced to a square cell in the ξ space, since

vector $\mathbf{d}_1$ means $\quad \xi_1 = 1, \quad \xi_2 = 0$
vector $\mathbf{d}_2$ means $\quad \xi_1 = 0, \quad \xi_2 = 1$

[1] BRILLOUIN, L., "Les Tenseurs en mécanique et en élasticité," pp. 27–30, 97, 101, 105, Masson, Paris, 1938.
STRATTON, J. A., "Electromagnetic Theory," p. 39, McGraw-Hill, New York, 1941.

Furthermore, according to the defining equation (25.3)

$$\xi_1 = (\mathbf{r} \cdot \mathbf{b}_1), \qquad \xi_2 = (\mathbf{r} \cdot \mathbf{b}_2) \tag{25.16}$$

A straight line in the plane (this line will become a plane in three dimensions) is represented by a linear relation.

$$\left.\begin{aligned} (\mathbf{a} \cdot \mathbf{r}) = a_1x + a_2y = c \\ \text{or} \quad \alpha_1\xi_1 + \alpha_2\xi_2 = c \qquad \alpha_1 = (\mathbf{a} \cdot \mathbf{d}_1) \\ \alpha_2 = (\mathbf{a} \cdot \mathbf{d}_2) \end{aligned}\right\} \tag{25.17}$$

as is easily seen by direct substitution. Conversely,

$$\mathbf{a} = \alpha_1\mathbf{b}_1 + \alpha_2\mathbf{b}_2 \tag{25.18}$$

In these equations $\mathbf{a}$ obviously represents a vector orthogonal to the straight line (25.17), and $c/|\mathbf{a}|$ is the distance δ of the line from the origin.

A lattice point is one with integral coordinates l_1 and l_2.

$$\xi_1 = l_1, \qquad \xi_2 = l_2, \qquad \mathbf{r} = l_1\mathbf{d}_1 + l_2\mathbf{d}_2 \tag{25.19}$$

and a vector $\mathbf{h}$ in the reciprocal lattice is

$$\mathbf{h} = h_1\mathbf{b}_1 + h_2\mathbf{b}_2 \qquad h_1 \text{ and } h_2 \text{ integers} \tag{25.20}$$

If such an $\mathbf{h}$ vector is taken as vector $\mathbf{a}$ in Eq. (25.17), it defines (for different values of c) a set of parallel lines, some of which go through an infinite number of points of the direct lattice. One of these lines is

$$(\mathbf{h} \cdot \mathbf{r}) = h_1(\mathbf{b}_1 \cdot \mathbf{r}) + h_2(\mathbf{b}_2 \cdot \mathbf{r}) = h_1\xi_1 + h_2\xi_2 = c \tag{25.21}$$

For $c = 0$ the line passes through the origin and through all lattice points for which

$$h_1l_1 + h_2l_2 = 0$$

such as

$$l_1 = h_2 \qquad \text{and} \qquad l_2 = -h_1$$

Other lattice rows will correspond to different c values. Now we ask the following question: What is the distance from the origin of the lattice row in this set nearest to the origin? This is the same as asking: What is the smallest nonzero value of $|c|$? Since h_1, ξ_1, h_2, and ξ_2 are all integers (positive or negative), c is also an integer for a lattice row, and the smallest nonzero value of $|c|$ is, provided h_1 h_2 have no common factor and $\mathbf{h}$ is the smallest possible vector.

$$|c| = 1$$

This means that the distance between each of the lattice rows in the set (h_1,h_2) is

$$\delta = \frac{|c|}{|\mathbf{h}|} = \frac{1}{|\mathbf{h}|} \tag{25.22}$$

Thus we have the following statement: A point (h_1,h_2) in the reciprocal lattice defines a set of lattice rows in the direct lattice. These straight rows are perpendicular to the vector $\mathbf{h}$ and are spaced at a distance of $1/|\mathbf{h}|$ from one another. This is known as the *Bravais* notation for crystal planes. In Fig. 25.1, the (1,0) rows are the vertical lines, and the (0,1) set is parallel to $\mathbf{d}_1$. The vector $\mathbf{d}'_1$ is in a (1,1) row, while $\mathbf{d}'_2$ is in $(1,-1)$.

According to the physical properties to be discussed, sometimes the direct and at other times the reciprocal lattice will yield the better description of the periodic structure.

26. Doubly and Triply Periodic Functions

We shall have use for doubly periodic functions only in this chapter. Since, however, triply periodic functions will arise in the theory of three-dimensional lattices, we shall treat the two together. By a doubly or triply periodic function we mean a function of two or three independent variables, periodic in each of its variables. The mathematical theory of such functions would be considerably simplified if we could split an arbitrary function, say $D(x,y)$, that is periodic in x and y into a product of two functions $F_1(x)$ and $F_2(y)$ periodic in x and y, respectively. This can be done, however, only in very special cases. Suppose, for instance, that

$$F(x,y) = \begin{cases} 1 & x,\ y \text{ both integers,} \\ 0 & \text{otherwise} \end{cases} \tag{26.1}$$

Figure 26.1 shows $F(x,y)$ plotted in the xy plane. The dots represent points at which $F(x,y)$ is not zero. Then

$$\begin{aligned} F_1(x) &= \begin{cases} 1 & x \text{ integer} \\ 0 & \text{otherwise} \end{cases} \\ F_2(y) &= \begin{cases} 1 & y \text{ integer} \\ 0 & \text{otherwise} \end{cases} \end{aligned} \tag{26.2}$$

are two functions of one variable each whose product is $F(x,y)$. Evidently $F_1(x)$ and $F_2(y)$ are both periodic functions. Consider, however, the function

$$F(x,y) = \begin{cases} 1 & x \text{ or } y \text{ integer} \\ 0 & \text{neither } x \text{ nor } y \text{ integer} \end{cases} \tag{26.3}$$

Figure 26.2 shows the function $F(x,y)$ plotted on the xy plane. The horizontal and vertical lines represent the points at which $F(x,y)$ is not zero. Let us assume that

$$F(x,y) = F_1(x)F_2(y) \tag{26.4}$$

holds for all x and y. Then, if x_1 and y_1 are neither integers,

$$F_1(x_1)F_2(y_1) = 0 \tag{26.5}$$

so that

$$F_1(x_1) = 0 \qquad \text{or} \qquad F_2(y_1) = 0 \tag{26.6}$$

Let us suppose $F_2(y_1) = 0$; then

$$F_1(n)F_2(y_1) = 0 \qquad n \text{ an integer} \tag{26.7}$$

contradicts the hypothesis that $F(x,y)$ defined by Eq. (26.3) has the form (26.4). Starting from $F_1(x_1)$ would lead to a similar

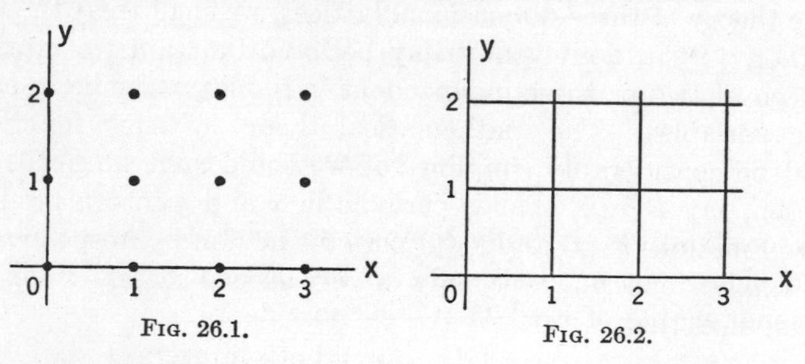

FIG. 26.1. FIG. 26.2.

conclusion; hence the decomposition is impossible. Many authors have also tried a sum.

$$F(x,y) = F_1(x) + F_2(y) \tag{26.8}$$

An example of this would be given by taking F_1 and F_2 as in Eq. (26.2).

$$F(x,y) = \begin{cases} 2 & x \text{ and } y \text{ integers} \\ 1 & x \text{ or } y \text{ integer} \\ 0 & \text{elsewhere} \end{cases}$$

Such an example is obviously a very special case of little practical use.

We shall, however, find it possible to expand doubly or triply periodic functions in double or triple Fourier series, and this will be done by means of the reciprocal lattice defined in Sec. 25.

A periodic function $F(x,y)$ in the direct lattice has the same value at points

$$\mathbf{r} = (x,y) \qquad \text{and} \qquad \mathbf{r}' = \mathbf{r} + l_1\mathbf{d}_1 + l_2\mathbf{d}_2 \tag{26.9}$$

Changing to coordinates ξ_1 and ξ_2 as in Eq. (25.15), we obtain a function $f(\xi_1,\xi_2)$ with period 1 in both ξ_1 and ξ_2. This periodic function can be expanded in a double Fourier series of imaginary exponentials.

$$F(x,y) = f(\xi_1,\xi_2) = \sum_{h_1h_2} C_{h_1h_2} e^{2\pi i(h_1\xi_1 + h_2\xi_2)} \tag{26.10}$$

where h_1 and h_2 are integers, and the coefficients of this series are given by

$$\int_0^1 \int_0^1 f(\xi_1,\xi_2) e^{-2\pi i(h'_1\xi_1 + h'_2\xi_2)} d\xi_1\, d\xi_2 = \sum_{h_1h_2} C_{h_1h_2} \int_0^1 \int_0^1 e^{2\pi i[(h_1-h'_1)\xi_1 + (h_2-h'_2)\xi_2]} d\xi_1\, d\xi_2$$

The integral is zero whenever $h_1 \neq h'_1$ or $h_2 \neq h'_2$ and the only remaining term is the one for which $h_1 = h'_1$ and $h_2 = h'_2$.

$$C_{h_1h_2} = \int_0^1 \int_0^1 f(\xi_1,\xi_2) e^{-2\pi i(h_1\xi_1 + h_2\xi_2)} d\xi_1\, d\xi_2 \tag{26.11}$$

The $C_{h_1h_2}$ coefficient is generally complex and includes the amplitude and phase angles. Returning to the original $F(x,y)$ function and making use of Eq. (25.21), we obtain

$$F(x,y) = \sum_{h_1h_2} C_{h_1h_2} e^{2\pi i(\mathbf{h}\cdot\mathbf{r})} = \sum_{h_1h_2} C_{h_1h_2} e^{2\pi i(h_1(\mathbf{b}_1\cdot\mathbf{r}) + h_2(\mathbf{b}_2\cdot\mathbf{r}))}$$
$$\mathbf{h} = h_1\mathbf{b}_1 + h_2\mathbf{b}_2 \tag{26.12}$$

where $\mathbf{h}$ defines one of the vectors of the reciprocal lattice. The periodic character of this expansion can be checked directly from Eqs. (25.20) and (25.3).

$$(\mathbf{h}\cdot\mathbf{r}') = [\mathbf{h}\cdot(\mathbf{r} + l_1\mathbf{d}_1 + l_2\mathbf{d}_2)] = (\mathbf{h}\cdot\mathbf{r}) + h_1l_1(\mathbf{b}_1\cdot\mathbf{d}_1) + h_2l_2(\mathbf{b}_2\cdot\mathbf{d}_2) = (\mathbf{h}\cdot\mathbf{r}) + h_1l_1 + h_2l_2$$

The imaginary exponential in Eq. (26.12) obviously has the same value at $(\mathbf{h}\cdot\mathbf{r})$ as at $[(\mathbf{h}\cdot\mathbf{r}) + \text{integer}]$.

In the transcription of Eq. (26.11) we must be cautious, since ξ_1 and ξ_2 correspond to oblique coordinates, and the length of a vector $\mathbf{r}$ is

$$|\mathbf{r}|^2 = x^2 + y^2 = |\mathbf{d}_1|^2\xi_1^2 + 2(\mathbf{d}_1 \cdot \mathbf{d}_2)\xi_1\xi_2 + |\mathbf{d}_2|^2\xi_2^2 \quad (26.13)$$

The area S_d of the $\mathbf{d}$ cell is transformed into an area 1 in the ξ system; hence

$$S_d = |\mathbf{d}_1||\mathbf{d}_2| \sin \theta, \qquad dx\, dy = S_d\, d\xi_1\, d\xi_2 \quad (26.14)$$

and

$$C_{h_1h_2} = \frac{1}{S_d} \int_0^{d_1} \int_0^{d_2} F(x,y) e^{-2\pi i(h\cdot r)} dx\, dy \quad (26.15)$$

To give a physical interpretation to expansion (26.12), we may say that the periodic function is decomposed into plane waves, corresponding to each of the lattice rows (lattice planes in three dimensions) defined by the points $\mathbf{h}$ in the reciprocal lattice. A periodic function $F(x,y)$ that can be represented by a product $F_1(x)F_2(y)$ offers the very special property that

$$C_{h_1h_2} = C_{h_1}C_{h_2} \qquad \text{with} \qquad C_{h_1} = \int_0^1 f_1(\xi_1) e^{-2\pi i h_1 \xi_1} d\xi_1 \quad (26.16)$$

and a similar equation for C_{h_2}. This, obviously, cannot be general, but it retains the whole set of coefficients C. The assumption in Eq. (26.8) of a sum $F_1(x) + F_2(y)$ is much more restricting since it knocks out all the coefficients except C_{h_10} and C_{0h_2}, which means that all oblique atomic rows are ruled out.

To emphasize the importance of these definitions, let us state that X-ray reflections from a crystal yield directly the values of $|C_{h_1h_2}|$ in the expansion of electronic density inside the crystal. Only the absolute value of the coefficients is obtained from the experimental data, but symmetry considerations often enable one to guess the phase angles and to reconstruct the whole periodic function representing the average density of electrons throughout the crystal lattice.

27. Zones in a Two-dimensional Lattice

In the discussion of the one-dimensional case, we found that the frequency was a periodic function of the wave number, and hence for a given frequency there was ambiguity in the wave length and the direction of propagation. We chose an interval containing one period of the frequency and taken symmetrically about the origin, and then we restricted the wave number to values in this interval. In the language of this section, we should call this interval the first *zone*. The second zone in one dimension would consist of two intervals containing half a period each, one on each side of the first zone, etc., for higher order zones. The zones for one dimension are shown in Fig. 27.1.

We now proceed to find the analogues of these zones in the two-dimensional case. The zones will be regions in the reciprocal lattice, since this is the lattice describing the periodicity of

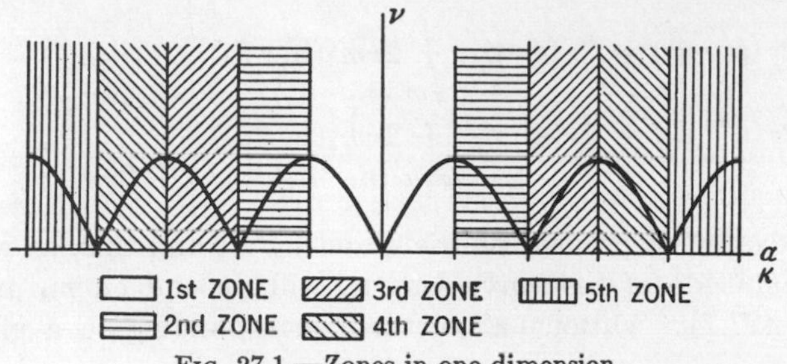

FIG. 27.1.—Zones in one dimension.

frequency as a function of wave number. Let us consider a plane wave propagating through the two-dimensional medium. It will have the form

$$\psi = Ae^{i(\omega t - 2\pi a_1 x - 2\pi a_2 y)} \tag{27.1}$$

or if we let $\mathbf{a}$ be a vector with components a_1 and a_2 and $\mathbf{r}$ a vector with components x and y,

$$\psi = Ae^{i[\omega t - 2\pi(\mathbf{a}\cdot\mathbf{r})]} \quad \text{and} \quad |\mathbf{a}|^2 = a_1^2 + a_2^2 = \frac{1}{\lambda^2} \tag{27.2}$$

$\mathbf{a}$ will be a vector in the direction of propagation, and its magnitude will be the reciprocal of the wave length λ. In a discontinuous medium, ψ is defined only at points $\mathbf{r}$ at which particles are located; *i.e.*, at the points $\mathbf{r}_{l_1 l_2}$ of the direct lattice. Thus

$$2\pi(\mathbf{a}\cdot\mathbf{r}_{l_1 l_2}) = 2\pi(\mathbf{a}\cdot l_1\mathbf{d}_1) + 2\pi(\mathbf{a}\cdot l_2\mathbf{d}_2) = l_1 k_1 + l_2 k_2 \tag{27.3}$$

where we have set

$$k_1 = 2\pi(\mathbf{a}\cdot\mathbf{d}_1) \quad \text{and} \quad k_2 = 2\pi(\mathbf{a}\cdot\mathbf{d}_2) \tag{27.4}$$

Accordingly, Eq. (27.2) may be written

$$\psi = Ae^{i(\omega t - k_1 l_1 - k_2 l_2)} \tag{27.5}$$

Now, as in the one-dimensional case, we may replace k_1 and k_2 by k'_1 and k'_2 where

$$k'_i = k_i + 2\pi m_i \qquad m_i \text{ integers} \tag{27.6}$$

without changing either the motion of the particles or the frequency. This ambiguity in the value of k_1 and k_2 is the analogue of that in k in the one-dimensional case (Sec. 4). The values of k'_1 and k'_2 in Eq. (27.6) correspond to the following value for $\mathbf{a}'$:

$$\mathbf{a}' = \mathbf{a} + m_1\mathbf{b}_1 + m_2\mathbf{b}_2 \tag{27.7}$$

for

$$\left.\begin{aligned} k'_1 = 2\pi(\mathbf{a}' \cdot \mathbf{d}_1) &= 2\pi(\mathbf{a} \cdot \mathbf{d}_1) + 2\pi m_1(\mathbf{b}_1 \cdot \mathbf{d}_1) \\ &\quad + 2\pi m_2(\mathbf{b}_2 \cdot \mathbf{d}_1) = k_1 + 2\pi m_1 \\ k'_2 = 2\pi(\mathbf{a}' \cdot \mathbf{d}_2) &= 2\pi(\mathbf{a} \cdot \mathbf{d}_2) + 2\pi m_1(\mathbf{b}_1 \cdot \mathbf{d}_2) \\ &\quad + 2\pi m_2(\mathbf{b}_2 \cdot \mathbf{d}_2) = k_2 + 2\pi m_2 \end{aligned}\right\} \tag{27.8}$$

The direction of propagation is given by $\mathbf{a}'$, and this, as well as the magnitude of the wave length, will depend on m_1 and m_2 in Eq. (27.7). Various $\mathbf{a}'$ vectors corresponding to a given $\mathbf{a}$

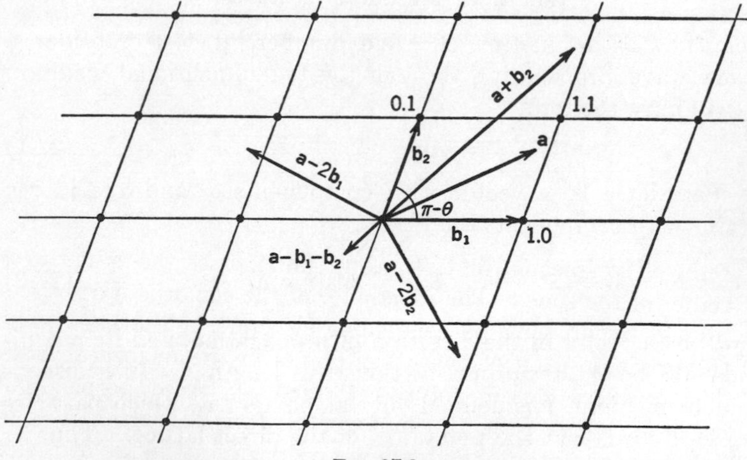

FIG. 27.2.

are shown drawn in the reciprocal lattice in Fig. 27.2. This discussion shows that the frequency ν of the wave, in a two-dimensional lattice, is a periodic function of the wave vector $\mathbf{a}$ in the reciprocal lattice with basis vectors $\mathbf{b}_1$ and $\mathbf{b}_2$.

We must now formulate a rule for choosing the area to which $\mathbf{a}$ is to be confined. We might start at the origin of the basis system and confine all vectors **a** to the first elementary cell of the reciprocal lattice—*i.e.*, to the parallelogram bounded by the points (0,0), (0,1), (1,0), and (1,1) in Fig. 27.2. There are two disadvantages to this. In the first place, this method singles out the directions contained in the angle $\pi - \theta$ as preferred directions of propagation for the waves. Further, it does not require the use of the longest possible wave length for a given disturbance and thus is inconsistent with the conventions set up for the one-dimensional case.

To do away with these objections, we try to construct a zone that will be analogous to the first zone in the one-dimensional

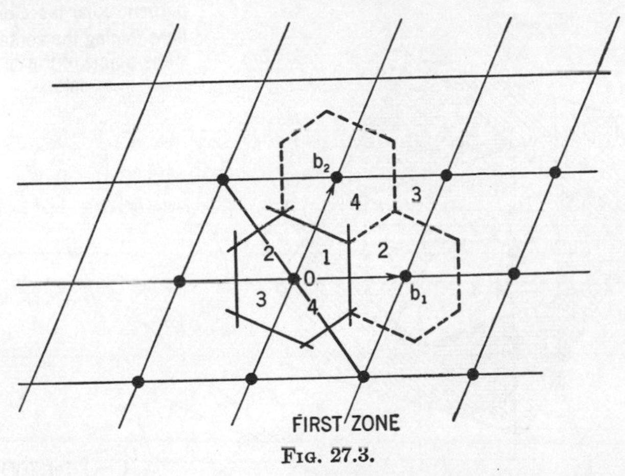

FIG. 27.3.

case. This means, first, that we must place the origin in the center of the zone. The remainder of the construction is accomplished by drawing perpendicular bisectors of the lines joining the origin to each of the other points in the reciprocal lattice. The smallest closed polygon formed by these perpendicular bisectors is taken as the first zone. It is independent of the basis system chosen and allows propagation in all directions. Furthermore, it requires the *longest wave length* describing a given disturbance to be used, as is easily seen by inspection since a complete period for each direction of propagation is included in the zone. There is still an ambiguity on the boundaries of the zone just as in the one-dimensional case. The construction for the first zone is shown in Fig. 27.3. The first zone has the same area as the first elementary cell of the reciprocal lattice, as may be seen by comparing elements of the two areas containing the same numbers. These elements are easily seen to be congruent from plane geometry.

The construction of the second zone and higher order zones is more complicated. They must all be bounded by perpendicular bisectors of lines joining the origin with other lattice points, and there can be no perpendicular bisectors passing through the interior of a zone. The significance of this will be seen later.

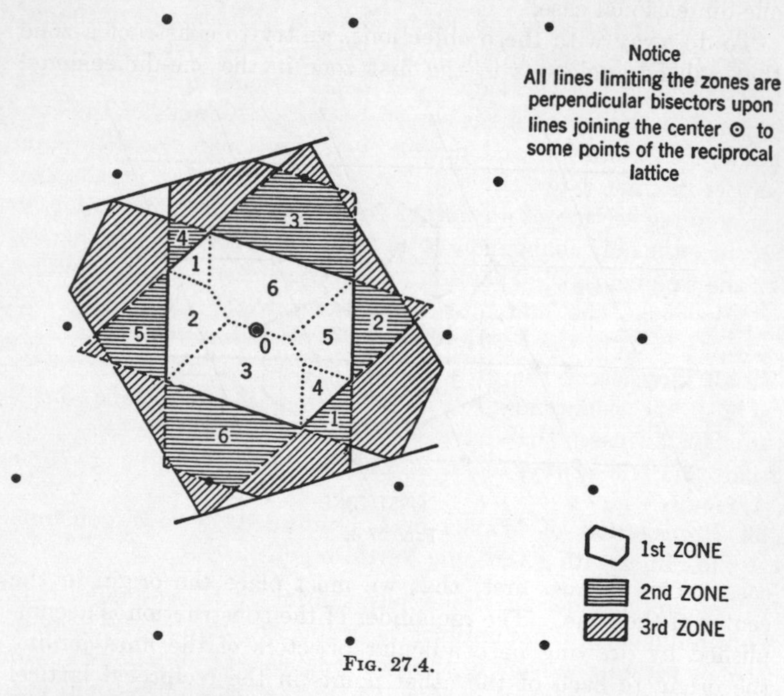

FIG. 27.4.

If a wave propagates through a continuous medium with small periodic variations in such a manner that its wave vector measured from the origin terminates on a perpendicular bisector of a line joining the origin with a lattice point, a discontinuity occurs in the ν vs. $|a|$ curve. The object of introducing zones is to eliminate discontinuities in the ν vs. $|a|$ curve except at the boundaries. This is exactly analogous to the one-dimensional case.

To construct the second zone, we draw the second smallest closed figure about the origin and bounded by perpendicular bisectors. The second zone is the area enclosed between the boundary of the first zone and the boundary of this second figure. The construction is shown in Fig. 27.4. Similarly, one may construct a third zone that is the area enclosed between the boundary of the second zone and the third smallest closed figure bounded by perpendicular bisectors. This is also shown in Fig. 27.4. Higher order zones are constructed in just the same manner. It should be noted that the $(n + 1)$st zone consists of figures having at least one side in common with one side of the nth zone and all vertices in common with the $(n - 1)$st zone.

Each zone has the same area as the elementary cell in the reciprocal lattice. This is shown by taking sections of the zone under consideration and noting their position relative to some lattice point. Now the wave vectors terminating in the corresponding section of any other cell will give the same value for ψ, since the only change in ψ is the addition of $2m\pi$ in the exponent of the exponential. Therefore, we may consider the two sections equivalent. The matching of sections in the elementary cell with sections in the first and second zones is shown in Fig. 27.4. In all these cases the area of each of the zones is equal to the area of the elementary cell in the reciprocal lattice, and this is true for all cases that have been worked out. A general proof that this will always be the case has been worked out. (See Appendix.)

28. Propagation of Waves in a Continuous Two-dimensional Medium with a Periodic Perturbation

We are considering waves propagating in a two-dimensional continuum with a nonuniformity in the structure of the medium that is periodic in each of the two independent directions. This problem was sketched in Sec. 17 for the one-dimensional case and will be fully discussed now. We can define a direct lattice with basis vectors pointing in the two directions $\mathbf{d}_1$ and $\mathbf{d}_2$ and having magnitudes equal to the periods of the structure in these two directions. Each point in the first elementary cell may be defined by a vector of the form [Eq. (25.15)]

$$\mathbf{r} = \xi_1\mathbf{d}_1 + \xi_2\mathbf{d}_2 \qquad \begin{matrix} 0 < \xi_1 < 1 \\ 0 < \xi_2 < 1 \end{matrix}$$

The vectors from the origin of the lattice for each point in the lattice are obtained by adding the vector for the corresponding point in the first cell to the vector of the origin of the cell in which the point lies.

$$\mathbf{r}' = (\xi_1\mathbf{d}_1 + \xi_2\mathbf{d}_2) + m_1\mathbf{d}_1 + m_2\mathbf{d}_2$$

A reciprocal lattice with basis vectors $\mathbf{b}_1$ and $\mathbf{b}_2$ defined by

$$(\mathbf{b}_i \cdot \mathbf{d}_k) = \delta_{ik}$$

as in Sec. 25 may be constructed. The vectors in this lattice are the propagation vectors of a wave propagating in the direct lattice, and the frequency of the wave is a function of the propagation vectors.

The general wave equation for a two-dimensional continuum with periodic nonuniformities is

$$\nabla^2\psi - \frac{1}{V^2}\ddot{\psi} = 0 \tag{28.1}$$

where ∇^2 is the two-dimensional Laplacian operator, ψ is the wave function, and V is the phase velocity of the wave, assumed to be a periodic function with periods $\mathbf{d}_1$ and $\mathbf{d}_2$. ψ is a function of (x,y) and of the time t. We assume that the time-dependent part of ψ is separable from the space-dependent part, *i.e.*,

$$\psi = u(x,y)e^{i\omega t} \tag{28.2}$$

from which we obtain a differential equation for u.

$$\nabla^2 u + \frac{\omega^2}{V^2}u = 0 \tag{28.3}$$

Now the wave equation for a two-dimensional homogeneous isotropic continuum is (after the time part is eliminated)

$$\nabla^2 u_0 + \frac{\omega_0^2}{V_0^2}u_0 = 0 \tag{28.4}$$

where V_0 is a constant depending on the constants of the medium. A solution of Eq. (28.4) is

$$u_0 = Ae^{-2\pi i(\mathbf{a}\cdot\mathbf{r})} \tag{28.5}$$

where

$$4\pi^2|\mathbf{a}|^2 = \frac{\omega_0^2}{V_0^2}, \qquad |\mathbf{a}|^2 = \frac{\nu_0^2}{V_0^2} \tag{28.6}$$

Equation (28.5) represents a plane wave. We may think of the wave as an ordinary sound wave or as an electromagnetic wave. Both of these have constant velocities in a homogeneous medium.

We solve the problem of propagation of waves through a continuum with periodic structure by perturbation methods. Thus we set

$$\left.\begin{aligned} u &= u_0 + \epsilon u_1 \\ \omega^2 &= \omega_0{}^2 + \epsilon k_1 \\ \frac{1}{V^2} &= \frac{1}{V_0{}^2} + \epsilon f \end{aligned}\right\} \tag{28.7}$$

We take **a**, the propagation vector, as fixed both in magnitude and in direction. u, $1/V^2$, and ω^2 are all functions of **a** in the reciprocal and **r** in the direct lattice. ϵ is a constant small enough so that any terms in ϵ^2, ϵ^3, . . . that we may encounter may be neglected in comparison with terms in ϵ, at least to a first approximation. The function f is periodic, and its average is zero in order to ensure

$$\frac{1}{V_0{}^2} = \overline{\left(\frac{1}{V^2}\right)}$$

We substitute Eq. (28.7) in the general wave equation (28.3).

$$\nabla^2 u + \frac{\omega^2}{V^2} u = 0 = \nabla^2 u_0 + \frac{\omega_0{}^2}{V_0{}^2} u_0 + \epsilon\left[\nabla^2 u_1 + \frac{\omega_0{}^2}{V_0{}^2} u_1 + \left(\frac{k_1}{V_0{}^2} + \omega_0{}^2 f\right) u_0\right] \tag{28.8}$$

if we neglect terms in ϵ^2 and higher powers of ϵ. The zero-order approximation is obtained by neglecting the term in ϵ. This is just the wave equation for the continuum without variations, and the solution has already been given. The first-order correction to the zero-order approximation is given by equating the term in ϵ to zero.

$$\nabla^2 u_1 + \frac{\omega_0{}^2}{V_0{}^2} u_1 = -\left(\frac{k_1}{V_0{}^2} + \omega_0{}^2 f\right) u_0 \tag{28.9}$$

This is an inhomogeneous differential equation as it stands. The homogeneous differential equation in u_1 is identical with the zero-order approximation and has the solutions.

$$u_1 = Be^{-2\pi i(a''\cdot r)} \tag{28.10}$$

where

$$4\pi^2|\mathbf{a}''|^2 = \frac{\omega_0^2}{V_0^2} = 4\pi^2|\mathbf{a}|^2, \qquad |\mathbf{a}''|^2 = |\mathbf{a}|^2 \tag{28.11}$$

To obtain the solution of the inhomogeneous equation we expand the periodic function f in a double Fourier series as in Sec. 26.

$$f = \Sigma C_{m_1m_2}e^{2\pi i(m_1\xi_1+m_2\xi_2)} \tag{28.12}$$

where the $C_{m_1m_2}$ are constants (in general complex to take care of phase factors) that may be evaluated from Fourier's theorem and $C_{00} = 0$. ξ_1 and ξ_2 are the coordinates of the point in the direct lattice at which f is to be evaluated with respect to the origin of the cell in which it lies, and m_1 and m_2 are integers. We may write f as a function of the vectors in the reciprocal lattice as in Eq. (26.12) by noting that

$$\left.\begin{aligned}(\mathbf{b}_1 \cdot \mathbf{r}) &= (\mathbf{b}_1 \cdot \xi_1\mathbf{d}_1) + (\mathbf{b}_1 \cdot \xi_2\mathbf{d}_2) = \xi_1\\(\mathbf{b}_2 \cdot \mathbf{r}) &= (\mathbf{b}_2 \cdot \xi_1\mathbf{d}_1) + (\mathbf{b}_2 \cdot \xi_2\mathbf{d}_2) = \xi_2\end{aligned}\right\} \tag{28.13}$$

and, therefore,

$$f = \Sigma C_{m_1m_2}e^{2\pi i[m_1(b_1\cdot r)+m_2(b_2\cdot r)]} \tag{28.14}$$

Substituting Eq. (28.14) into Eq. (28.9), substituting the solution [Eq. (28.5)] of Eq. (28.4) for u_0, and introducing the abbreviation

$$\mathbf{a}'_{m_1m_2} = \mathbf{a} - m_1\mathbf{b}_1 - m_2\mathbf{b}_2 \tag{28.15}$$

yields

$$\nabla^2 u_1 + \frac{\omega_0^2}{V_0^2}u_1 = -A\left(\frac{k_1}{V_0^2}e^{-2\pi i(a\cdot r)} + \omega_0^2\sum C_{m_1m_2}e^{-2\pi i(a'_{m_1m_2}\cdot r)}\right) = R(\mathbf{r}) \tag{28.16}$$

This is an equation with right-hand term of the type

$$\nabla^2 u_1 + \frac{\omega_0^2}{V_0^2}u_1 = R(\mathbf{r})$$

As is well known, such an equation possesses a *finite solution only* if the *right-hand term is orthogonal to all solutions of the homogeneous equation*, by which we understand the condition

$$\iint\limits_{\text{all space}} u_1^* R(\mathbf{r})d\tau = 0$$

where u_1^* is the complex conjugate of u_1 in Eq. (28.10). In our problem this means that first of all we must write

$$\iint\limits_{\text{all space}} R(\mathbf{r})e^{2\pi i(\mathbf{a}''\cdot\mathbf{r})}d\tau = 0, \qquad |\mathbf{a}''| = |\mathbf{a}| \tag{28.17}$$

where $\mathbf{a}''$ is any vector of length $|\mathbf{a}|$ according to Eq. (28.11). Once this condition is satisfied, the general solution of Eq. (28.16) has the form

$$u_1 = \Sigma B_{m_1m_2}e^{-2\pi i(\mathbf{a}'_{m_1m_2}\cdot\mathbf{r})} \tag{28.18}$$

and we shall be able to evaluate the $B_{m_1m_2}$ coefficients of this expansion in terms of known quantities. The general character of the solution will perhaps be better understood if it is written in a slightly different way.

$$u_1 = e^{-2\pi i(\mathbf{a}\cdot\mathbf{r})}F(\mathbf{r}); \qquad F(\mathbf{r}) = \Sigma B_{m_1m_2}e^{2\pi i[m_1(\mathbf{b}_1\cdot\mathbf{r})+m_2(\mathbf{b}_2\cdot\mathbf{r})]}$$

This means that the solution ψ is a plane wave.

$$\psi = e^{i\omega t}(u_0 + \epsilon u_1) = e^{2\pi i[\nu t-(\mathbf{a}\cdot\mathbf{r})]}A(\mathbf{r}); \qquad A(\mathbf{r}) = A + \epsilon F(\mathbf{r})$$

with an amplitude $A(\mathbf{r})$ that is a periodic function in the direct lattice.

In the discussion of condition (28.17) two cases must be distinguished:

1. Among all vectors $\mathbf{a}''$ having the same magnitude as vector $\mathbf{a}$, $\mathbf{a}$ must be considered separately, but there is no other vector $\mathbf{a}''$ coinciding with any of the $\mathbf{a}'_{m_1m_2}$ vectors.

$$\mathbf{a}'' \neq \text{all } \mathbf{a}'_{m_1m_2}$$

2. An exact (or approximate) coincidence can be found for a certain vector $\mathbf{a}''$ and a corresponding $\mathbf{a}'_{m_1m_2}$.

$$\mathbf{a}'' \approx \mathbf{a}'_{m_1m_2} \qquad \text{and} \qquad \mathbf{a}'_{m_1m_2} = \mathbf{a} - m_1\mathbf{b}_1 - m_2\mathbf{b}_2$$

which implies the condition

$$|\mathbf{a}'_{mm_{12}}| \approx |\mathbf{a}|$$

If this happens, both $\mathbf{a}$ and this special $\mathbf{a}''$ must be singled out in the discussion of condition (28.17).

Case 1.—In this case we first write the necessary condition (28.17) for vector $\mathbf{a}$, and we obtain a relation that determines the value of the unknown coefficient k_1. The integral in Eq. (28.17) becomes

$$\int e^{2\pi i(a\cdot r)}\left(\frac{k_1}{V_0^2}e^{-2\pi i(a\cdot r)} + \omega_0^2\sum C_{m_1m_2}e^{-2\pi i(a'\cdot r)}\right)d\tau$$

$$= \frac{k_1}{V_0^2}\int d\tau = 0$$

or

$$k_1 = 0 \tag{28.19}$$

since

$$\mathbf{a} - \mathbf{a}' = m_1\mathbf{b}_1 + m_2\mathbf{b}_2$$

is zero only for $m_1 = m_2 = 0$ and $C_{00} = 0$, and hence all the exponential terms become zero on integration. Equation (28.19) means that the average perturbation on the unperturbed wave is zero for this case. For all other vectors $\mathbf{a}''$ we have $\mathbf{a}'' \neq \mathbf{a}$ and $|\mathbf{a}''| \neq |\mathbf{a}'_{m_1m_2}|$ for all m_1 and m_2 values. This condition implies that none of the $\mathbf{a}'$ vectors may have the same magnitude as $\mathbf{a}$. The orthogonality condition (28.17) is automatically fulfilled for these other $\mathbf{a}''$ values, since the integrals will all go to zero. Using now our value $k_1 = 0$, we may attempt to solve Eq. (28.16) with an expansion of the type (28.18).

$$\nabla^2 u_1 + \frac{\omega_0^2}{V_0^2}u_1 = \sum \frac{-\omega_{m_1m_2}^2 + \omega_0^2}{V_0^2}B_{m_1m_2}e^{-2\pi i(a'_{m_1m_2}\cdot r)}$$

$$= -A\omega_0^2\sum C_{m_1m_2}e^{-2\pi i(a'_{m_1m_2}\cdot r)} \tag{28.20}$$

where

$$\frac{\omega_{m_1m_2}^2}{V_0^2} = 4\pi^2|\mathbf{a}'_{m_1m_2}|^2 \tag{28.21}$$

We may combine the two sums in Eq. (28.20) and set the coefficients of $e^{-2\pi i(a'_{m_1m_2}\cdot r)}$ equal to zero. This gives

$$\frac{\omega_0^2 - \omega_{m_1m_2}^2}{V_0^2}B_{m_1m_2} = -A\omega_0^2 C_{m_1m_2} \tag{28.22}$$

and solving for $B_{m_1m_2}$ in terms of $C_{m_1m_2}$, we obtain

$$B_{m_1m_2} = -\frac{A\omega_0^2V_0^2}{\omega_0^2 - \omega_{m_1m_2}^2}C_{m_1m_2} \tag{28.23}$$

We have assumed that $|\mathbf{a}'_{m_1m_2}| \neq |\mathbf{a}|$, and therefore $\omega_0^2 \neq \omega_{m_1m_2}^2$, so that $B_{m_1m_2}$ is always finite. Summarizing the *results for case* 1, we see that there is *no first-order correction to the frequency* (since $k_1 = 0$) and the *shape of the waves is slightly perturbed*, in accordance with the general scheme (28.18). Case 1 is characterized by the fact that *one* of the coefficients in A is much larger than the others, which are all of the order of ϵ.

Case 2.—We first discuss the case of an exact coincidence: $\mathbf{a}'' \neq \mathbf{a}$; $\mathbf{a}'' = \mathbf{a}'_{m_1m_2}$ for some m_1 and m_2 values, say n_1 and n_2.

In this case then

$$|\mathbf{a}'_{n_1n_2}| = |\mathbf{a}|, \qquad \mathbf{a}'_{n_1n_2} = \mathbf{a} - n_1\mathbf{b}_1 - n_2\mathbf{b}_2 \tag{28.24}$$

This means that there are two values of $\mathbf{a}$ that describe the motion equally well; *i.e.*, there are two solutions for the unperturbed problem that are equivalent. This degenerate motion is the analogue of the motion in the one-dimensional case when $a = \pm 1/2d$. We must write u_0 as a linear combination of two exponentials in this case, one for each of the solutions.

$$u_0 = Ce^{-2\pi i(a\cdot r)} + C'e^{-2\pi i(a'_{n_1n_2}\cdot r)} \tag{28.25}$$

with arbitrary coefficients C and C' to be discussed later. The terms in $\mathbf{a}'_{n_1n_2}$ will turn out to represent the reflected wave in Bragg reflection. Substituting Eq. (28.25) into Eq. (28.9) and using Eq. (28.14) will yield

$$\begin{aligned}
\nabla^2 u_1 + \frac{\omega_0^2}{V_0^2} u_1 = &- \frac{k_1}{V_0^2}\left(Ce^{-2\pi i(a\cdot r)} + C'e^{-2\pi i(a'_{n_1n_2}\cdot r)}\right) \\
&- \omega_0^2\Big(\sum CC_{m_1m_2}e^{-2\pi i[(a-m_1b_1-m_2b_2)\cdot r]} \\
&\qquad + \sum C'C_{m_1m_2}e^{-2\pi i[(a'_{n_1n_2}-m_1b_1-m_2b_2)\cdot r]}\Big) \\
= &- \Bigg[\left(\frac{k_1C}{V_0^2} + \omega_0^2C'C_{-n_1-n_2}\right)e^{-2\pi i(a\cdot r)} \\
&+ \omega_0^2 \sum_{\substack{m_1\neq -n_1\\ m_2\neq -n_2}} C'C_{m_1m_2}e^{-2\pi i[(a'_{n_1n_2}-m_1b_1-m_2b_2)\cdot r]}\Bigg] \\
&- \Bigg[\left(\frac{k_1C'}{V_0^2} + \omega_0^2CC_{n_1n_2}\right)e^{-2\pi i(a'_{n_1n_2}\cdot r)} \\
&\qquad + \omega_0^2 \sum_{\substack{m_1\neq n_1\\ m_2\neq n_2}} CC_{m_1m_2}e^{-2\pi i(a'_{m_1m_2}\cdot r)}\Bigg]
\end{aligned} \tag{28.26}$$

The two sums give no trouble since their exponentials are never zero, even when multiplied by $e^{2\pi i(a''\cdot r)}$ in the orthogonality relation (28.17). Therefore, we need consider only terms in $e^{-2\pi i(a\cdot r)}$ and $e^{-2\pi i(a'_{n_1n_2}\cdot r)}$. We use the orthogonality relation to determine k_1. All terms in the integral (28.17) vanish except the two already noted. We must allow two values for **a**″, one corresponding to **a** and one to $\mathbf{a}'_{n_1n_2}$. The first gives the equation

$$\int e^{2\pi i(a\cdot r)}\left[\left(\frac{k_1C}{V_0^2}+\omega_0^2C'C_{-n_1-n_2}\right)e^{-2\pi i(a\cdot r)} + \left(\frac{k_1C'}{V_0^2}+\omega_0^2CC_{n_1n_2}\right)e^{-2\pi i(a'_{n_1n_2}\cdot r)}\right]d\tau = \left(\frac{k_1C}{V_0^2}+\omega_0^2C'C_{-n_1-n_2}\right)\int d\tau = 0$$

Since $\mathbf{a} \neq \mathbf{a}'$ except in magnitude, the second term vanishes on integration. The constant coefficient of the integral must vanish, and this gives one equation in k_1, C, and C'.

$$\frac{k_1C}{V_0^2}+\omega_0^2C'C_{-n_1-n_2} = 0 \tag{28.27a}$$

The other orthogonality relation is

$$\int e^{2\pi i(a'_{n_1n_2}\cdot r)}\left[\left(\frac{k_1C}{V_0^2}+\omega_0^2C'C_{-n_1-n_2}\right)e^{-2\pi i(a\cdot r)} + \left(\frac{k_1C'}{V_0^2}+\omega_0^2CC_{n_1n_2}\right)e^{-2\pi i(a'_{n_1n_2}\cdot r)}\right]d\tau = \left(\frac{k_1C'}{V_0^2}+\omega_0^2CC_{n_1n_2}\right)\int d\tau = 0$$

by the same reasoning, and this gives a second equation in k_1, C, and C'.

$$\frac{k_1C'}{V_0^2}+\omega_0^2CC_{n_1n_2} = 0 \tag{28.27b}$$

These two equations must give the same ratio of C to C'. The condition for this is that the determinant of the coefficients of C and C' vanish. Thus

$$\begin{vmatrix} \dfrac{k_1}{V_0^2} & \omega_0^2C_{-n_1-n_2} \\ \omega_0^2C_{n_1n_2} & \dfrac{k_1}{V_0^2} \end{vmatrix} = 0 = \begin{vmatrix} \dfrac{k_1}{V_0^2} & \omega_0^2C_{n_1n_2}{}^* \\ \omega_0^2C_{n_1n_2} & \dfrac{k_1}{V_0^2} \end{vmatrix} \tag{28.28}$$

since $C_{-n_1-n_2} = C_{n_1n_2}^*$ is necessary to keep f real. Solving Eq. (28.28) for k_1 gives

$$\left(\frac{k_1}{V_0^2}\right)^2 - \omega_0^4|C_{n_1n_2}|^2 = 0 \qquad \text{or} \qquad k_1 = \pm\omega_0^2V_0^2|C_{n_1n_2}| \qquad (28.29)$$

Once k_1 is obtained, the ratio C'/C results from Eq. (28.27), and the remaining coefficients of expansion (28.18) are computed without difficulty.

Summarizing the *results for case* 2, we obtain a *first-order correction* on the frequency

$$\omega^2 = \omega_0^2 + \epsilon k_1 = \omega_0^2 \pm \epsilon\omega_0^2V_0^2|C_{n_1n_2}| \qquad (28.30)$$

and a wave whose general shape is still represented by Eq. (28.18), but which has *two* large coefficients (C and C') in its expansion instead of a single one as in case 1. All other coefficients in the amplitude function $A(\mathbf{r})$ are of the first order in ϵ.

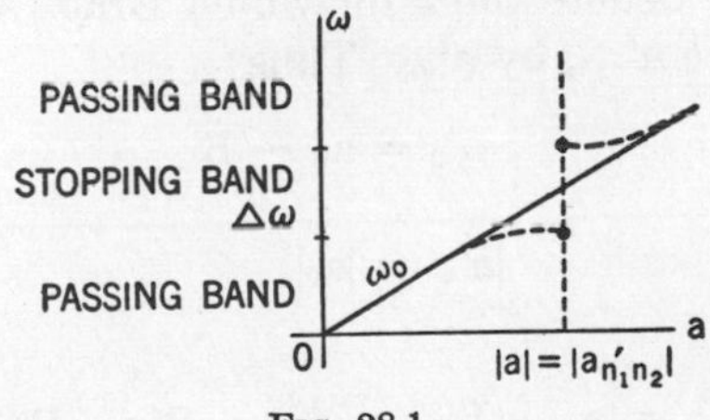

FIG. 28.1.

We have already seen in case 1 that the perturbation is small when $\mathbf{a}$ is not too close to any $\mathbf{a}'_{n_1n_2}$. When it is, however, the perturbation becomes larger and when $\mathbf{a} = \mathbf{a}'_{n_1n_2}$, the frequency has two possible values, one for each of the values of k_1 given by Eq. (28.29). Thus for the unperturbed wave the frequency is a linear function of $|\mathbf{a}|$ as shown by the solid line in Fig. 28.1. The dotted line shows ω as a function of $\mathbf{a}$ for the perturbed wave. For a certain value of $\mathbf{a}$ the curve splits up and the perturbation becomes less as $\mathbf{a}$ gets farther away from $\mathbf{a}'_{n_1n_2}$.

29. The Exceptional Waves of Case 2 and Bragg Reflection

We shall discuss later the transition from the portion of the curve that remains unperturbed and the exceptional point at which the splitting occurs, but first we wish to compare the conditions for case 2 with Bragg's formula for reflection from crystal planes. Bragg discovered that X rays can be selectively reflected from some of the atomic planes in crystal lattices, provided a certain relation among wave length, the distance of separation of the planes, and the direction of propagation is satisfied. We want to prove that this condition is equivalent to

$$|\mathbf{a}| = |\mathbf{a}_{n_1n_2}| \tag{29.1}$$

for the (n_1,n_2) values that define the atomic planes (which in the two-dimensional case are just rows of atoms). This is, of course, exactly the condition for case 2 of Sec. 28.

We consider the vector in the reciprocal lattice

$$\mathbf{B} = n_1\mathbf{b}_1 + n_2\mathbf{b}_2$$

This vector defines a direction in the two-dimensional reciprocal lattice and a row of atoms perpendicular to this direction in the plane of the direct lattice. This row is the row responsible for the Bragg reflection. For the reflection to take place, Eq. (29.1) must hold. We denote the $\mathbf{a}$ for which Bragg's condition holds by $\mathbf{a}_0$ and replace $\mathbf{a}'_{n_1n_2}$ by $\mathbf{a}'_0$. Thus

$$\mathbf{a}'_0 = \mathbf{a}_0 - \mathbf{B} \tag{29.2}$$

and

$$|\mathbf{a}'_0| = |\mathbf{a}_0| \tag{29.1}$$

In other words,

$$|\mathbf{a}'_0|^2 = |\mathbf{a}_0|^2 = |\mathbf{a}_0 - \mathbf{B}|^2 = |\mathbf{a}_0{}^2| - 2(\mathbf{a}_0 \cdot \mathbf{B}) + |\mathbf{B}|^2$$

and

$$|\mathbf{a}_0|^2 = |\mathbf{a}'_0|^2 = |\mathbf{a}'_0 + \mathbf{B}|^2 = |\mathbf{a}'_0|^2 + 2(\mathbf{a}'_0 \cdot \mathbf{B}) + |\mathbf{B}|^2$$

These two equations yield

$$|\mathbf{B}|^2 = 2(\mathbf{a}_0 \cdot \mathbf{B}) = -2(\mathbf{a}'_0 \cdot \mathbf{B})$$

or

$$|\mathbf{a}_0| \cos(\mathbf{a}_0,\mathbf{B}) = -|\mathbf{a}'_0| \cos(\mathbf{a}'_0,\mathbf{B}) = \tfrac{1}{2}|\mathbf{B}| \tag{29.3}$$

and since $\mathbf{a}_0$ and $\mathbf{a}'_0$ differ only in direction but have the same length,

$$\cos(\mathbf{a}_0,\mathbf{B}) = -\cos(\mathbf{a}'_0,\mathbf{B})$$

or $\mathbf{a}_0$ makes the same angle with $\mathbf{B}$ that $\mathbf{a}'_0$ makes with $-\mathbf{B}$. From Eq. (29.3) it now follows at once that $\mathbf{a}_0$ terminates on the perpendicular bisector of $\mathbf{B}$, while $\mathbf{a}'_0$ terminates on the perpendicular bisector of $-\mathbf{B}$. This means that the projection of $\mathbf{a}$ on

B has magnitude $|\mathbf{B}|/2$ or

$$|\mathbf{a}| \cos \varphi = \frac{1}{\lambda} \cos \varphi = \frac{|\mathbf{B}|}{2} = \frac{1}{2\delta}$$

or

$$\lambda = 2\delta \cos \varphi \tag{29.4}$$

where φ is the angle between **a** and **B** and δ is the distance between successive rows passing through the lattice points in the direct lattice and perpendicular to the basis vector conjugate to **B** [Eq. (25.22)]. This is illustrated in Fig. 29.1, showing a set of parallel rows in the direct lattice, with a distance of separation δ, with the incident beam $\mathbf{a}_0$, and with the reflected beam $\mathbf{a}'_0$. The elementary theory of Bragg reflection is as follows:

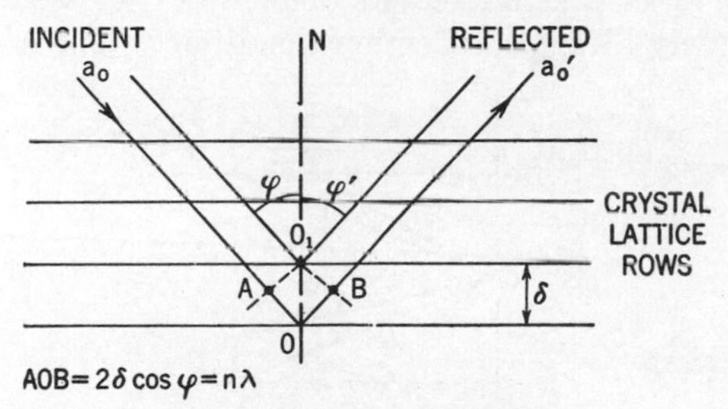

FIG. 29.1.—Bragg's reflection.

1. Angles φ and φ' must be equal, ensuring a uniform reflection from each lattice row.

2. Waves reflected from two successive lattice rows must be in phase; hence

$$AOB = 2\delta \cos \varphi = m\lambda \tag{29.5}$$

This is Bragg's formula, which checks with Eq. (29.4) when $m = 1$. Let us specify the integers defining the particular vector **B** corresponding to $m = 1$ by n_1 and n_2. We note that other vectors $\mathbf{B}_m$ of the reciprocal lattice are obtained if we take

$$\mathbf{B}_m = m\mathbf{B} = mn_1\mathbf{b}_1 + mn_2\mathbf{b}_2$$

and yield rows in the direct lattice separated by a distance

$$\delta_m = \frac{1}{|\mathbf{B}_m|} = \frac{1}{m|\mathbf{B}|} = \frac{\delta}{m}$$

from which we obtain the generalization contained in Eq. (29.5).

All this proves that case 2, with its two large components in the wave, corresponds exactly to Bragg's condition for reflection; *i.e.*, to the situation in which an incident C wave ($\mathbf{a}_0$) can be reflected from atomic rows in the lattice and generate a C' wave ($\mathbf{a}'_0$) of large amplitude.

30. Transition near the Discontinuity

We wish now to investigate the region where $\mathbf{a}$ almost satisfies Bragg's condition but not quite; *i.e.*, we allow

$$\mathbf{a} = \mathbf{a}_0 + \eta\mathbf{B} \qquad \text{where } \eta \text{ is small} \tag{30.1}$$

Then

$$\mathbf{a}' = \mathbf{a} - \mathbf{B} = \mathbf{a}_0 - \mathbf{B} + \eta\mathbf{B} = \mathbf{a}'_0 + \eta\mathbf{B} \tag{30.2}$$

where $\mathbf{a}_0$ and $\mathbf{a}'_0$ are the vectors defined in Secs. 28 and 29 and exactly satisfy Bragg's reflection condition. The new vectors

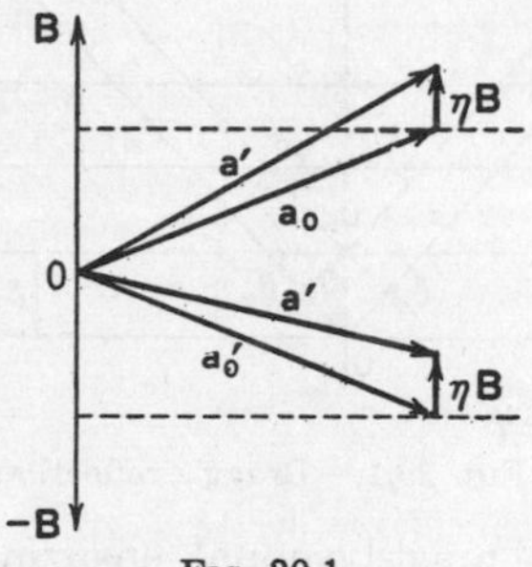

FIG. 30.1.

$\mathbf{a}$ and $\mathbf{a}'$ satisfy these same conditions approximately only, according to the η terms. This is shown in Fig. 30.1. The squares of the absolute values of $\mathbf{a}$ and $\mathbf{a}'$ are given by

$$\left.\begin{aligned} |\mathbf{a}|^2 &= |\mathbf{a}_0|^2 + 2\eta(\mathbf{a}_0 \cdot \mathbf{B}) \\ |\mathbf{a}'|^2 &= |\mathbf{a}'_0|^2 + 2\eta(\mathbf{a}'_0 \cdot \mathbf{B}) = |\mathbf{a}_0|^2 - 2\eta(\mathbf{a}_0 \cdot \mathbf{B}) \end{aligned}\right\} \tag{30.3}$$

according to Eq. (29.3) and by dropping η^2 term. Furthermore, we define the following expressions:

$$\left.\begin{aligned} \frac{\omega_0^2}{V_0^2} &= 4\pi^2|\mathbf{a}_0|^2 \\ \frac{\omega_a^2}{V_0^2} &= 4\pi^2|\mathbf{a}|^2 = \frac{\omega_0^2}{V_0^2} + 8\pi^2\eta(\mathbf{a}_0 \cdot \mathbf{B}) \\ \frac{\omega_{a'}^2}{V_0^2} &= 4\pi^2|\mathbf{a}'|^2 = \frac{\omega_0^2}{V_0^2} - 8\pi^2\eta(\mathbf{a}_0 \cdot \mathbf{B}) \end{aligned}\right\} \tag{30.4}$$

Also

$$u_0 = Ce^{-2\pi i(a\cdot r)} + C'e^{-2\pi i(a'\cdot r)} \tag{30.5}$$

as in Eq. (28.25), and

$$u = u_0 + \epsilon u_1$$
$$\frac{1}{V^2} = \frac{1}{V_0{}^2} + \epsilon f \tag{30.6}$$

The frequency ω of the u_0 wave is given by

$$\omega^2 = \omega_0{}^2 + \epsilon k_1$$

as in Eq. (28.7). This frequency ω is the same for both terms entering u_0 and should not be confused with ω_a and $\omega_{a'}$, which represent the frequencies of the (C,C') waves in the unperturbed medium, while ω is the common frequency of both terms in the medium with periodic perturbation.

We start again from Eq. (28.8), and we take Eq. (30.4) into account. The $\nabla^2 u_0$ term yields

$$\begin{aligned}\nabla^2 u_0 &= \nabla^2(Ce^{-2\pi i(a\cdot r)} + C'e^{-2\pi i(a'\cdot r)}) \\ &= -4\pi^2|\mathbf{a}|^2Ce^{-2\pi i(a\cdot r)} - 4\pi^2|\mathbf{a}'|^2C'e^{-2\pi i(a'\cdot r)} \\ &= -\frac{\omega_0{}^2}{V_0{}^2}u_0 - 8\pi^2\eta(\mathbf{a}_0\cdot\mathbf{B})(Ce^{-2\pi i(a\cdot r)} - C'e^{-2\pi i(a'\cdot r)})\end{aligned} \tag{30.7}$$

The new η terms characterize our present problem. η and ϵ are both perturbation coefficients and are assumed to be of the same order of magnitude. We set

$$h = \frac{\eta}{\epsilon} \tag{30.8}$$

We now separate the perturbation terms from the rest of the equation and set them equal to zero as before.

$$\begin{aligned}\nabla^2 u_1 + \frac{\omega_0{}^2}{V_0{}^2}u_1 = &-\left(\frac{k_1}{V_0{}^2} + \omega_0{}^2 f\right)(Ce^{-2\pi i(a\cdot r)} + C'e^{-2\pi i(a'\cdot r)}) \\ &+ 8\pi^2 h(\mathbf{a}_0\cdot\mathbf{B})(Ce^{-2\pi i(a\cdot r)} - C'e^{-2\pi i(a'\cdot r)})\end{aligned} \tag{30.9}$$

This is exactly Eq. (28.9) but for the additional h term. The discussion from now on parallels that given in Sec. 28, case 2. We again expand f according to Eq. (28.14) and group the terms that contribute to the perturbation as in Eq. (28.26). The two important terms are

$$\left.\begin{aligned}&\left[\frac{k_1C}{V_0^2} + \omega_0^2C'C_{-n_1-n_2} - 8\pi^2h(\mathbf{a}_0 \cdot \mathbf{B})C\right] e^{-2\pi i(a \cdot r)}\\ \text{and}\qquad&\\ &\left[\frac{k_1C'}{V_0^2} + \omega_0^2CC_{n_1n_2} + 8\pi^2h(\mathbf{a}_0 \cdot \mathbf{B})C'\right] e^{-2\pi i(a' \cdot r)}\end{aligned}\right\} \tag{30.10}$$

When we substitute the right-hand side of Eq. (30.9) in the orthogonality relation (28.17), all terms contribute zero to the integral except the two above. The first will give rise to one equation similar to Eq. (28.27*a*) for C and C' when the solution $e^{-2\pi i(a \cdot r)}$ of the homogeneous equation for u_1 is used.

$$\frac{k_1C}{V_0^2} + \omega_0^2C'C_{-n_1-n_2} - 8\pi^2h(\mathbf{a}_0 \cdot \mathbf{B})C = 0 \tag{30.11a}$$

The second one gives another relation similar to Eq. (28.27*b*), when $u_1 = e^{-2\pi i(a' \cdot r)}$ is used.

$$\frac{k_1C'}{V_0^2} + \omega_0^2CC_{n_1n_2} + 8\pi^2h(\mathbf{a}_0 \cdot \mathbf{B})C' = 0 \tag{30.11b}$$

The determinant of the coefficients of C and C' must vanish as before. This determinant is

$$\begin{vmatrix} \dfrac{k_1}{V_0^2} - 8\pi^2h(\mathbf{a}_0 \cdot \mathbf{B}) & \omega_0^2C_{n_1n_2}^* \\ \omega_0^2C_{n_1n_2} & \dfrac{k_1}{V_0^2} + 8\pi^2h(\mathbf{a}_0 \cdot \mathbf{B}) \end{vmatrix} = 0 \tag{30.12}$$

Solving for k_1 yields

$$\frac{k_1}{V_0^2} = \pm\sqrt{\omega_0^4|C_{n_1n_2}|^2 + [8\pi^2h(\mathbf{a}_0 \cdot \mathbf{B})]^2} \tag{30.13}$$

For $h = 0$ we have the Bragg condition and the same results as before. When h is large,

$$\frac{k_1}{V_0^2} = \pm 8\pi^2h(\mathbf{a}_0 \cdot \mathbf{B}) \qquad h >> 1 \tag{30.14}$$

But

$$\frac{\omega^2}{V_0^2} = \frac{\omega_0^2}{V_0^2} + \epsilon\frac{k_1}{V_0^2} = \frac{\omega_0^2}{V_0^2} \pm \epsilon 8\pi^2h(\mathbf{a}_0 \cdot \mathbf{B}) = \begin{cases} \dfrac{\omega_a^2}{V_0^2} \\[2ex] \dfrac{\omega_{a'}^2}{V_0^2} \end{cases}$$

according to Eq. (30.4). Thus **a** will be in one zone and **a**′ in another, and the values for ω will lie on the dotted transition curve shown in Fig. 28.1.

The whole discussion of Secs. 28 and 30 shows that discontinuities in the function $\nu(a)$ appear only when the **a** vector has its extremity on the perpendicular bisector of the vectors in the reciprocal lattice. This justifies the rule given in Sec. 27 for the construction of successive zones. Some examples of the shape of the first zone have been found by various authors, and the general rule was given by the present writer, with a comprehensive discussion of the structure of higher zones in two and three dimensions.

31. Examples and Discussion of Zones in Two Dimensions

The theory just developed in Secs. 28, 29, and 30 contains the principle of X-ray reflection from crystal lattices. X rays propagate through the crystal with the velocity of light in vacuum, and atoms or molecules may just slightly perturb the propagation. The perturbation is practically proportional to the electronic density, and an equation of propagation of the type of Eq. (28.8) is obtained, with a perturbation term f proportional to the electronic density. In a crystal lattice, atoms are regularly distributed along a direct lattice, each atomic nucleus being surrounded by a cloud of electrons that may partly overlap that of its neighbors. The electronic density is a periodic function with the periodicity of the lattice and can be expanded in a multiple Fourier series like Eq. (28.14). In the final results given by Eq. (28.30) or Eq. (30.13) only the absolute value $|C_{m_1m_2}|$ of the coefficients of the Fourier terms appeared. Hence, any experiment on wave propagation through the crystal lattice will give only the absolute value and not the phase angle. This latter may often be obtained from symmetry considerations and some general knowledge of the lattice structure, and then the whole Fourier expansion of the electronic space charge is found, from which the distribution of the space charge at any point can be computed. Figure 31.1 gives an example of such experimental results.

This is the principle of the procedure announced at the end of Sec. 26. As a rule, *all* coefficients C_m of the Fourier expansion are required, and there is practically no example of actual lattices where simplified assumptions such as Eq. (26.1) or (26.8) could be used. Sometimes a few exceptional terms may happen to be zero, but this is not very frequent.

The relation between the conditions yielding discontinuities in the $\nu(a)$ curve and Bragg's reflection condition was explained in Sec. 29. In principle the explanation is the same as for the relation between passing bands and stopping bands in the one-dimensional lattices discussed in Sec. 16: Let a certain direction

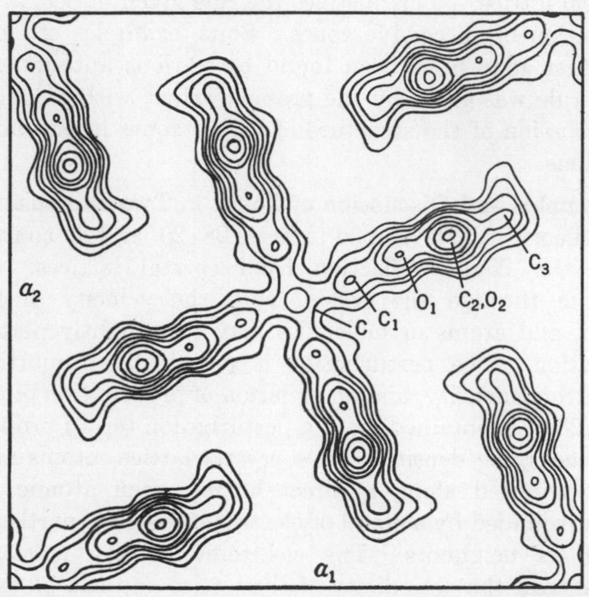

FIG. 31.1.—Crystal structure of pentaerythritol tetracetate $C\cdot(CH_2O\cdot CO\cdot CH_3)_4$ showing the position of carbon and oxygen atoms as resulting from a Fourier analysis based on X-rays diffraction. (*Courtesy of T. H. Goodwin and R. Hardy, Proc. Roy. Soc.* (*London*) *A, vol.* 164 (1938), *p.* 369.)

of propagation be given (direction of **a**) and the frequency ν of the wave be varied. If the frequency corresponds to a passing band, then the wave falling upon the lattice with this direction of propagation and frequency may be propagated through the crystal. Surface conditions at the boundary of the crystal will give only partial reflection from the surface. If, however, the frequency ν falls inside one of the stopping bands, like the intervals obtained in Fig. 28.1, then the corresponding wave cannot be propagated through the crystal and must be totally reflected from the surface.

The elementary Bragg theory, as sketched in Fig. 29.1, predicted reflection for just one frequency, while our more comprehensive treatment yields reflection for the whole stopping band $\Delta\nu$. For X rays, the perturbation of the wave by the crystal lattice is extremely small and the $\Delta\nu$ bands for ideal crystals are very narrow.

All this was explained here for a two-dimensional lattice structure, but X-ray reflection actually occurs in three-dimensional structures. Electron reflection according to wave mechanics (electrons being represented by De Broglie waves) is a more

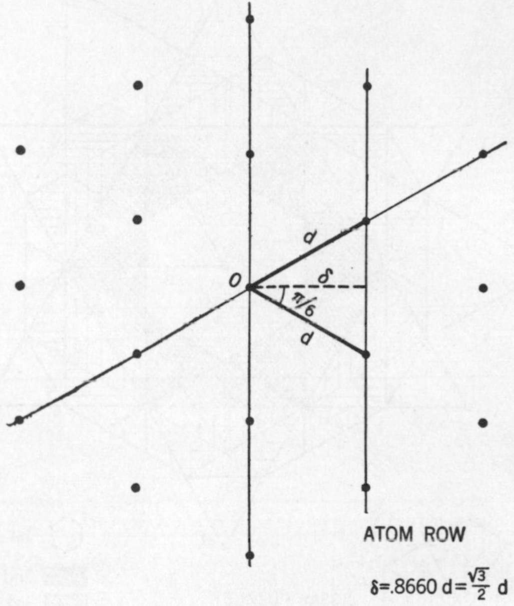

FIG. 31.2.—Hexagonal lattice.

accurate example of a two-dimensional problem, since in many experiments (Davisson and Germer) the reflection takes place on the surface of the crystal (two dimensions) and electronic waves do not penetrate inside the crystal.

We now give a few examples of direct and reciprocal lattices in two dimensions, with the corresponding zone structures. Where a certain direct lattice is given, the shortest way to find the reciprocal lattice is to use Eq. (25.22) and look for some parallel rows of lattice points in the direct lattice, compute their distance of separation δ, and obtain a vector of the reciprocal lattice by taking a length $1/\delta$ in the direction perpendicular to the rows. This is shown in Fig. 31.2 for a hexagonal lattice based on two vectors **d** making an angle $\pi/3$. The reciprocal lattice is another hexagonal lattice, turned through an angle $\pi/6$ and with vectors **b**.

$$|\mathbf{b}| = \frac{2}{\sqrt{3}} \frac{1}{|\mathbf{d}|}$$

as shown in Fig. 31.3. The first five zones have been drawn and

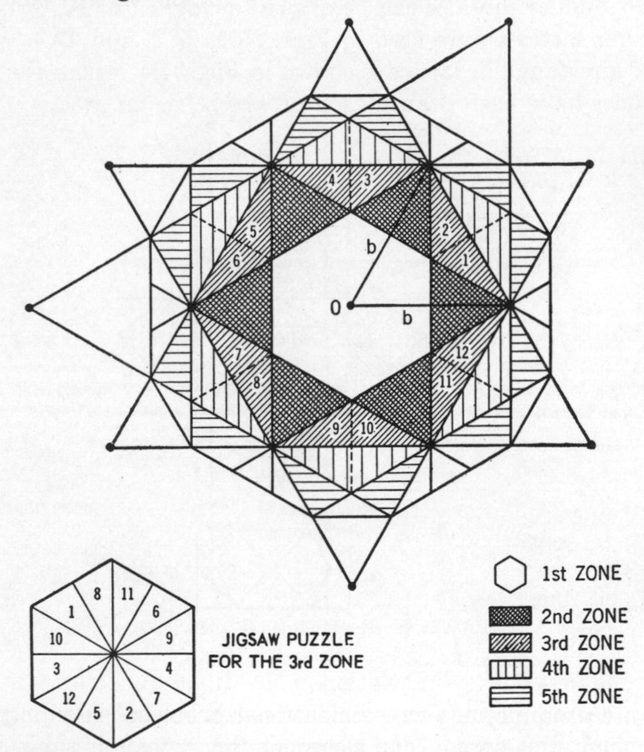

FIG. 31.3.—Zones for a hexagonal lattice.

the sixth one is easily recognized. Each zone covers an area equal to that of the first one or to that of the (**b**,**b**) parallelogram.

$$A_b = |\mathbf{b}|^2 \sin\frac{\pi}{3} = \frac{\sqrt{3}}{2}|\mathbf{b}|^2 = \frac{2}{\sqrt{3}}\frac{1}{|\mathbf{d}|^2}$$

while the area of the cell in the direct lattice is

$$A_d = |\mathbf{d}|^2 \sin\frac{\pi}{3} = \frac{\sqrt{3}}{2}|\mathbf{d}|^2 = \frac{1}{A_b}$$

Each zone can be reduced to the first zone by taking its sections and giving them a translation parallel and equal to one of the vectors of the reciprocal lattice. This is obvious for the second zone in Fig. 31.3. The case of the third zone is illustrated by a mosaic showing how the different sections of the third zone exactly cover the first one after being given the necessary translation. Similar mosaics can be drawn for higher zones.

Oblique lattices were used in Figs. 25.1, 27.2, and 27.4. The case of a rectangular lattice is shown in Fig. 31.4, where the first four zones have been drawn, each of which has an area equal to

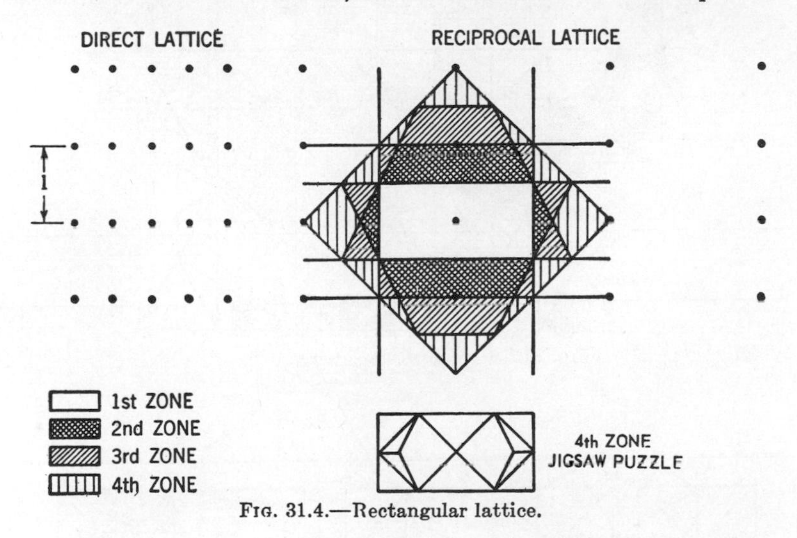

FIG. 31.4.—Rectangular lattice.

that of the first one. Translation of the different sections of one zone by vectors of the reciprocal lattice can be used to superpose them on the first zone. The corresponding mosaic is shown for the fourth zone. Figures 31.5 and 31.6 refer to the square-lattice structure and are original drawings given by the writer in a paper published in 1930. Figure 31.6 contains the mosaics for the successive zones in the square lattice.

All this theory is based upon the assumption of the periodicity of the function f of Sec. 28. It is not inconceivable that in certain physical problems the perturbation function f (the electronic density, for instance) may have a lower symmetry than the atomic lattice, and that its periodicity may offer a different character. In such cases the zone structure would

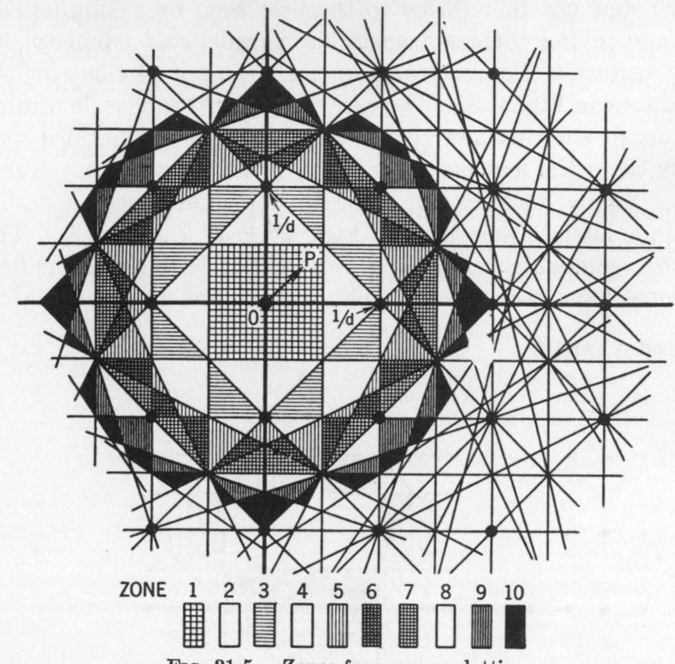

FIG. 31.5.—Zones for a square lattice.

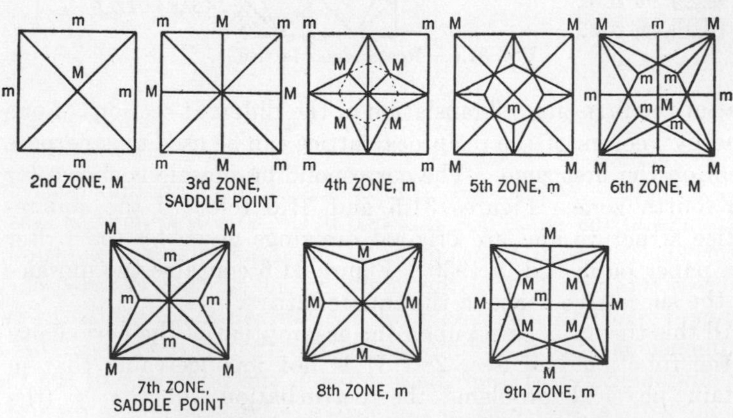

FIG. 31.6.—Square lattice, reduction of the first zones.

correspond to the actual periodicity and symmetry of the perturbation function and not to those of the lattice itself. This may be the case when the individual electronic clouds around each atomic nucleus already possess a certain structure (atoms in P, D, . . . states) and do not exhibit spherical symmetry (S state) for the isolated atoms.

Once the zonal structure has been obtained, most of the results established in the first chapters for one-dimensional structures can be readily extended to two-dimensional problems. Zones

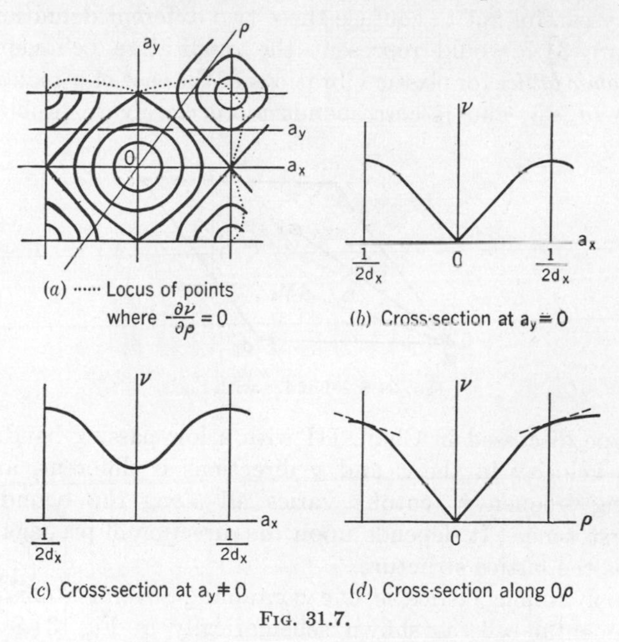

FIG. 31.7.

1, 2, 3, . . . correspond to intervals of similar numbers in one dimension, as explained in Fig. 27.1. The frequency ν was a periodic function of period $1/d$ in one dimension, and continuity across the boundary of the first zone meant that the $\nu(a)$ curve should reach this boundary with a horizontal tangent. In two dimensions $\nu(\mathbf{a})$ is a function of the two variables a_x and a_y (components of $\mathbf{a}$), and it must reach the boundary of the first zone with a zero normal derivative. We can plot a map of ν inside the zone, using lines of equal ν values (like lines of equal altitude on a map), and obtain a drawing like the one represented in Fig. 31.7a. A cross section of the map along Ox yields a curve similar to those of Chaps. I, II, and III (Fig. 31.7*b*). Another cross section at a_{y_0} gives the curve of Fig. 31.7*c* with horizontal tangents in the middle and at the ends of the interval. A radial cross section along $O\rho$, as shown in Fig. 31.7*d*, shows no horizontal tangents at the ends of the interval. The distinction between the radial derivative $\partial\nu/\partial\rho$ or a normal derivative is also exemplified in Fig. 31.7*a*, where the normal derivative is zero along the border of the zone, while the locus of point $\partial\nu/\partial\rho = 0$ is represented by the dotted curve. One must always be very careful not to confuse these two different definitions.

Figure 31.7 would represent the qualitative behavior of a *monatomic lattice* for elastic vibrations in the case of a rectangular lattice (d_x,d_y), and it corresponds more closely to problems of

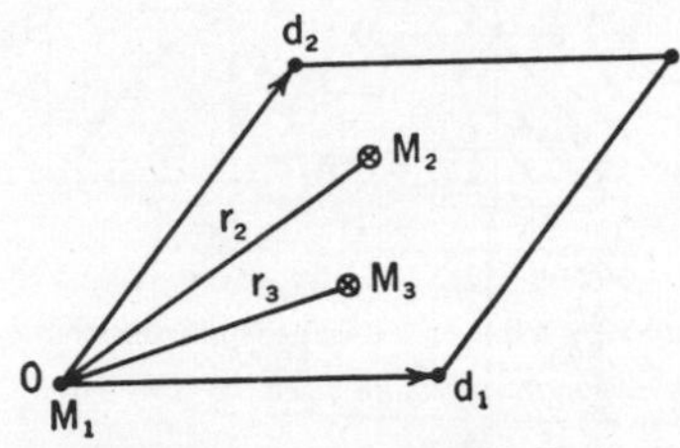

FIG. 31.8.—Lattice with basis.

the type discussed in Chap. III with a low passing band. The phase velocity in the x and y directions is different, and the limiting frequency (cutoff) varies all along the boundary of the first zone. It depends upon the direction of propagation as well as the lattice structure.

A polyatomic lattice is one containing several atoms in the fundamental cell, as shown schematically in Fig. 31.8. It is often called a *lattice with basis*, where the word "basis" is used for the bundle of vectors $r_2, r_3, r_4, \ldots, r_n$ defining the positions of particles $M_2, M_3, \ldots, M_n$ of the cell with respect to a certain particle M_1 taken as the origin. This is the two-dimensional generalization of Fig. 17.1. Such problems resulted, in the one-dimensional case, in a $\nu(a)$ curve with N branches, one acoustical and the remaining $(N - 1)$ optical. Here we obtain N surfaces covering the first zone. The cross section of these N surfaces along a given direction is very similar to the curves in Figs. 3.2 and 3.9 in one dimension.

The NaCl problem may be discussed more accurately in connection with the theory developed in Chap. IV. When the particles M_1 and M_2 differ in mass, the lattice is a square-centered lattice as shown in Fig. 31.9 and represents a lattice with basis, built upon two equal orthogonal vectors **d** and **d**. Its first two zones are shown at the bottom of the drawing. When, however, $M_1 = M_2$, the lattice suddenly changes its character and becomes a simple square lattice, built on two vectors $d' = d/\sqrt{2}$ at 45 deg. Its first zone includes both the

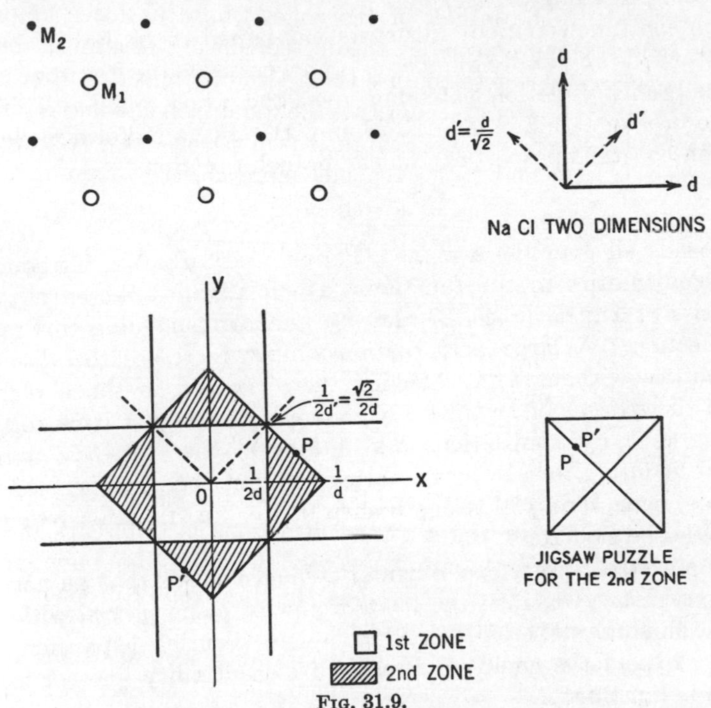

FIG. 31.9.

first and the second zones of the previous structure. In this case ($M_1 = M_2$) we obtain $\nu(\mathbf{a})$ as a single-valued function of **a** over the whole big zone. When $M_1 \neq M_2$, the four outer triangular sections (second zone) must be translated to the reduced first zone, and $\nu(\mathbf{a})$ becomes a double-valued function of **a** inside this new first zone. The limits of these zones are at $\pm 1/2d$ and $\pm 1/d$ along the x or the y axis (as in the one-dimensional problem) except for directions at 45 deg.; here the limits of the zones coincide. The mosaic of the sections of the second zone shows how two points P and P' come in contact with the new representation. Since ν obviously has the same values at P and P', by symmetry there is *no discontinuity* of $\nu(\mathbf{a})$ along the diagonals of the mosaic. Both branches of the $\nu(\mathbf{a})$ function are continuous except at the boundary of the new first zone.

N particles per cell mean N branches in the $\nu(\mathbf{a})$ function when $\mathbf{a}$ is restricted to the interior of the first zone. It may also be thought of as an extension of one branch $\nu(\mathbf{a})$ over N zones, as in the preceding paragraph.

A continuous periodic structure is obtained at the limit $N \rightarrow \infty$ and yields an infinite number of branches inside the first zone or a one-branch function extending over the whole plane. This is the problem studied in Secs. 28 and 30. For a uniform medium with constant properties, the one-branch function

$$\nu = W|\mathbf{a}|$$

extends all over the $\mathbf{a}$ plane. Periodic perturbation introduces discontinuities in the function $\nu(\mathbf{a})$ on all lines chosen as the limits of a zone (Secs. 27 and 29) and corresponding to Bragg reflection. A large perturbation simply increases the discontinuities without ever changing their location in the $\mathbf{a}$ plane. All the *sections* of an arbitrary zone can be brought back to the first zone by translations $h_1\mathbf{b}_1 + h_2\mathbf{b}_2$ in the *reciprocal lattice* and fit into a mosaic just covering the first zone. When this is done, each zone yields one branch of the $\nu(\mathbf{a})$ function reduced inside the first zone.

As stated before, experimental evidence shows that an actual crystal lattice exhibits the *complete* row or plane *system*, with no set missing. Therefore, the complete Fourier expansion of Sec. 26 and the complete system of discontinuity lines or zone limits must occur.

CHAPTER VII

THREE-DIMENSIONAL LATTICES

32. Direct and Reciprocal Lattices in Three Dimensions

The lattice in three dimensions is usually defined by three oblique coordinates. The elementary cell is thus a parallelepiped. We take the basis vectors $\mathbf{d}_1$, $\mathbf{d}_2$, and $\mathbf{d}_3$ to be the vectors joining the origin of the lattice with three particles in the lattice that do not all lie in the same plane. These vectors define the first elementary cell. Then any other set of basis vectors[1] is defined by

$$\left.\begin{aligned} \mathbf{d}'_1 &= \alpha_{11}\mathbf{d}_1 + \alpha_{12}\mathbf{d}_2 + \alpha_{13}\mathbf{d}_3 \\ \mathbf{d}'_2 &= \alpha_{21}\mathbf{d}_1 + \alpha_{22}\mathbf{d}_2 + \alpha_{23}\mathbf{d}_3 \\ \mathbf{d}'_3 &= \alpha_{31}\mathbf{d}_1 + \alpha_{32}\mathbf{d}_2 + \alpha_{33}\mathbf{d}_3 \end{aligned} \quad \begin{aligned} &\alpha_{ik} = \text{positive or} \\ &\text{negative integers} \end{aligned}\right\} \tag{32.1}$$

where the determinant of the α_{ik} must not be zero to ensure that $\mathbf{d}'_1$, $\mathbf{d}'_2$, and $\mathbf{d}'_3$ are not linearly dependent; *i.e.*, $\mathbf{d}'_1$, $\mathbf{d}'_2$, and $\mathbf{d}'_3$ do not all lie in the same plane. A lattice point is given by the vector

$$\mathbf{R}_{l_1l_2l_3} = l_1\mathbf{d}_1 + l_2\mathbf{d}_2 + l_3\mathbf{d}_3 \tag{32.2}$$

where l_1, l_2, and l_3 are integers. Points in the first elementary cell have vectors of the form

$$\mathbf{r} = \xi_1\mathbf{d}_1 + \xi_2\mathbf{d}_2 + \xi_3\mathbf{d}_3 \tag{32.3}$$

where $|\xi_i| < 1$. Any other point in the lattice may be obtained by adding vectorially the vector for the origin of the cell in which the point lies to its vector from the origin of its cell.

The *reciprocal lattice* is defined in exactly the same fashion as for two dimensions: Its basis vectors $\mathbf{b}_1$, $\mathbf{b}_2$, and $\mathbf{b}_3$ satisfy the nine equations analogous to Eq. (25.3).

$$(\mathbf{b}_i \cdot \mathbf{d}_k) = \delta_{ik} \tag{32.4}$$

The propagation vector for a wave propagating in the direct lattice is drawn in the reciprocal lattice as before. The analogue

[1] See footnote on p. 95.

to the fact that direct and reciprocal cells have reciprocal areas in two dimensions [Eq. (25.14)] is that they have reciprocal volumes in three dimensions.

$$V_d V_b = 1 \tag{32.5}$$

To prove this, we note that $\mathbf{b}_3$ is perpendicular to $\mathbf{d}_1$ and $\mathbf{d}_2$ from Eq. (32.4). Thus we may write

$$\mathbf{b}_3 = k(\mathbf{d}_1 \times \mathbf{d}_2) \tag{32.6}$$

Now

$$(\mathbf{b}_3 \cdot \mathbf{d}_3) = 1 = k[\mathbf{d}_3 \cdot (\mathbf{d}_1 \times \mathbf{d}_2)] = kV_d \tag{32.7}$$

Therefore, $k = 1/V_d$, and from Eq. (32.6) it follows that

$$\mathbf{b}_3 = \frac{1}{V_d}(\mathbf{d}_1 \times \mathbf{d}_2) \tag{32.8}$$

Similarly,

$$\left.\begin{aligned} \mathbf{b}_1 &= \frac{1}{V_d}(\mathbf{d}_2 \times \mathbf{d}_3) \\ \mathbf{b}_2 &= \frac{1}{V_d}(\mathbf{d}_3 \times \mathbf{d}_1) \end{aligned}\right\} \tag{32.9}$$

and conversely

$$\mathbf{d}_3 = \frac{1}{V_b}(\mathbf{b}_1 \times \mathbf{b}_2), \qquad \mathbf{d}_1 = \frac{1}{V_b}(\mathbf{b}_2 \times \mathbf{b}_3),$$

$$\mathbf{d}_2 = \frac{1}{V_b}(\mathbf{b}_3 \times \mathbf{b}_1) \tag{32.10}$$

Therefore,

$$(\mathbf{b}_3 \cdot \mathbf{d}_3) = 1 = \frac{[(\mathbf{d}_1 \times \mathbf{d}_2) \cdot (\mathbf{b}_1 \times \mathbf{b}_2)]}{V_d V_b}$$

and if we break the vectors in the numerator up into their Cartesian components and rearrange them, it becomes

$$(\mathbf{d}_1 \cdot \mathbf{b}_1)(\mathbf{d}_2 \cdot \mathbf{b}_2) - (\mathbf{d}_2 \cdot \mathbf{b}_1)(\mathbf{d}_1 \cdot \mathbf{b}_2) = 1$$

so that we obtain the desired relation.

Another theorem that we shall find useful is that the position vector of any lattice point in the reciprocal lattice is perpendicular to an infinite set of lattice planes in the direct lattice [the two-dimensional analogue is expressed by Eq. (25.22)] where a lattice plane is defined as a plane passing through a set of lattice points. Thus, if we denote the position vector of a lattice point in the reciprocal lattice by

$$\mathbf{H} = h_1\mathbf{b}_1 + h_2\mathbf{b}_2 + h_3\mathbf{b}_3 \tag{32.11}$$

where h_1, h_2, and h_3 are integers, and let

$$\mathbf{n} = \frac{\mathbf{H}}{|\mathbf{H}|} \tag{32.12}$$

be the unit vector in the direction **H**, the vector equation representing a plane perpendicular to the vector **H** is

$$(\mathbf{n} \cdot \mathbf{r}) = \frac{(\mathbf{H} \cdot \mathbf{r})}{|\mathbf{H}|} = C \tag{32.13}$$

where C represents the distance of the plane from the origin. Such a plane passes through a point $\mathbf{R}_{l_1l_2l_3}$ of the direct lattice if

$$\frac{\mathbf{H} \cdot \mathbf{R}_{l_1l_2l_3}}{|\mathbf{H}|} = \frac{h_1l_1 + h_2l_2 + h_3l_3}{|\mathbf{H}|} = C \tag{32.14}$$

by direct substitution for **H** and $\mathbf{R}_{l_1l_2l_3}$ from Eqs. (32.2) and (32.11). The numerator is an integer m. Now the distance between these lattice planes in the direct lattice is given by the smallest allowable variation of the right-hand member of Eq. (32.14). Since the numerator must be integral,[1] its smallest value is 1 and the distance:

$$\delta = \frac{1}{|\mathbf{H}|} \tag{32.15}$$

if Eq. (32.14) is reduced to lowest terms. One may also state this theorem by saying that the distance between the lattice planes perpendicular to a given direction **n** is the reciprocal of the distance of the lattice point in the reciprocal lattice nearest to the origin and in the direction **n** from the origin. An analogous theorem may be stated and proved in the reciprocal lattice.

The density of points in the lattice planes is proportional to $\delta = \frac{1}{|\mathbf{H}|}$. For the volume density is constant, and hence the number of points per unit area of the plane is directly proportional to δ. This result is, of course, also true for reciprocal lattices with appropriate changes in notation.

A vector in the direct lattice may be written

$$\mathbf{r} = \xi_1\mathbf{d}_1 + \xi_2\mathbf{d}_2 + \xi_3\mathbf{d}_3 \tag{32.16}$$

[1] See last sentence on p. 98.

where we have the relations

$$\xi_1 = (\mathbf{b}_1 \cdot \mathbf{r}), \qquad \xi_2 = (\mathbf{b}_2 \cdot \mathbf{r}), \qquad \xi_3 = (\mathbf{b}_3 \cdot \mathbf{r})$$

as may easily be verified. Similarly, for a vector in the reciprocal lattice

$$\mathbf{H} = \eta_1\mathbf{b}_1 + \eta_2\mathbf{b}_2 + \eta_3\mathbf{b}_3 \tag{32.17}$$

we have

$$\eta_1 = (\mathbf{d}_1 \cdot \mathbf{H}), \qquad \eta_2 = (\mathbf{d}_2 \cdot \mathbf{H}), \qquad \eta_3 = (\mathbf{d}_3 \cdot \mathbf{H})$$

Before going on to the propagation of waves, it is well to give some examples of three-dimensional lattices and their reciprocals.

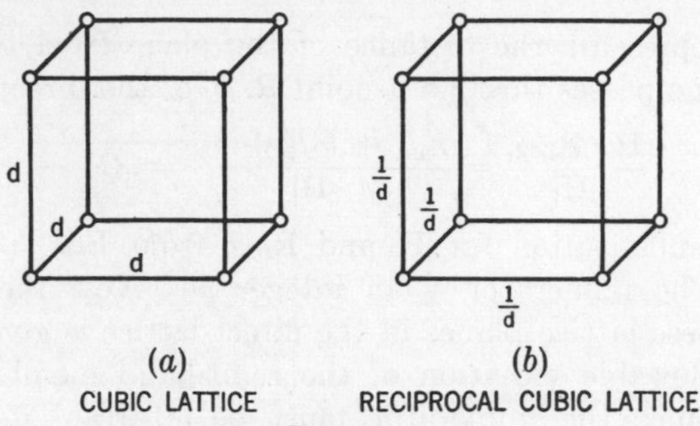

FIG. 32.1.

The simplest three-dimensional lattice structure is probably the *cubic lattice* shown in Fig. 32.1*a*. Here

$$(\mathbf{d}_i \cdot \mathbf{d}_k) = \begin{Bmatrix} d^2 & i = k \\ 0 & i \neq k \end{Bmatrix}$$

where d is the length of one edge of the cube. From Eq. (32.9) we obtain the reciprocal lattice $|\mathbf{b}_i| = 1/d$ and $\mathbf{b}_i$ parallel to $\mathbf{d}_i$. This reciprocal lattice, shown in Fig. 32.1*b*, is also cubic.

The simple cubic lattice does not occur naturally. There are, however, some related lattices that do. Let us consider the *face-centered cubic lattice* shown in Fig. 32.2*a*. This lattice has atoms in the center of each of the faces of the cube as well as at the corners. We think of the *elementary cell* in this lattice as the parallelepiped determined by the lines AE, AF, and AG. The volume of this cell is $V_d = d^3/4$ if the edge of the cube is d. The cell based on these vectors contains only one atom A, all others being considered as belonging to similar adjacent cells. It is easily verified that linear combinations of these three fundamental vectors give all the points in the lattice. The sum of the three vectors leads to B, while $AE + AF - AG$ yields point D. The cube d cannot be used as a fundamental cell, since it contains four atoms instead of one. If the atoms located in the faces of the cube were different from those at the corners, the lattice would become a cubic lattice with a basis $AEFG$, but this point of view is not logical for equal particles.

To obtain the reciprocal of the face-centered cubic lattice we make use of the theorem that a vector in the reciprocal lattice drawn to the point nearest to the origin in a given direction is perpendicular to a set of lattice planes in the direct lattice and has a magnitude equal to the reciprocal of the distance between

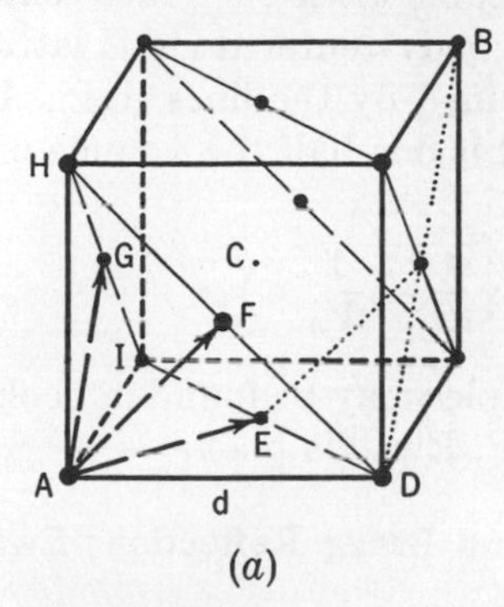

(a)

FACE CENTERED CUBIC LATTICE
AE, AF, AG BASIC VECTORS

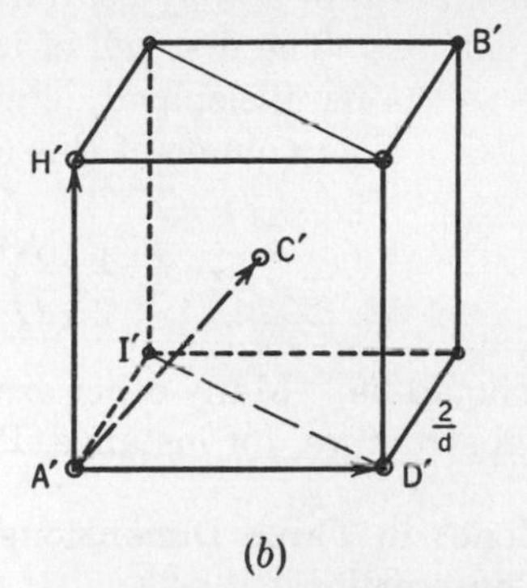

(b)

BODY CENTERED CUBIC LATTICE
A′D′, A′C′, A′H′ BASIC VECTORS

FIG. 32.2.

these lattice planes. The distance between the lattice planes in the direction AD is $d/2$, and hence there is a point D' of the reciprocal lattice in this direction at a distance $2/d$ from the point A' (see Fig. 32.2*b*). Similarly, there are points at distance $d/2$ from A in the directions AI and AH. The corresponding points are indicated by I' and H' in the reciprocal lattice. There is only one set of planes in the direct lattice separated by a distance greater than $d/2$, *viz.*, those parallel to the plane determined by $DEIGHF$. Thus there can be only one point in the first cube of the reciprocal lattice besides those already found. All other points will be in different cells. The planes are shown in Fig. 32.2*a*. These planes are separated by a distance

$$\delta = \frac{1}{3} AB = \frac{1}{3}\sqrt{3}\, d = \frac{d}{\sqrt{3}}$$

and hence

$$\frac{1}{\delta} = \frac{\sqrt{3}}{d} = \frac{\sqrt{3}}{2}\frac{2}{d} = \frac{\sqrt{3}}{2}b \qquad \text{where} \qquad b = \frac{2}{d}$$

gives the position of a lattice point in the reciprocal lattice in the direction $A'B'$. This point is at the center C' of the cube. This structure—a cube with a point at its center—is called a *body-centered cube.* Thus the reciprocal of the face-centered cubic lattice is a body-centered cubic lattice. It may easily be shown by similar reasoning that the converse statement is true: The reciprocal of a body-centered cubic lattice is a face-centered cubic lattice. The first cell of the body-centered cubic lattice is taken as the parallelepiped determined by the lines $A'D'$, $A'H'$, and $A'C'$. The volume of this cell is one-half the volume of the cube

$$V_b = \frac{1}{2}\left(\frac{2}{d}\right)^3 = \frac{4}{d^3} = \frac{1}{V_d}$$

as it should be. Many other examples may be found in books on crystal structure, for instance, P. P. Ewald's book.

33. Zones in Three Dimensions and Bragg Reflection; Ewald's Construction

The discussion given in Chap. VI can be used without any change for three-dimensional problems. We used vector notation, which works just as well for three as for two components. The areas S_d and S_b are to be replaced by the volumes V_d and V_b as in Eq. (32.5), and atomic planes in the direct lattice replace the atomic rows occurring in two dimensions, as explained in Eq. (32.14).

Triply periodic functions are expanded in triple Fourier series in exactly the same way as in Sec. 26 for two dimensions. The coefficients $C_{h_1h_2h_3}$ with three integral indices h_1, h_2, h_3 will simply be written C_h for convenience. The proof of the periodicity of ν as a function of $\mathbf{a}$ is carried out exactly as in Sec. 27 and may be briefly repeated here on account of its importance.

A point in the direct lattice is given by

$$\mathbf{R} = l_1\mathbf{d}_1 + l_2\mathbf{d}_2 + l_3\mathbf{d}_3 \tag{33.1}$$

where l_1, l_2, and l_3 are integers and $\mathbf{d}_1$, $\mathbf{d}_2$, and $\mathbf{d}_3$ are the lattice vectors. An arbitrary vector in the direct lattice is given by

$$\mathbf{r} = \xi_1\mathbf{d}_1 + \xi_2\mathbf{d}_2 + \xi_3\mathbf{d}_3 \tag{33.2}$$

where ξ_1, ξ_2, and ξ_3 are the components of $\mathbf{r}$ in the directions $\mathbf{d}_1$, $\mathbf{d}_2$, and $\mathbf{d}_3$, respectively. If a wave is propagating through the lattice and can be observed only at the lattice points $\mathbf{R}$, we may express the disturbance ψ by

$$\psi = Ae^{2\pi i[\nu t - (\mathbf{a}\cdot\mathbf{R})]} \tag{33.3}$$

where $\mathbf{a}$ is the wave vector and is regarded as a vector of the reciprocal lattice. The function ψ is evidently periodic in $\mathbf{a}$ and $\mathbf{R}$. The vector

$$\mathbf{a}'_h = \mathbf{a} + h_1\mathbf{b}_1 + h_2\mathbf{b}_2 + h_3\mathbf{b}_3 \tag{33.4}$$

where h_1, h_2, and h_3 are integers, will describe the motion at the lattice points just as well as $\mathbf{a}$; for

$$\begin{aligned}(\mathbf{a}'_h \cdot \mathbf{R}) &= (\mathbf{a}\cdot\mathbf{R}) + h_1(\mathbf{b}_1\cdot\mathbf{R}) + h_2(\mathbf{b}_2\cdot\mathbf{R}) + h_3(\mathbf{b}_3\cdot\mathbf{R}) \\ &= (\mathbf{a}\cdot\mathbf{R}) + h_1l_1 + h_2l_2 + h_3l_3 = (\mathbf{a}\cdot\mathbf{R}) + \text{integer}\end{aligned}$$

Since the same motion can be represented by $\mathbf{a}$ or any arbitrary $\mathbf{a}'_h$, the frequency must be a periodic function of $\mathbf{a}$ also, with the periodicity $\mathbf{b}_1$, $\mathbf{b}_2$, and $\mathbf{b}_3$ of the reciprocal lattice.

We wish to set up conventions for eliminating all but one of the values for $\mathbf{a}$, *i.e.*, define zones to which $\mathbf{a}$ is to be restricted, as was done in Sec. 27 for the two-dimensional case. The method is exactly the same, and we take the first zone to be a volume centered upon the origin O of the reciprocal lattice and limited by plane perpendicular bisectors of vectors in the reciprocal lattice. The first zone has a volume V_b equal to the volume of the elementary cell in the reciprocal lattice, and any point in space can be brought back into the first zone by $\mathbf{H}$ translations in the reciprocal lattice.

$$\mathbf{H} = h_1\mathbf{b}_1 + h_2\mathbf{b}_2 + h_3\mathbf{b}_3$$

Higher zones surrounding the first one are built in a similar way, and some actual examples will be given below.

The choice of these particular planes, bisecting and perpendicular to the vectors of the reciprocal lattice, is based on the analysis previously given in Secs. 28 and 30 for two dimensions. The theory of waves propagating through a continuous medium with a small periodic perturbation is identical with the two-dimensional theory, and one must distinguish between

$$\left.\begin{array}{ll} \textit{Case 1, where all} & |\mathbf{a}'_h| \neq |\mathbf{a}| \\ \textit{Case 2, where one certain } \mathbf{a}'_h\textit{, say } \mathbf{a}'_n\textit{, is} & |\mathbf{a}'_n| \approx |\mathbf{a}| \end{array}\right\} \tag{33.5}$$

where $\mathbf{a}'_h$ is a vector (33.4). Case 2 arises when two vectors $\mathbf{a}'_n$ and $\mathbf{a}$ having almost the same length can be found, such that their difference is a vector of the reciprocal lattice.

$$\mathbf{a}'_n - \mathbf{a} = \mathbf{H} = h_1\mathbf{b}_1 + h_2\mathbf{b}_2 + h_3\mathbf{b}_3 \tag{33.6}$$

A geometrical interpretation of this condition was presented in Sec. 29 where it was proved that the circumstances leading to case 2 were identical with those yielding Bragg's reflections in the crystal. This is always true if atomic rows are replaced by atomic planes in the direct lattice.

Another geometrical interpretation was given by P. P. Ewald. From point O of the reciprocal lattice he draws a vector $\mathbf{a}$ to point P. A sphere is drawn with radius $|\mathbf{a}|$ about the point P at the end of the vector $\mathbf{a}$. If it happens that this sphere passes through or near to a second point $\mathbf{B}$ of the reciprocal lattice, we obtain a discontinuity in the frequency as a function of $\mathbf{a}$.

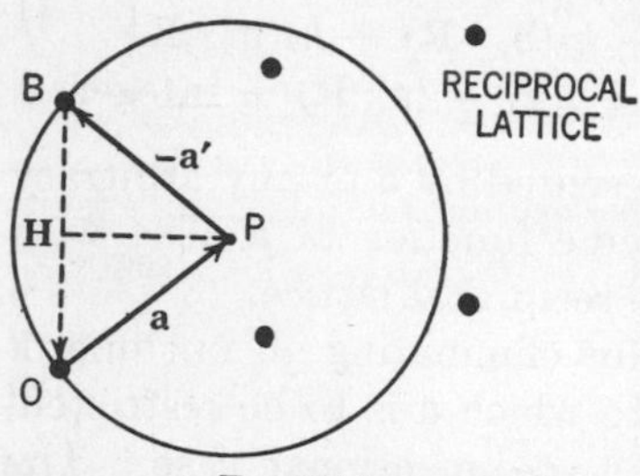

FIG. 33.1.

The reason for this is that there is some $\mathbf{a}'_n$ that just fulfills Eq. (33.6). There is no way of telling from the motion of the lattice points which of vectors $\mathbf{a}$ and $\mathbf{a}'_n$ should be preferred. Since the two vectors have different directions, we must assume that the motion is given by a superposition of the two waves. One of these is an incident wave and the other a reflected wave (Bragg wave). There will be two values for the frequency for this single value of $|\mathbf{a}|$ and hence a discontinuity in the ν vs. $\mathbf{a}$ curve.

We note that when Bragg reflection occurs, the vector terminates on a plane that is the perpendicular bisector of the line $\mathbf{H}$ joining two lattice points of the reciprocal lattice. This justifies the rule for constructing zones. We construct planes that are perpendicular bisectors of lines joining lattice points with the origin. The smallest polyhedron bounded by such planes is the first zone. The area bounded by the first zone and the second smallest polyhedron is the second zone and similarly for higher order zones.

34. General Results for a Wave Propagating in a Three-dimensional Periodic Medium

The problem of wave propagation in a continuous medium with a small periodic perturbation was discussed in Secs. 28 to 30 for two dimensions. The results immediately extend to three dimensions without any difficulty.

We shall now discuss the general problem of wave propagation in a periodic medium, without restricting our discussion to the case of a small periodic perturbation. The following sections will contain various applications and examples of this general theory.

The three-dimensional wave equation is

$$\nabla^2\psi + \frac{\omega^2}{V^2}\psi = 0 \tag{34.1}$$

We confine ourselves to waves in a periodic medium, and therefore we may assume

$$\frac{1}{V^2} = F(\mathbf{r}) \tag{34.2}$$

where $F(\mathbf{r})$ is periodic in the three directions specified by the lattice vectors $\mathbf{d}_1$, $\mathbf{d}_2$, and $\mathbf{d}_3$; *i.e.*,

$$F(\mathbf{r}) = F(\mathbf{r} + n_1\mathbf{d}_1 + n_2\mathbf{d}_2 + n_3\mathbf{d}_3) \qquad n_1,\ n_2,\ \text{and } n_3 \text{ integers}$$

The basis vectors of the reciprocal lattice are $\mathbf{b}_1$, $\mathbf{b}_2$, and $\mathbf{b}_3$, where

$$(\mathbf{b}_i \cdot \mathbf{d}_j) = \delta_{ij}$$

$F(\mathbf{r})$ may be expanded in a triple Fourier sum.

$$F = \Sigma C_{m_1m_2m_3}e^{2\pi i[m_1(b_1\cdot r)+m_2(b_2\cdot r)+m_3(b_3\cdot r)]} \tag{34.3}$$

The *solution* of Eq. (34.1) may also be expressed as a Fourier sum.

$$\psi = A(\mathbf{r})e^{2\pi i[\nu t-(a\cdot r)]} \tag{34.4}$$

where A is to be periodic in $\mathbf{r}$ and may be written

$$A(\mathbf{r}) = \Sigma A_{m_1m_2m_3}e^{2\pi i[m_1(b_1\cdot r)+m_2(b_2\cdot r)+m_3(b_3\cdot r)]} \tag{34.5}$$

The form taken for the ψ solution in Eq. (34.4) will be justified by the following discussion. It is generally known as F. Bloch's theorem and represents the generalization for three dimensions of an old theorem dating back to Floquet for the one-dimensional problem of Mathieu's equation, which is discussed in the next chapter. Combining Eq. (34.4) with Eq. (34.5) yields ψ as a Fourier sum.

$$\psi = e^{i\omega t}\Sigma A_{m_1m_2m_3}e^{-2\pi i(a'_{m_1m_2m_3}\cdot r)} \tag{34.6}$$

where

$$\mathbf{a}'_{m_1m_2m_3} = \mathbf{a} - m_1\mathbf{b}_1 - m_2\mathbf{b}_2 - m_3\mathbf{b}_3 \tag{34.7}$$

The last three terms in Eq. (34.7) specify a lattice point in the reciprocal lattice.

Substitution of the solution (34.6) into the wave equation gives a relation between ω and $\mathbf{a}$. The Laplacian ∇^2 of an arbitrary term of the sum in Eq. (34.6) is

$$\nabla^2 e^{-2\pi i(a'_{m_1m_2m_3}\cdot r)} = -4\pi^2|\mathbf{a}'_{m_1m_2m_3}|^2 e^{-2\pi i(a'_{m_1m_2m_3}\cdot r)}$$

and substitution in Eq. (34.1) gives

$$\begin{aligned}\nabla^2\psi &= -4\pi^2\sum_{m_i} A_{m_1m_2m_3}|\mathbf{a}'_{m_1m_2m_3}|^2 e^{-2\pi i(a'_{m_1m_2m_3}\cdot r)} = -\omega^2 F(\mathbf{r})\psi \\ &= -\omega^2\sum_{n_i} C_{n_1n_2n_3}e^{2\pi i\Sigma n_i(b_i\cdot r)}\cdot\sum_{p_i} A_{p_1p_2p_3}e^{-2\pi i[(a\cdot r)-\Sigma p_i(b_i\cdot r)]}\end{aligned} \tag{34.8}$$

replacing $\mathbf{a}'_{p_1p_2p_3}$ by its equivalent given in Eq. (34.7). We introduce new subscripts m_1, m_2, and m_3 in the last form of Eq. (34.8) as follows:

$$m_i = n_i + p_i \tag{34.9}$$

Equation (34.8) may now be written in the form

$$\begin{aligned}&\frac{4\pi^2}{\omega^2}\sum_{m_i} A_{m_1m_2m_3}|\mathbf{a}'_{m_1m_2m_3}|^2 e^{-2\pi i(a'_{m_1m_2m_3}\cdot r)} \\ &\qquad = \sum_{m_i}\sum_{p_i} C_{m_1-p_1,m_2-p_2,m_3-p_3}A_{p_1p_2p_3}e^{-2\pi i(a'_{m_1m_2m_3}\cdot r)}\end{aligned} \tag{34.10}$$

and equating corresponding terms, we obtain, finally,

$$\frac{1}{\nu^2}A_m|\mathbf{a}'_m|^2 = \sum_{p=-\infty}^{\infty} C_{m-p}A_p \tag{34.11}$$

where m and p stand for each set of three indices $m_1m_2m_3$ and $p_1p_2p_3$, respectively. This gives an infinite set of linear homogeneous equations to be solved simultaneously for the A's. This can be written

$$\sum_p \left(C_{m-p} - \frac{1}{\nu^2} |\mathbf{a}'_m|^2 \delta_{m,p} \right) A_p = 0 \tag{34.12}$$

where $\delta_{m,p}$ is a Kronecker symbol that is unity when $m_1 = p_1$, $m_2 = p_2$, and $m_3 = p_3$, and zero otherwise. After dividing by $|\mathbf{a}'_m|^2$ the equation reads

$$\sum_p \left(\frac{C_{m-p}}{|\mathbf{a}'_m|^2} - \frac{1}{\nu^2} \delta_{m,p} \right) A_p = 0 \tag{34.13}$$

This set of simultaneous homogeneous equations in the A_p's has a nontrivial solution only if the infinite determinant is zero.

$$\left| \frac{C_{m-p}}{|\mathbf{a}'_m|^2} - \frac{1}{\nu^2} \delta_{m,p} \right| = 0 \tag{34.14}$$

This means that the $1/\nu^2$ are the proper values of the infinite determinant $\left| \dfrac{C_{m-p}}{|\mathbf{a}'_m|^2} \right|$. The structure of the general equation is better understood if the determinant is explicitly written, with a one-dimensional problem (one subscript m or p instead of three) as an example.

$$\begin{array}{r|cccccc|}
p = & \cdots\ -2 & -1 & 0 & 1 & 2 & \cdots \\
 & \vdots & & & & & \\
m = -2 & \cdots\ \dfrac{C_0}{|a'_{-2}|^2} - \dfrac{1}{\nu^2} & \dfrac{C_{-1}}{|a'_{-2}|^2} & \dfrac{C_{-2}}{|a'_{-2}|^2} & \dfrac{C_{-3}}{|a'_{-2}|^2} & \cdots & \\
-1 & \cdots\ \dfrac{C_1}{|a'_{-1}|^2} & \dfrac{C_0}{|a'_{-1}|^2} - \dfrac{1}{\nu^2} & \dfrac{C_{-1}}{|a'_{-1}|^2} & \dfrac{C_{-2}}{|a'_{-1}|^2} & \cdots & \\
0 & \cdots\ \dfrac{C_2}{|a'_0|^2} & \dfrac{C_1}{|a'_0|^2} & \dfrac{C_0}{|a'_0|^2} - \dfrac{1}{\nu^2} & \dfrac{C_{-1}}{|a'_0|^2} & \dfrac{C_{-2}}{|a'_0|^2} & \cdots \\
1 & \cdots\ \dfrac{C_3}{|a'_1|^2} & \dfrac{C_2}{|a'_1|^2} & \dfrac{C_1}{|a'_1|^2} & \dfrac{C_0}{|a'_1|^2} - \dfrac{1}{\nu^2} & \dfrac{C_{-1}}{|a'_1|^2} & \cdots \\
 & \vdots & & & & & \\
 & \cdots & \cdots & \cdots & \cdots & \cdots & \cdots \\
 & \vdots & & & & &
\end{array} \tag{34.15}$$

where one should remember that expansion (34.3) must represent a *real* function F, hence the relation

$$C_{-n} = C_n^*$$

The equation is obviously *symmetrical in all* $|\mathbf{a}'_m|^2$, and so are the solutions

$$\nu^2 = f(\cdot\ \cdot\ \cdot|\mathbf{a}'_m|^2\ \cdot\ \cdot\ \cdot) \tag{34.16}$$

Some general results are thus provided:

a. The frequency ν is a periodic function of the $\mathbf{a}$ vectors, with the periods $\mathbf{b}_1$, $\mathbf{b}_2$, and $\mathbf{b}_3$ of the reciprocal lattice, since replacing $\mathbf{a}$ by any $\mathbf{a}'_m$ just changes the names of the $\mathbf{a}$ vectors without changing the set of $\mathbf{a}$ vectors as a whole. This is also shown by the fact that the wave itself [Eq. (34.6)] contains all the $\mathbf{a}'_m$ vectors in a similar way and offers no possibility of assigning to any one of these vectors special importance.

b. Changing $\mathbf{a}$ into $-\mathbf{a}$ makes a similar change in all vectors, since

$$-\mathbf{a}'_m = -(\mathbf{a} - m_1\mathbf{b}_1 - m_2\mathbf{b}_2 - m_3\mathbf{b}_3) = -\mathbf{a} + m_1\mathbf{b}_1 + m_2\mathbf{b}_2 + m_3\mathbf{b}_3 = (-\mathbf{a})'_{-m} \tag{34.17}$$

Hence, the same frequency is obtained for two similar waves propagating in opposite directions.

c. The frequency ν depends *symmetrically* upon all vectors $\mathbf{a}'_m$ and contains *only the absolute value of these vectors*, not their direction. This supports the rule used for the definition of the boundary of the zones, which was based only on the existence of certain relations between the lengths of the vectors $\mathbf{a}'_m$. The zone boundaries are obtained for a small periodic perturbation, as discussed in the next section.

Zone boundary:
$$|\mathbf{a}| = |\mathbf{a}'_m| \tag{34.18}$$

The definition of the first zone, for instance, is justified in this way. Among all the $\mathbf{a}'_m$ entering the expansion of the wave [Eq. (34.6)] we chose the smallest $|\mathbf{a}|$ as the parameter. This special vector $\mathbf{a}$ is used to specify the wave, but for each $\mathbf{a}$ we obtain an infinite number of waves, with an infinite number of frequencies that are the roots of the infinite determinant [Eq. (34.14)].

These infinite determinants will be encountered in the theory of Mathieu's equation, which will be discussed in the next chapter. The Mathieu problem corresponds to one dimension when the determinant (34.15) is obtained, and this special case has been completely computed by Hill and Whittaker (see Sec. 43). It would be very interesting to obtain an extension of Hill's results for three dimensions, but this problem has not yet been discussed.

We shall now examine the problem for the case of a small periodic perturbation.

35. Waves in a Homogeneous Isotropic Medium with a Small Periodic Perturbation

The problem of the propagation of waves through a three-dimensional homogeneous isotropic medium with a small periodic perturbation does not differ from that for two dimensions treated in Sec. 28. We assume that $1/V^2$ is almost constant with a small periodic variation.

$$\frac{1}{V^2} = \frac{1}{V_0^2} + \epsilon f \tag{35.1}$$

To continue the discussion we expand f in Eq. (35.1) as a Fourier sum.

$$f = \Sigma c_{m_1m_2m_3} e^{2\pi i \Sigma m_i (b_i \cdot r)} \text{ with } c_{000} = 0 \tag{35.2}$$

Then $C_{n_1n_2n_3}$ in the expansion of $F(\mathbf{r}) = 1/V^2$ may be written in the following form:

$$C_{n_1n_2n_3} = \frac{1}{V_0^2} \delta_{0n_1}\delta_{0n_2}\delta_{0n_3} + \epsilon c_{n_1n_2n_3} \tag{35.3}$$

with Kronecker symbols δ, which mean

$$\left.\begin{aligned} C_{000} &= \frac{1}{V_0^2} && \text{finite} \\ \text{and all other} \quad C_{n_1n_2n_3} &= \epsilon c_{n_1n_2n_3} && \text{infinitely small} \end{aligned}\right\} \tag{35.4}$$

This means that the determinant (34.14) or (34.15) has finite terms only along the principal diagonal, while all off-diagonal terms are infinitely small. We want to expand the determinant in powers of ϵ. The term independent of ϵ is the diagonal term

$$\prod_m \left(\frac{C_{000}}{|\mathbf{a}'_m|^2} - \frac{1}{\nu^2} \right) \tag{35.5}$$

which we may write as

$$\prod_m \left(\frac{1}{\nu_m^2} - \frac{1}{\nu^2}\right); \qquad \frac{1}{\nu_m^2} = \frac{C_{000}}{|\mathbf{a}'_m|^2} = \frac{1}{V_0^2|\mathbf{a}'_m|^2} \tag{35.6}$$

The next terms in the expansion are in ϵ^2 and are obtained by replacing the terms n and p on the diagonal by the $(n \cdot p)$ and $(p \cdot n)$ nondiagonal terms. These terms have a minus sign according to the law of determinants.

$$-\epsilon^2 \sum_{n,p} \prod_{\substack{m\neq n\\ m\neq p}} \left(\frac{1}{\nu_m^2} - \frac{1}{\nu^2}\right) \frac{c_{n-p}c_{p-n}}{|a'_,|^2|a'_p|^2}$$

$$= -\epsilon^2 V_0^4 \sum_{n,p} \prod_{\substack{m\\ n\neq m\neq p}} \left(\frac{1}{\nu_m^2} - \frac{1}{\nu^2}\right) \frac{|c_{n-p}|^2}{\nu_n^2\nu_p^2}. \tag{35.7}$$

To make this process clear, let us consider the determinant (34.15) and write the term $n = 0$, $p = 1$.

$$\cdots \left(\frac{C_0}{|\mathbf{a}'_{-2}|^2} - \frac{1}{\nu^2}\right)\left(\frac{C_0}{|\mathbf{a}'_{-1}|^2} - \frac{1}{\nu^2}\right)\left(-\epsilon^2 \frac{c_{-1}}{|\mathbf{a}'_0|^2}\frac{c_1}{|\mathbf{a}'_1|^2}\right)\left(\frac{C_0}{|\mathbf{a}'_2|^2} - \frac{1}{\nu^2}\right)\cdots$$

We shall not attempt to compute terms in ϵ^3, ϵ^4, ... Grouping terms (35.6) and (35.7) together, we obtain for our determinant

$$D = 0 = \sum_{n,p} \prod_{\substack{m\\ n\neq m\neq p}}$$

$$\left(\frac{1}{\nu_m^2} - \frac{1}{\nu^2}\right)\left[\left(\frac{1}{\nu_n^2} - \frac{1}{\nu^2}\right)\left(\frac{1}{\nu_p^2} - \frac{1}{\nu^2}\right) - \epsilon^2 V_0^4 \frac{|c_{n-p}|^2}{\nu_n^2\nu_p^2}\right] \tag{35.8}$$

We can now discuss the solution of this equation. The *first approximation* is obviously obtained by making the product (35.6) of the diagonal terms zero, which means that ν must be equal to one of the ν_m's:

$$\nu = \nu_m \tag{35.9}$$

This is correct as long as no two values ν_n and ν_p are too close together, which means

Case 1:

$$\text{All} \quad \nu_n \neq \nu_p \quad \text{or all} \quad |\mathbf{a}'_n|^2 \neq |\mathbf{a}'_p|^2 \tag{35.10}$$

An exception arises when two values ν_n and ν_p are close enough to make both terms of equal order of magnitude in one of the square brackets of expansion (35.8).

Case 2:

$$\nu_n \approx \nu_p \qquad \text{or} \qquad |\mathbf{a}'_n|^2 \approx |\mathbf{a}'_p|^2 \tag{35.11}$$

When this occurs, we can no longer neglect the ϵ^2 terms, and instead of simply writing

$$\left(\frac{1}{\nu_n^2} - \frac{1}{\nu^2}\right)\left(\frac{1}{\nu_p^2} - \frac{1}{\nu^2}\right) = 0$$

we must take the complete square bracket from Eq. (35.8) and write

$$\left(\frac{1}{\nu_n^2} - \frac{1}{\nu^2}\right)\left(\frac{1}{\nu_p^2} - \frac{1}{\nu^2}\right) - \epsilon^2 V_0{}^4 \frac{|c_{n-p}|^2}{\nu_n{}^2\nu_p{}^2} = 0 \tag{35.12}$$

an equation that includes both case 2 of Sec. 28 and the case discussed in Sec. 30.

In order to see this clearly, let us use the same notation as in Chap. VI, Secs. 28 and 30, and choose one of our two vectors, $\mathbf{a}'_n$ for instance, as vector $\mathbf{a}$. This is always allowed on account of the equivalence of all vectors $\mathbf{a}'_m$. Hence we write, instead of (35.11),

$$\nu_n = \nu_0, \qquad |\mathbf{a}'_n| = |\mathbf{a} - n_1\mathbf{b}_1 - n_2\mathbf{b}_2 - n_3\mathbf{b}_3| \approx |\mathbf{a}| \tag{35.13}$$

To make the comparison with Sec. 30 easier, let us call $\mathbf{a}_0$ the vector for which the relation (35.13) would be exactly satisfied and take

$$|\mathbf{a}_0 - \mathbf{B}| = |\mathbf{a}_0|, \qquad \mathbf{B} = n_1\mathbf{b}_1 + n_2\mathbf{b}_2 + n_3\mathbf{b}_3 \tag{35.14}$$

Then the case of the approximate condition (35.13) is defined by

$$\left.\begin{aligned} \mathbf{a} &= \mathbf{a}_0 + \eta\mathbf{B} \\ \mathbf{a}'_n &= \mathbf{a}_0 - \mathbf{B} + \eta\mathbf{B} \end{aligned} \qquad \eta \text{ small} \right\} \tag{35.15}$$

which corresponds to the definitions (30.1) and yields, as in Eqs. (30.3) and (30.4),

$$\left.\begin{aligned} |\mathbf{a}|^2 &= |\mathbf{a}_0|^2 + 2\eta(\mathbf{a}_0 \cdot \mathbf{B}) \\ |\mathbf{a}'_n|^2 &= |\mathbf{a}_0|^2 - 2\eta(\mathbf{a}_0 \cdot \mathbf{B}) \end{aligned}\right\} \tag{35.16}$$

or

$$\left.\begin{aligned} \nu^2 &= \nu_0{}^2 + 2\eta V_0{}^2(\mathbf{a}_0 \cdot \mathbf{B}) \\ \nu_n{}^2 &= \nu_0{}^2 - 2\eta V_0{}^2(\mathbf{a}_0 \cdot \mathbf{B}) \end{aligned}\right\} \tag{35.17}$$

With this notation, Eq. (35.12) can be transcribed as

$$\left[\frac{1}{\nu_0^2} + \frac{2\eta}{\nu_0^4} V_0^2(\mathbf{a}_0 \cdot \mathbf{B}) - \frac{1}{\nu^2}\right]\left[\frac{1}{\nu_0^2} - \frac{2\eta}{\nu_0^4} V_0^2(\mathbf{a}_0 \cdot \mathbf{B}) - \frac{1}{\nu^2}\right] - \epsilon^2 V_0^4 \frac{|c_n|^2}{\nu_n^2\nu^2} = 0$$

but $\nu_n^2\nu^2$ can be replaced by ν_0^4 in the last term, which is already small like ϵ^2.

$$\left(\frac{1}{\nu^2} - \frac{1}{\nu_0^2}\right)^2 - \frac{4\eta^2}{\nu_0^8} V_0^4(\mathbf{a}_0 \cdot \mathbf{B})^2 - \epsilon^2 V_0^4 \frac{|c_n|^2}{\nu_0^4} = 0 \qquad (35.18)$$

which yields

$$\frac{1}{\nu^2} = \frac{1}{\nu_0^2} \pm \epsilon \frac{V_0^2}{\nu_0^4} \sqrt{\nu_0^4|c_n|^2 + [2h(\mathbf{a}_0 \cdot \mathbf{B})]^2}, \qquad h = \frac{\eta}{\epsilon} \qquad (35.19)$$

This is exactly the same as Eq. (30.13), where we had

$$\omega^2 = \omega_0^2 + \epsilon k_1 \qquad (28.7)$$

$$k_1 = \pm V_0^2 4\pi^2 \sqrt{\nu_0^4|c_n|^2 + [2h(\mathbf{a}_0 \cdot \mathbf{B})]^2} \qquad (30.13)$$

which means

$$\nu^2 = \nu_0^2 + \frac{\epsilon}{4\pi^2} k_1$$

$$\frac{1}{\nu^2} = \frac{1}{\nu_0^2} - \frac{\epsilon}{4\pi^2\nu_0^4} k_1$$

and checks with Eq. (35.19).

Thus the general method developed in Sec. 34 checks completely with the approximation previously discussed in Secs. 28 and 30. Just as in this previous discussion, case 1 is characterized by one amplitude coefficient A much larger than all other A coefficients in expansion (35.6), and the definition that gives the best connection with the problem of the uniform homogeneous medium consists in calling A_{000} this specially large coefficient, as was done in Sec. 28. In case 2, two A coefficients are of the same order of magnitude, and according to the notation (35.14) one of them is called A_{000} and the other one $A_{n_1n_2n_3}$.

The whole theory of zone structure was based on the discussion of Secs. 28 and 30 and finds here a more complete and general foundation.

36. General Remarks on Waves in a Discontinuous Lattice

We have defined in Sec. 31 a *lattice with basis* for two dimensions (Fig. 31.8), and the same definition applies for three dimensions. The whole lattice is based on three vectors $\mathbf{d}_1$, $\mathbf{d}_2$, and $\mathbf{d}_3$ as before, and inside each $\mathbf{d}$ cell there is a certain number N of particles, whose positions with respect to the origin of the cell are

$$\mathbf{r}_1, \mathbf{r}_2, \cdots, \mathbf{r}_N$$

and whose masses are taken as $M_1, M_2, \ldots M_N$, respectively. If $N = 1$, we obtain the monatomic lattice, with one particle per cell, and it is convenient to take $r_1 = 0$ and have this particle at the origin of the cell. In the general case, an arbitrary particle k anywhere in the lattice is located at

$$\mathbf{r} = \mathbf{r}_j + n_1\mathbf{d}_1 + n_2\mathbf{d}_2 + n_3\mathbf{d}_3 \tag{36.1}$$

where particle k is the jth particle in cell (n_1,n_2,n_3). A general scheme for propagation of waves through such a lattice was given in Sec. 17 for the one-dimensional case. It could be developed in a similar way for three dimensions. For each j type of particle in the lattice we could write a wave

$$\psi_j = A'_j e^{2\pi i(\nu t - \mathbf{a}\cdot\mathbf{r})} \tag{36.2}$$

but it is more comvenient to include the exponential $e^{-2\pi i(\mathbf{a}\cdot\mathbf{r}_j)}$ in the complex amplitude A_j and to keep the same imaginary exponential in all the j waves.

$$\left.\begin{array}{c} e^{i(\omega t - n_1k_1 - n_2k_2 - n_3k_3)} \\ k_1 = 2\pi(\mathbf{a}\cdot\mathbf{d}_1), \qquad k_2 = 2\pi(\mathbf{a}\cdot\mathbf{d}_2), \qquad k_3 = 2\pi(\mathbf{a}\cdot\mathbf{d}_3) \end{array}\right\} \tag{36.3}$$

as we did in Sec. 27 for two dimensions. The wave motion of particles j is then described by

$$\psi_j = A_j e^{i(\omega t - n_1k_1 - n_2k_2 - n_3k_3)}, \qquad A_j = A'_j e^{-2\pi i(\mathbf{a}\cdot\mathbf{r}_j)} \tag{36.4}$$

There will be N constants: $A_1, A_2, \ldots, A_N$, in general complex to include the phase of particle j with particle 1.

As in the one-dimensional case we will have N equations of motion, and substitution of Eq. (36.4) in the equations of motion will yield N linear equations in the A_i. Each A_i is a vector function and has therefore three components, thus yielding altogether $3N$ linear homogeneous equations to be solved simultaneously. As before, we equate the determinant of the coefficients of the A_j to zero, which yields an equation of degree $3N$ in ω^2. This means that for each value of a in the first zone of the reciprocal lattice, there will be $3N$ values for the frequency. This is shown schematically in Fig. 36.1.

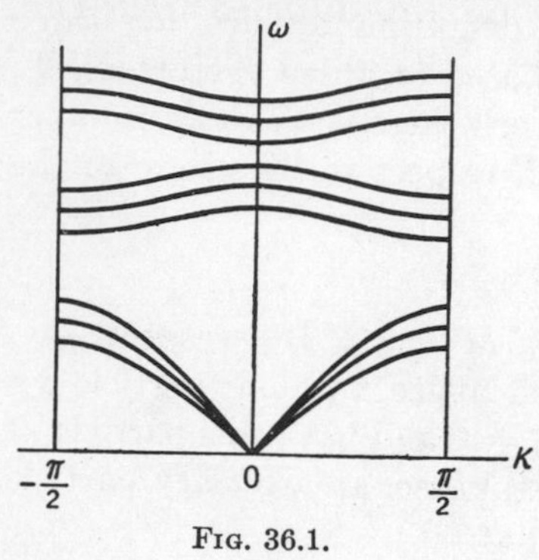

FIG. 36.1.

The number of branches for the function $\nu(\mathbf{a})$ is thus equal to three times the number N of particles per cell. A continuous periodic medium may be regarded as the limit $N \to \infty$. Uncertainty in the wave vector $\mathbf{a}$ is best avoided by restricting $\mathbf{a}$ to the interior of the first zone.

37. Some Examples of Zones in Three Dimensions

The face-centered and body-centered cubic lattices were discussed in Sec. 32 (Fig. 32.2) where it was proved that they are mutually reciprocal. The *face-centered cubic lattice* is of special

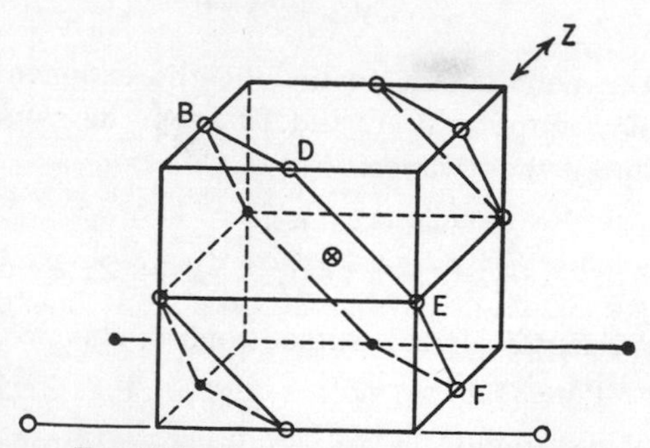

FIG. 37.1.—Face-centered cubic lattice.

importance since it represents one of the possible structures for close-packed spheres. The lattice can be described as in Fig. 32.2*a*, and also as in Fig. 37.1, which obviously represents the same structure since it is derived from Fig. 32.2*a* by translation of ½*d* parallel to the axis. Looking at this cubic structure from the direction of the arrow and taking the diagonal *OZ* as the vertical axis, we obtain the drawing of Fig. 37.2, which represents the same lattice as the hexagonal structure shown in Fig. 37.3. This is one of the possible structures obtained by piling up equal spheres provided that the distance from the central sphere to its *twelve neighbors* is the same, and this is the case for

$$\frac{c}{d} = 2\sqrt{\frac{2}{3}} = 1.633 \tag{37.1}$$

where the distance c measured vertically from A to B is slightly less than the distance $BE = \sqrt{3}\,d = 1.732d$. The structure repeats itself after a vertical distance $(3/2)c$.

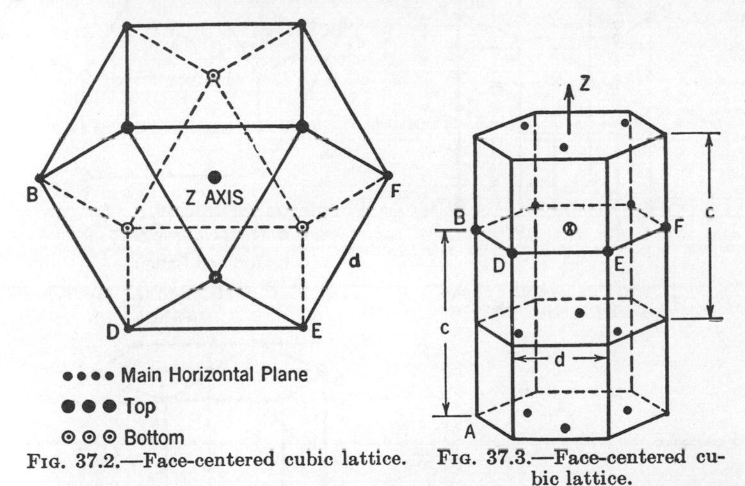

FIG. 37.2.—Face-centered cubic lattice. FIG. 37.3.—Face-centered cubic lattice.

There is *another possible structure* for *close-packed spheres* shown in Figs. 37.4 and 37.5. It obviously has exactly the same density as the face-centered cubic lattice. Comparing Fig. 37.3 with Fig. 37.4, we notice that in Fig. 37.3 the lower atoms are diagonally opposite to the upper ones. In Fig. 37.4, on the other hand, the lower atoms lie just below the upper ones, and the structure repeats itself after a vertical distance c. This remark shows immediately that the *hexagonal lattice* of Figs. 37.4 and 37.5 is *not a simple Bravais lattice* built on three vectors $\mathbf{d}_1$, $\mathbf{d}_2$, and $\mathbf{d}_3$, but that it represents a *lattice with basis* according to the definition given in Sec. 31 (Fig. 31.8).

In the case of lattices containing only one type of particle, the following criterion can be used to distinguish between a simple

Bravais lattice and lattices with a basis: Taking a vector OA from one particle O to another A, we construct its negative OA' (Fig. 37.6). If the lattice is a simple Bravais lattice, there must be an atom at the point A' (as in Figs. 37.2 and 37.3). If there is no atom at A' (as in Figs. 37.4 and 37.5), the lattice has a basis. Hence, the face-centered cubic structure, which

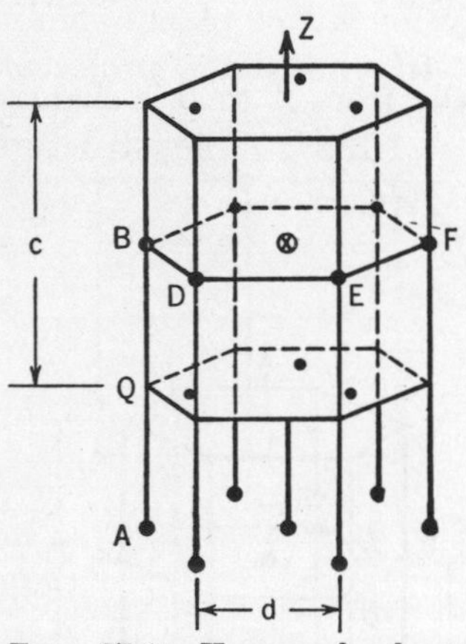

Fig. 37.4.—Hexagonal close-packed lattice.

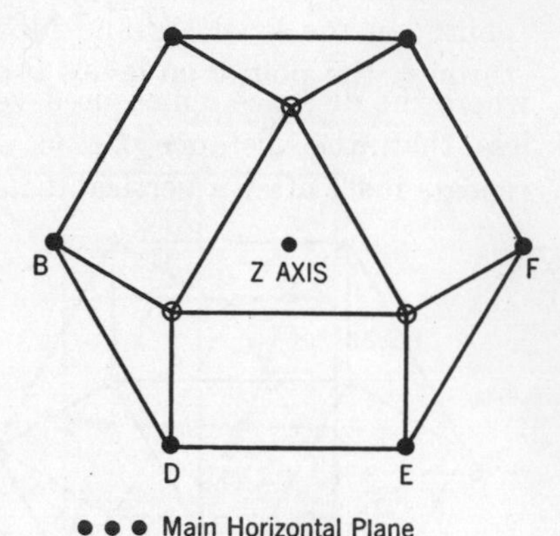

Fig. 37.5.—Hexagonal close-packed lattice.

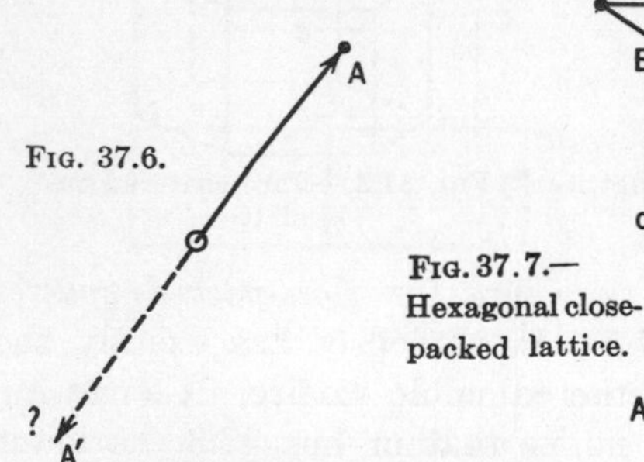

Fig. 37.6.

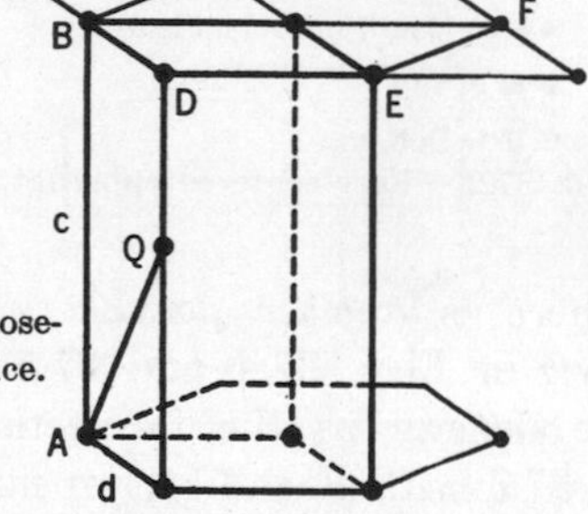

Fig. 37.7.—Hexagonal close-packed lattice.

Note that point Q is *not* on the vertical line going to D but well inside the parallelepiped, as can be seen on Fig. 37.4.

looked like a structure with a basis, actually represents a simple Bravais lattice. The hexagonal close-packed lattice, however, cannot be represented that way and actually possesses a basis. The fundamental cell contains two atoms as shown in Fig. 37.7 where AQ represents the basis vector. In this hexagonal lattice as in the face-centered cubic lattice of Fig. 37.3

$$AB = c = 1.633d, \qquad BE = 1.732d$$

for spherical particles. Both structures can be projected on a vertical plane passing through DF as shown in Fig. 37.8. In the reciprocal-lattice discussion of a lattice with a basis, all additional atoms inside the basis must be ignored, and the discussion refers only to the three fundamental vectors $\mathbf{d}_1$, $\mathbf{d}_2$, and $\mathbf{d}_3$. In the hexagonal structure of Fig. 37.7, for instance, we ignore the Q points on the level $\frac{1}{2}c$ and look only for lattice planes running through the points on levels O or c. In a horizontal projection,

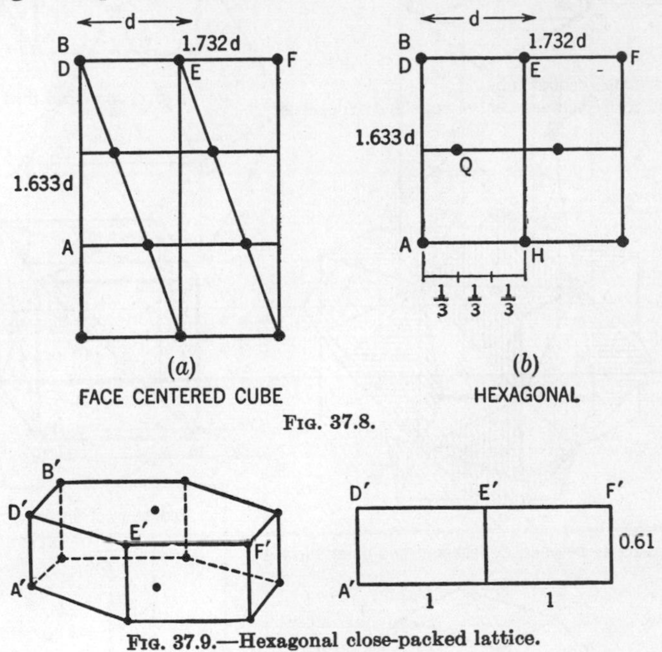

FIG. 37.8.

FIG. 37.9.—Hexagonal close-packed lattice.

the hexagonal structure is the same as in Fig. 31.2 for two dimensions and the reciprocal is another hexagonal structure with the side

$$b = \frac{2}{\sqrt{3}\,d} \tag{37.2}$$

as drawn in Fig. 31.3. Looking at the vertical projection in Fig. 37.8*b*, we obtain the fundamental cell represented by $ABEH$ with dimensions

$$BE = \frac{\sqrt{3}}{2}\,d \qquad \text{and} \qquad AB = c = 2\sqrt{\frac{2}{3}}\,d \tag{37.3}$$

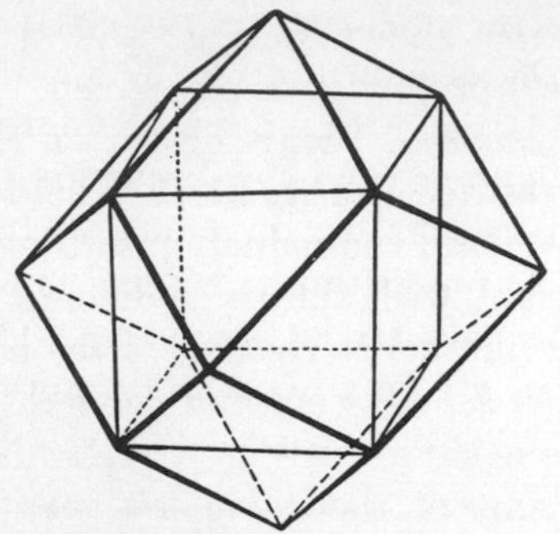

1st zone – central cube
2nd zone – between central cube and dodecaeder

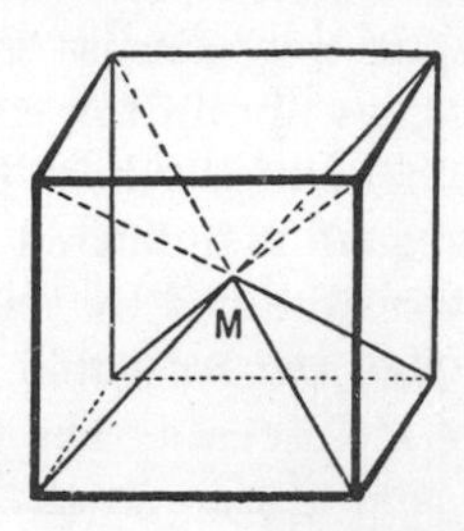

Reduction of 2nd zone

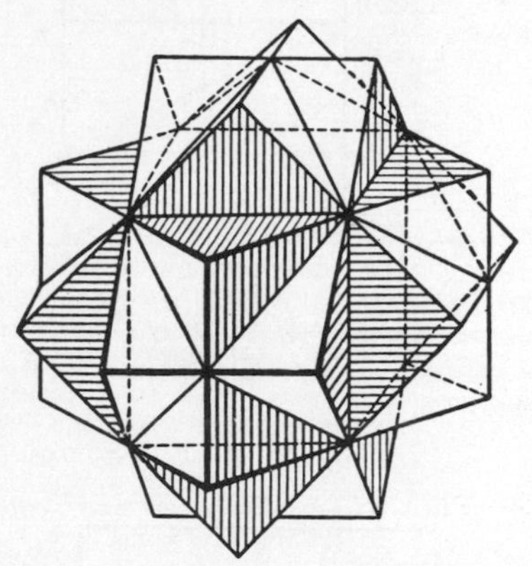

3rd zone – between dodecaeder and outer surface

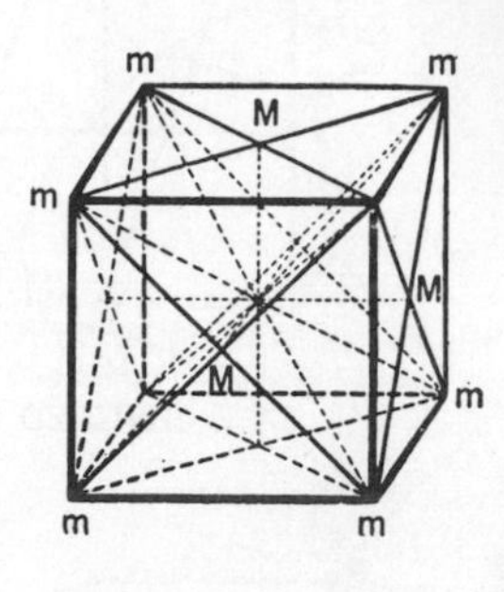

Reduction of 3rd zone

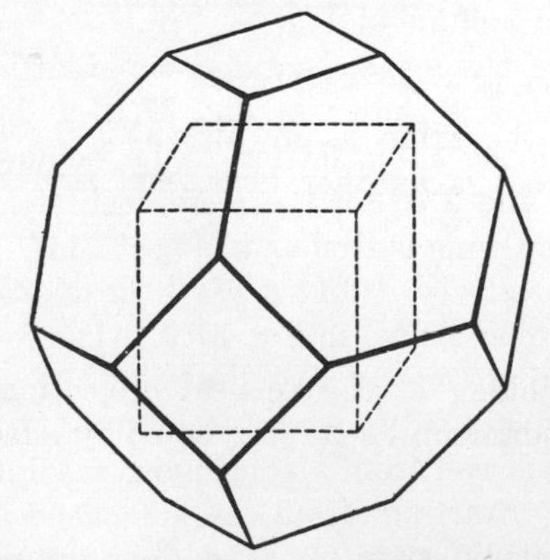

4th zone – between 3rd zone and new outer surface

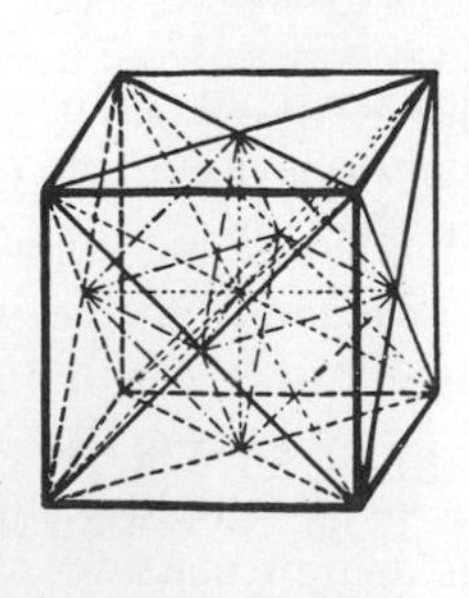

Reduction of 4th zone

FIG. 37.10.—Cubic lattice, zones 1, 2, 3 and 4.

This gives us the reciprocal lattice shown in Fig. 37.9, a flat hexagonal structure whose vertical projection is also given.

Let us now discuss the *zone structures*. Starting with a *cubic lattice*, we obtain the zones represented in Fig. 37.10, where the first four surfaces have been drawn and the reduction to the first cubic zone is indicated on the right with the three-dimensional mosaics obtained by translations parallel to the side of the cube.

A *face-centered* cubic lattice has a body-centered cubic lattice as its reciprocal. The first zone is shown in Fig. 37.11 and has the same shape as the fourth zone of the cubic lattice. The fundamental cell of the direct lattice has a volume $\frac{1}{4}d^3$ (four

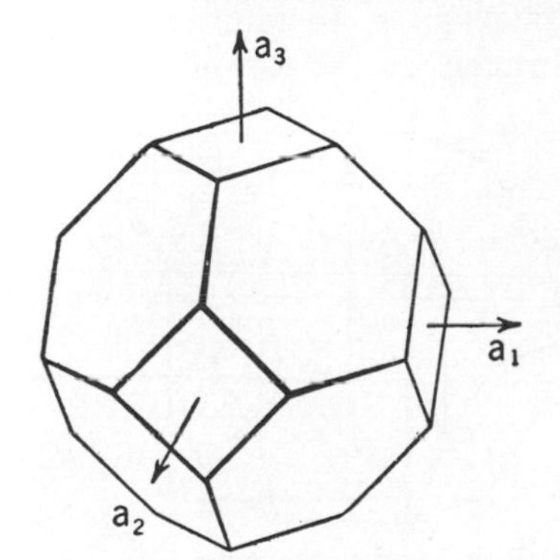

FIG. 37.11.—Face-centered cubic lattice, first zone.

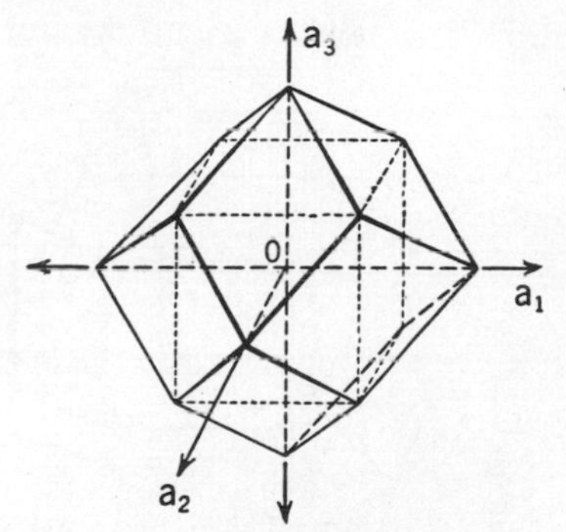

FIG. 37.12.—Body-centered cubic lattice, first zone.

points per cube); hence the first zone and each fundamental cell of the reciprocal lattice have a volume of $4/d^3$.

A *body-centered* cubic lattice has a face-centered cubic lattice as its reciprocal. The first zone is shown in Fig. 37.12 and is similar to the second zone of the cubic lattice. The volumes are $\frac{1}{2}d^3$ for the direct lattice and $2/d^3$ for the reciprocal lattice and the first zone. The second zone is similar to Fig. 37.11.

A hexagonal lattice with arbitrary d and c has a hexagonal reciprocal with $2/\sqrt{3}\,d$ and $1/c$ as shown in Fig. 37.9. The first zone is a hexagonal cell looking exactly like Fig. 37.9. First and second zones are shown in Fig. 37.13.

Let us now consider the transition from a continuous medium to a discontinuous lattice. Starting from a homogeneous isotropic continuum and a certain type of wave (longitudinal elastic waves, for instance), we first introduce a slight periodic perturbation with the face-centered cubic distribution. This introduces discontinuities in the $\nu(\mathbf{a})$ relation on all plane surfaces corresponding to zone boundaries. Instead of letting **a** run from 0 to ∞, we may reduce all vectors **a** inside the first zone, since each higher zone possesses sections that give a continuous $\nu(\mathbf{a})$ branch inside the first zone, and finally we obtain an infinite set of successive branches inside the first zone. This is the three-dimensional equivalent of the process described by Fig. 17.2 for one dimension. Increasing the periodic perturbation, we finally reduce the structure to the discrete atoms located at the points of the face-centered lattice. In this process all the upper branches of the $\nu(a)$ curves rise to infinity and disappear. The only remaining branch is the lower one, and

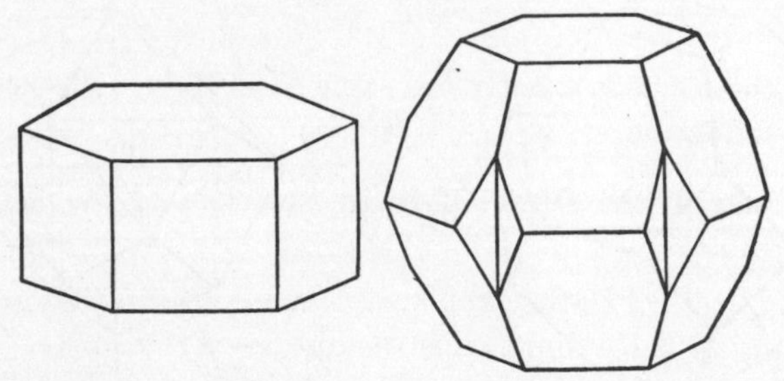

FIG. 37.13.—Hexagonal lattice, first and second zone.

Fig. 17.2 reduces to Fig. 2.4*b*. A very similar process of transformation was discussed at the beginning of Sec. 16.

Let us now follow the same procedure with a hexagonal close packing. The periodicity is hexagonal, but there are two atoms in each cell. The transformation will leave us with *two branches* in the first zone instead of one. The final $\nu(\mathbf{a})$ will be similar to the double curve or the one-dimensional NaCl lattice (Fig. 16.1), instead of the single curve of Fig. 2.4*b*. In Sec. 16 we discussed the transition from the case of two different masses $M_1 \neq M_2$ to two equal masses $M_1 = M_2$, and Fig. 16.1 explained the transformation. A similar discussion could be applied to the transformation indicated in Fig. 37.14 and obtained by straightening the vertical atomic line, thus going from the close-packed hexagonal lattice of height c to the simple Bravais hexagonal lattice of height $\frac{1}{2}c$. The fundamental cell of the latter has a volume one-half that of the original. Its first zone has a double volume, being twice as high as the original one of Fig. 37.13. In this first zone we should find just *one* $\nu(\mathbf{a})$ branch, but as soon as the perturbation corresponding to the zigzag of the vertical lines is introduced, this zone is cut in two, and the single branch splits into two branches in the new first zone. The procedure

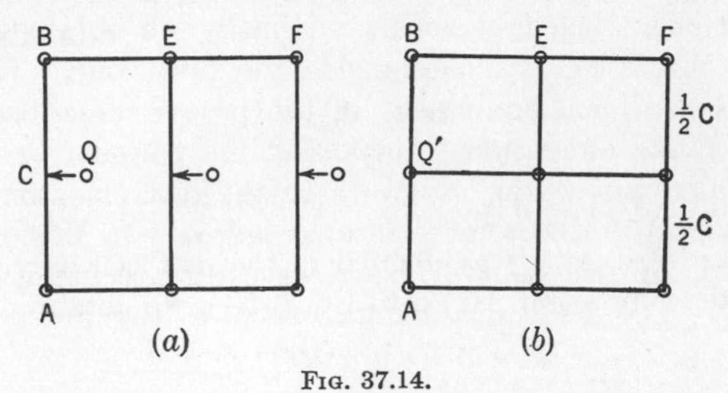

FIG. 37.14.

along the z axis is exactly the same as in Born's discussion of the NaCl reduction.

38. Zones in the Direct Lattice; Principle of the Wigner-Seitz Method

Let us return to the problem of wave propagation in a periodic medium for three dimensions, as discussed in Sec. 34. We found that the general solution could be written as in Eq. (34.4).

$$\psi = A(\mathbf{r})e^{2\pi i[\nu t-(a\cdot r)]} \tag{34.4}$$

with an amplitude $A(\mathbf{r})$ that is a periodic function in the direct lattice. This offers the possibility of defining the function $A(\mathbf{r})$ inside a single $\mathbf{d}$ cell or inside a closed surface containing a volume equal to that of an elementary $\mathbf{d}$ cell.

This is the basis of the Wigner-Seitz method of treating the theory of solids that we shall discuss briefly in this section. To do this, we break the vector $\mathbf{r}$ of a point in the cell $(n_1n_2n_3)$ into a number of terms.

$$\mathbf{r} = \mathbf{r}_0 + \mathbf{r}' + n_1\mathbf{d}_1 + n_2\mathbf{d}_2 + n_3\mathbf{d}_3 \tag{38.1}$$

$\mathbf{r}_0$ is the vector for some point in the first cell relative to the origin of the cell, $n_1\mathbf{d}_1 + n_2\mathbf{d}_2 + n_3\mathbf{d}_3$ the vector for the origin of the cell $(n_1n_2n_3)$ relative to the origin of the lattice, and $\mathbf{r}'$ the coordinate of the point under consideration relative to the point $\mathbf{r}_0$ in the cell $(n_1n_2n_3)$. $\mathbf{r}'$ is to be restricted to values inside a single cell or an equivalent surface. This is illustrated in Fig. 38.1.

Now we must rewrite the solution (34.4) in terms of $\mathbf{r}'$. First, we note that $(\mathbf{a} \cdot \mathbf{r})$ becomes

$$(\mathbf{a} \cdot \mathbf{r}) = (\mathbf{a} \cdot \mathbf{r}_0) + (\mathbf{a} \cdot \mathbf{r}') + n_1(\mathbf{a} \cdot \mathbf{d}_1) + n_2(\mathbf{a} \cdot \mathbf{d}_2) + n_3(\mathbf{a} \cdot \mathbf{d}_3) \quad (38.2)$$

We set

$$2\pi(\mathbf{a} \cdot \mathbf{d}_i) = k_i \quad (38.3)$$

Then

$$A(\mathbf{r}) = A(\mathbf{r}_0 + \mathbf{r}') = e^{2\pi i[(a\cdot r_0)+(a\cdot r')]}A''(\mathbf{r}') \quad (38.4)$$

and we regard $A''(\mathbf{r}')$ as defined in the first cell only. Substituting the expression $A(\mathbf{r})$ into Eq. (34.4), we obtain

$$\psi = A''(\mathbf{r}')e^{i(\omega t - n_1k_1 - n_2k_2 - n_3k_3)} \quad (38.5)$$

This is the wave function inside the cell $(n_1n_2n_3)$. The amplitude A'' is defined inside the first cell and is independent of (n_1,n_2,n_3).

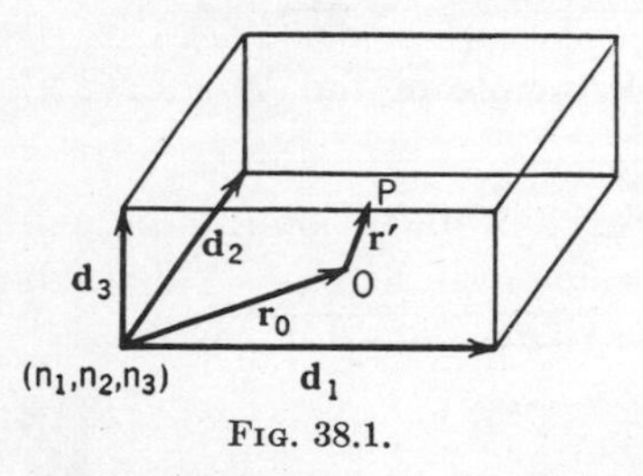

FIG. 38.1.

One may notice immediately that Eq. (38.5) is the translation for a continuous medium of the type of definitions recommended in Sec. 36 for a discontinuous structure. The choice of the first cell is, of course, arbitrary since the choice of the basis vectors in the direct lattice is arbitrary. Wigner and Seitz choose their elementary cell in a manner similar to that in which zones are constructed for the reciprocal lattice, *viz.*, by constructing a polyhedron about a lattice point. The faces of the polyhedron are planes that are perpendicular bisectors of the lines joining the point taken as the origin with neighboring lattice points. This is shown schematically in Fig. 38.2 for a two-dimensional lattice.

Some conditions are required to insure continuity of the ψ function throughout the lattice and to prevent any discontinuity across the border of the zone in the direct lattice. Let $\mathbf{r}'$ be a point on the boundary; the vector $\mathbf{r}$ defining the analogous point in the next cell (Fig. 38.2) is then

$$\mathbf{r} = \mathbf{r}' + n_1\mathbf{d}_1 + n_2\mathbf{d}_2 + n_3\mathbf{d}_3 \quad (38.6)$$

This results from the definition of the zones in the direct lattice, and n_1, n_2, and n_3 are small integers such as 0 or ± 1 if the first zone is being used. We must obtain a continuity condition for ψ and its normal derivative at $\mathbf{r}'$. The condition

$$A''(\mathbf{r}') = A''(\mathbf{r})e^{-i(n_1k_1+n_2k_2+n_3k_3)} \tag{38.7}$$

ensures the continuity of the wave function ψ. A similar condition holds for the normal derivative. For very long wave length, k_1, k_2, and k_3 are small, as are n_1, n_2, and n_3, and one may *approximately* state

$$A''(\mathbf{r}') = A''(\mathbf{r}) \tag{38.8}$$

along the boundary.

This is a first approximation, but it is generally necessary to use a second simplifying assumption, since the polyhedron

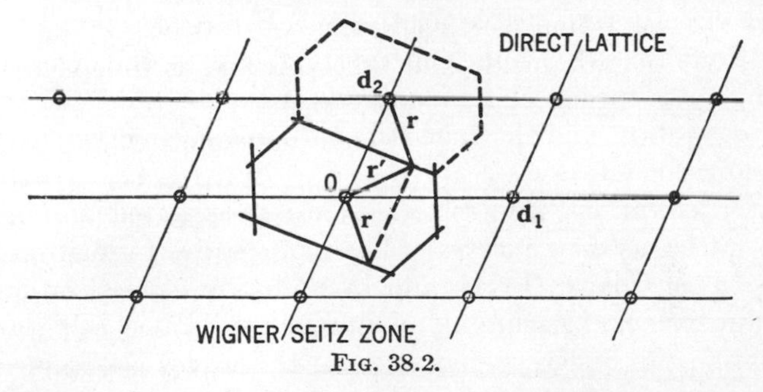

FIG. 38.2.

limiting the Wigner-Seitz zone offers considerable difficulty as a boundary. The simplification used is to replace the polyhedron by a *sphere* of equal inside volume and radius R. The corresponding points $\mathbf{r}'$ and $\mathbf{r}$ are replaced by diametrically opposite points $\pm\mathbf{r}'$.

$$\left.\begin{aligned} A''(\mathbf{r}') &= A''(-\mathbf{r}') \\ \frac{\partial A''}{\partial R} &= 0 \end{aligned}\right\} \tag{38.9}$$

This can give only a first approximation for long wave lengths, and the discussion of corrections for small wave lengths offers serious difficulties.

39. Frequency Distribution for Waves in an Actual Crystal

The general discussion of the preceding sections leads to very important results, which play a prominent role in a number of problems in theoretical physics. We do not intend to discuss all these problems, but we shall select the oldest one as the most typical: the theory of specific heat of solid bodies. Let us first summarize our main results:

For any kind of waves (elastic, electromagnetic, or wave mechanical De Broglie waves) propagating in a medium with periodic structure, discontinuities are found in the relation between the frequency ν and the wave vector $\mathbf{a}$ (a vector of length $|\mathbf{a}| = 1/\lambda$ and pointing in the direction of propagation). These discontinuities are obtained whenever the vector $\mathbf{a}$ terminates on a plane that is a perpendicular bisector of one of the vectors of the reciprocal lattice. These planes play the same role for all waves, whatever their particular nature may be. For instance, in electromagnetic waves the discontinuities in $\nu(\mathbf{a})$ are directly responsible for the selective reflection of X rays (Bragg-Laue spots). This general property is the reason for choosing these special planes as limits of the *zones* defined in the preceding section, and the zone structure in a given crystal lattice is the same for all waves.

Elastic vibrations, for instance, are propagated through a crystal lattice as *elastic waves*. Their properties result from the discussions of Chaps. II, III, and IV and their generalizations in three dimensions. Assuming N atoms per lattice cell (lattice with basis), the best representation of the waves is obtained by restricting the $\mathbf{a}$ vector to the *first zone*. Each $\mathbf{a}$ vector yields $3N$ different wave motions, of which three are of the acoustic type and $3(N - 1)$ of the optical type, as Fig. 36.1 shows schematically for the case $N = 3$. The three acoustic waves correspond to the well-known waves in an isotropic solid: one longitudinal and two transverse vibrations. In an ideal continuous anisotropic medium three vibrations at right angles are obtained, none of which is exactly longitudinal or transverse. In the crystal lattice with discontinuous structure, there are still three different acoustic waves for each $\mathbf{a}$ vector, but their properties are much more complicated than for a continuous medium. We may, for the sake of visualization, call the waves longitudinal (l) and transverse (t_1,t_2), but these names do not correspond exactly to the properties of waves in a lattice structure.

The hexagonal lattice, although it contains only one type of atom, is a lattice with basis and yields three acoustic branches and three branches of higher frequency, which may be called *optical*. A real *monatomic* crystal lattice (such as the face- or body-centered cubic structure) is one without basis and contains only one atom per cell. It yields only three acoustic branches and no optical branches.

The volume of the first zone equals the volume V_b of the fundamental cell in the reciprocal lattice, and

$$V_b = \frac{1}{V_d} \tag{39.1}$$

where V_d is the volume of the cell in the direct lattice.

All this refers to an infinite crystal lattice. Now what can be said about a finite piece of crystal of volume V, containing, for instance, one gram molecule and a total of $\mathfrak{N}$ atoms?

$$\mathfrak{N} = 6.06 \times 10^{23} \qquad \text{Avogadro's number} \tag{39.2}$$

The vibrations of such a bounded crystal lattice depend upon the properties of the infinite lattice and upon the *boundary conditions*. These conditions are usually very troublesome in all problems of elasticity. Even in the case of an isotropic continuum, boundary conditions generally result in mixing all the wave types. A longitudinal wave, for instance, falling upon a plane boundary gives a reflected longitudinal wave but also excites a transverse reflected wave. For an ideal isotropic continuum, there is a boundary condition that avoids these complications—a perfect, smooth, and rigid boundary—but it does not work for crystal lattices. M. Born invented for that purpose a very ingenious type of condition which he characterizes as *cyclic condition*. He takes an infinite unbounded medium through which plane waves can propagate freely and selects inside this infinite medium a finite volume V, which is a rectangular parallelepiped.

$$0 \leqq x \leqq L_1, \qquad 0 \leqq y \leqq L_2, \qquad 0 \leqq z \leqq L_3, \qquad V = L_1L_2L_3 \tag{39.3}$$

The condition for the waves is to take the same value at a point (x,y,z) and at points $(x + n_1L_1)$, $(y + n_2L_2)$, and $(z + n_3L_3)$ where n_1, n_2, and n_3 are any arbitrary integers.

$$\psi(x + n_1L_1, y + n_2L_2, z + n_3L_3) = \psi(x,y,z) \tag{39.4}$$

Since

$$\psi = e^{i\omega t - 2\pi i(ax+by+cz)} \qquad n_1n_2n_3 \text{ integer} \tag{39.5}$$

this requires that

$$a = \frac{m_1}{L_1}, \qquad b = \frac{m_2}{L_2}, \qquad c = \frac{m_3}{L_3} \qquad m_1 m_2 m_3 \text{ integer} \tag{39.6}$$

A characteristic frequency of the crystal will be excited whenever the wave vector terminates on a point with components given by Eq. (39.6). The number of such points per unit volume of the reciprocal lattice is $L_1L_2L_3$ (since the points are spaced at intervals $1/L_1$, $1/L_2$, and $1/L_3$ along the x, y, and z axes, respectively).

The number $\mathfrak{N}$ of atoms contained in the volume V is stupendous [Eq. (39.2)], and L_1, L_2, and L_3 are very large, compared with the dimensions d_1, d_2, and d_3 of the elementary lattice cell. This means that the density of the vibration points given by Eq. (39.6) is extremely high. Even if we take a very small volume element $d\tau$ in the abc space, we may obtain the average number of points inside $d\tau$ by just taking

$$dn = L_1L_2L_3\, d\tau = V\, d\tau$$

Let us, for instance, consider a certain direction of propagation and a small cone of aperture $d\Omega$ around this average direction. The number of **a** vectors that terminate inside this cone between the distances r and $r + dr$ is

$$dn = L_1L_2L_3r^2dr\, d\Omega = Vr^2dr\, d\Omega \tag{39.7}$$

$$r = |\mathbf{a}| = \frac{1}{\lambda} \tag{39.8}$$

Hence

$$dn = V\, d\Omega \frac{1}{\lambda^2} d\left(\frac{1}{\lambda}\right) = V\, d\Omega \frac{\nu^2}{W^2} d\left(\frac{\nu}{W}\right)$$

where W is the *phase velocity* for one special type of wave. According to the definitions given in Sec. 21, the *group velocity* U is defined by

$$W = \frac{\nu}{|\mathbf{a}|}, \qquad U = \frac{d\nu}{d|\mathbf{a}|}, \qquad \frac{1}{U} = \frac{d}{d\nu}\left(\frac{\nu}{W}\right) \tag{39.9}$$

and we finally obtain

$$dn = V\, d\Omega \frac{\nu^2 d\nu}{W^2 U} \tag{39.10}$$

In a crystal lattice the difficulty is that phase and group velocities depend upon both ν and the orientation of the cone. In an ideal isotropic body this last dependence disappears, and one may immediately integrate about all orientations, thus replacing $d\Omega$ by 4π.

$$dn = 4\pi V \frac{\nu^2 d\nu}{W^2 U} \qquad \text{isotropic in all directions} \qquad (39.11)$$

There is, however, a general result that can be deduced directly from Eq. (39.7): For *each type of elastic wave*, the *total number of vibrations* (with cyclic conditions) is exactly *equal* to the *number* $\mathfrak{N}$ *of atoms* in the volume V. This is easily seen, since the total number of vibrations of a certain type is obtained by integrating Eq. (39.7) over the whole first zone, the volume of which is V_b.

$$\left.\begin{aligned} &\int r^2 dr\, d\Omega = V_b \\ &n = \int dn = V\, V_b = \frac{V}{V_d} = \mathfrak{N} \end{aligned}\right\} \qquad (39.12)$$

according to Eq. (39.1). This is a very important and general result of the zone theory.

How can this general scheme be simplified to be applied to the problem of an *ideal isotropic solid body?* The word "Ideal" is necessary to remind us of the somewhat artificial character of the assumptions: actual so-called *isotropic* solids are only mixtures of tiny crystals oriented at random. Our ideal isotropic solid will represent a sort of average of crystal properties for the purpose of simplification. *Two assumptions* will be made:

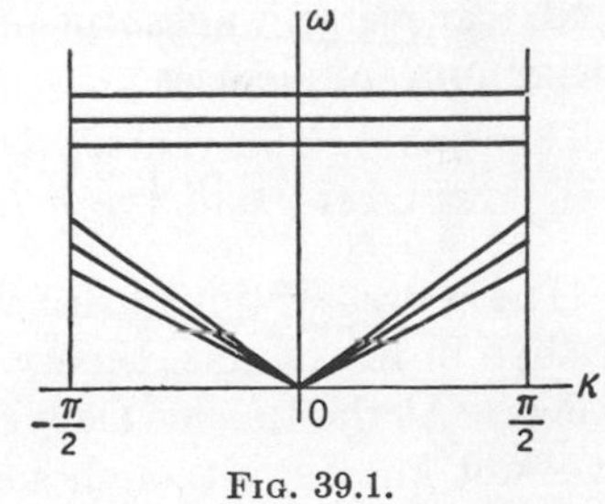

FIG. 39.1.

a. We assume that the curves of Fig. 36.1 are replaced by straight lines, as shown in Fig. 39.1. This means that the upper optical branches are supposed to correspond to single frequencies (instead of the actual frequency bands of finite width) and that for the *acoustic branches* we assume a *constant phase velocity*

$$W = U = \text{const.} \qquad (39.13)$$

b. We simplify the *shape of the first zone* and replace it by a *sphere*. But here we must not forget the general results emphasized at the beginning of this section, and we assume the *same spherical first zone for all waves* (whether electromagnetic or longitudinal and transverse acoustical waves). Let the sphere have a radius R. Then the volume is

$$\frac{4}{3}\pi R^3 = V_b = \frac{1}{V_d} = \frac{\mathfrak{N}}{V} \tag{39.14}$$

where V_d is the volume of the cell in the direct lattice and $\mathfrak{N}$ the number of atoms in a total volume V. Accordingly, we maintain the validity of Eq. (39.12) as necessary.

In order to comply with the requirements of the general theory we see that we have to introduce the same R for all types of waves, hence the same limit for the wave length.

$$\left.\begin{aligned} R &= |\mathbf{a}|_{\max} = \frac{1}{\lambda_{\min}} && \text{cutoff wave length} \\ \lambda_{\min} &= \left(\frac{4\pi V}{3\mathfrak{N}}\right)^{1/3} && \text{common to all waves} \end{aligned}\right\} \tag{39.15}$$

which means different cutoff frequencies for different waves. We may speak now of longitudinal waves (phase velocity W_l) and transverse waves (phase velocity W_t), and we obtain the maximum frequencies

$$\nu_{lc} = W_l\left(\frac{3\mathfrak{N}}{4\pi V}\right)^{1/3}, \qquad \nu_{tc} = W_t\left(\frac{3\mathfrak{N}}{4\pi V}\right)^{1/3} \tag{39.16}$$

These assumptions are very close to the ones introduced by Debye in his famous theory of specific heats. but not quite the same. At the time of Debye's original paper, the theory of zones was not known, although some of the main results had already been obtained by Born. Hence, Debye did not realize the necessity of taking the same minimum wave length (and different cutoff frequencies) for the different waves. He found it easier to assume the same cutoff frequency and different cutoff wave lengths and stated the condition

$$\nu_D = \left(\frac{1}{W_l^3} + \frac{2}{W_t^3}\right)^{-1/3}\left(\frac{9\mathfrak{N}}{4\pi V}\right)^{1/3} \tag{39.17}$$

ν_D is Debye's single cutoff frequency. His reasoning was as follows: Starting from Eq. (39.11) and taking

$$W_l = U_l = \text{const.}$$
$$W_t = U_t = \text{const.}$$

he first computed the total number of vibrations in the frequency interval $(\nu, \nu + d\nu)$ for all waves (one longitudinal and two transverse) and wrote

$$dn_l + 2dn_t = 4\pi V \nu^2 d\nu \left(\frac{1}{W_l^3} + \frac{2}{W_t^3} \right) \tag{39.18}$$

Then he integrated from $\nu = 0$ to ν_D and assumed that the total number of vibrations was $3\mathfrak{N}$. Hence

$$3\mathfrak{N} = \frac{4}{3} \pi V \nu^3 \left(\frac{1}{W_l^3} + \frac{2}{W_t^3} \right) \tag{39.19}$$

which is the same as Eq. (39.17). The weak point in Debye's argument is that this oversimplification does not satisfy the

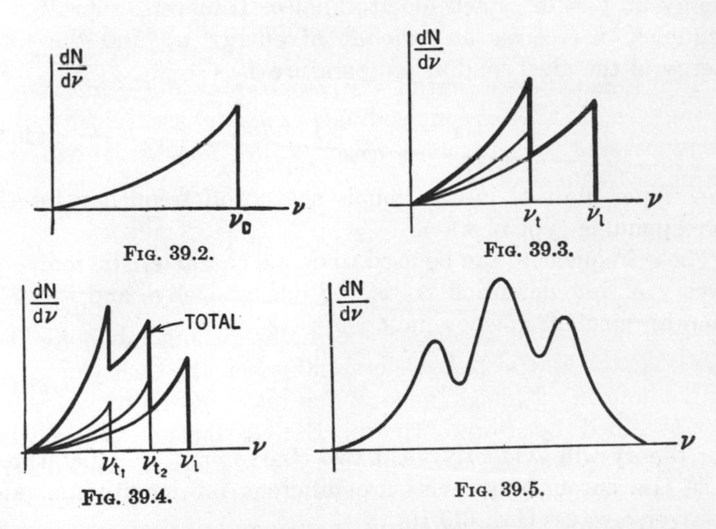

FIG. 39.2. FIG. 39.3. FIG. 39.4. FIG. 39.5.

necessary condition (39.12). We must always have $\mathfrak{N}$ longitudinal and $2\mathfrak{N}$ transverse vibrations. With Debye's assumption the distribution between longitudinal and transverse modes is modified; only the total number is maintained by $3\mathfrak{N}$.

Figure 39.2 shows Debye's distribution function, while Fig. 39.3 shows ours. In Fig. 39.3 the two curves are to be added (the sum is given by the heavy curve) to obtain the actual distribution. Figure 39.4 shows the curves that would be obtained for an anisotropic medium. The sharp points on our curves are due to the assumption of a spherical first zone. A better approximation yields a curve of the type shown in Fig. 39.5.

40. The Energy of a Solid; the Characteristic Temperatures

We regard the solid as made up of $3\mathfrak{N}$ harmonic oscillators. The energy of a harmonic oscillator vibrating with frequency ν is, according to Planck (quantum theory),

$$u_\nu = \frac{h\nu}{e^{h\nu/kT} - 1} + \frac{1}{2}h\nu \tag{40.1}$$

where k is Boltzmann's constant, h is Planck's constant, and T is the absolute temperature. The constant $\frac{1}{2}h\nu$ did not appear in the original Planck treatment, but quantum mechanical considerations indicate that this, and not zero, is the correct energy at $T = 0$. Each longitudinal or transverse vibration of frequency ν receives an amount of energy u_ν, and the total energy of the ideal solid at temperature T is

$$U_T = \sum_{m=l,t_1,t_2} \int u_\nu dn_m \tag{40.2}$$

The upper limit of integration is the cutoff frequency for the corresponding type of wave.

These frequencies can be used to define characteristic temperatures. A first definition Θ_D is the one of Debye and is based upon his single frequency limit ν_D.

$$k\Theta_D = h\nu_D \qquad \text{or} \qquad \Theta_D = \frac{h\nu_D}{k} \tag{40.3}$$

Our theory will evidently yield two characteristic temperatures, since the cutoff frequencies are different for longitudinal and transverse waves [Eq. (39.16)].

$$\left.\begin{aligned} \Theta_l &= \frac{h\nu_l}{k} = \frac{hW_l}{k}\left(\frac{3\mathfrak{N}}{4\pi V}\right)^{1/3} \\ \Theta_t &= \frac{h\nu_t}{k} = \frac{hW_t}{k}\left(\frac{3\mathfrak{N}}{4\pi V}\right)^{1/3} \end{aligned}\right\} \tag{40.4}$$

If we denote the type of wave by the subscript m, the total energy at temperature T is, according to Eqs. (39.11), (40.1), and (40.2),

$$U_T = \sum_{m=l_1t_1,t_2} \frac{4\pi V}{W_m{}^3} \int_0^{\nu_m} \nu^2 d\nu \left[\frac{h\nu}{e^{h\nu/kT} - 1} + \frac{1}{2} h\nu \right] \tag{40.5}$$

We make the following change of variables:

$$\xi = \frac{h\nu}{kT}, \qquad \xi_m = \frac{h\nu_m}{kT} = \frac{\Theta_m}{T}$$

and Eq. (40.5) becomes

$$U_T = \sum_{l,t_1,t_2} \frac{4\pi V}{W_m{}^3} \frac{(kT)^4}{h^3} \int_0^{\xi_m} \xi^3 d\xi \left[\frac{1}{e^\xi - 1} + \frac{1}{2} \right] \tag{40.6}$$

This integration must be performed by approximate methods for most cases. We define the Debye function

$$D(x) = \frac{3}{x^3} \int_0^x \left[\frac{1}{e^\xi - 1} + \frac{1}{2} \right] \xi^3 d\xi \tag{40.7}$$

Now the coefficient of the integral in Eq. (40.6) is given by

$$\frac{4\pi V}{W_m{}^3} \frac{(kT)^4}{h^3} \tag{40.8}$$

and, if we multiply by $\xi_m{}^3/3$, we can replace the integral by the Debye function. Then

$$\begin{aligned} \frac{4\pi V}{W_m{}^3} \frac{(kT)^4}{h^3} \frac{\xi_m{}^3}{3} &= \frac{4\pi V}{3W_m{}^3} \frac{(kT)^4}{h^3} \frac{h^3 \nu_m{}^3}{k^3 T^3} \\ &= \frac{4\pi V}{3} \frac{\nu_m{}^3}{W_m{}^3} kT = \frac{4\pi V}{3} kT \left(\frac{3\mathfrak{N}}{4\pi V} \right) = \mathfrak{N}kT = RT \end{aligned}$$

Thus we may write Eq. (40.6) in the form

$$U_T = \sum_m U_{T_m} = RT \sum_{l,t_1,t_2} D\left(\frac{\Theta_m}{T}\right)$$

and, if the two transverse waves are alike, this becomes

$$U_T = RT \left[D\left(\frac{\Theta_l}{T}\right) + 2D\left(\frac{\Theta_t}{T}\right) \right] \tag{40.9}$$

The Debye treatment gives

$$U_T = 3RTD\left(\frac{\Theta_D}{T}\right) \tag{40.10}$$

In general, Eq. (40.9) is more reliable than Eq. (40.10). However, the two characteristic temperatures Θ_l and Θ_t are often both fairly close to Θ_D and for very high or very low temperatures the two theories agree.

For very high temperatures, classical thermodynamics holds with equipartition of energy, as can be seen from Eq. (40.1).

$$u_\nu = kT\left(\frac{\xi}{e^\xi - 1} + \frac{1}{2}\,\xi\right) = kT\left(\frac{\xi}{\xi + \frac{1}{2}\xi^2 + \cdots} + \frac{1}{2}\,\xi\right)$$
$$\approx kT\left(1 - \frac{\xi}{2} + \frac{\xi}{2}\right) = kT \quad (40.11)$$

Each of the oscillators has an energy kT. Both theories have been formulated in such a way as to yield the correct number $3\mathfrak{N}$ for the total number of degrees of freedom; hence we obtain a total energy $3\mathfrak{N}kT$ or $3RT$ in both cases. This may also be seen from Eq. (40.7), since for very high temperatures Debye's function approaches one and both theories yield the result

$$U_T = 3RT \quad (40.12)$$

which is just the law of Dulong and Petit. For temperatures so small that

$$T << \Theta_e,\ \Theta_D,\ \Theta_t$$

holds, Θ_m/T is very large, and the upper limit in the integral of Eq. (40.5) may be replaced by ∞. Physically this means that only the low frequencies are excited and the number and value of the higher frequencies is unimportant. The Debye function becomes

$$\lim_{x\to\infty} D(x) = \lim_{x\to\infty} \frac{3}{x^3}\int_0^x \left(\frac{1}{e^\xi - 1} + \frac{1}{2}\right)\xi^3 d\xi$$
$$= \lim_{x\to\infty} \frac{3}{x^3}\left(\frac{x^4}{8} + \int_0^\infty \frac{1}{e^\xi - 1}\,\xi^3 d\xi\right) \quad (40.13)$$

The last integral is a constant that is found equal to $\pi^4/15$.

$$U_T = \sum_m \left[RT\,\frac{3}{8}\,\frac{\Theta_m}{T} + 3RT\,\frac{\pi^4}{15}\left(\frac{T}{\Theta_m}\right)^3\right]$$
$$= \frac{3}{8}\,R\,(\Theta_l + 2\Theta_t) + RT\,\frac{\pi^4}{5}\left[\left(\frac{T}{\Theta_l}\right)^3 + 2\left(\frac{T}{\Theta_t}\right)^3\right] \quad (40.14)$$

The first term is a constant and will not enter into the applications to specific heats, etc., since these involve derivatives of U_T. Debye's solution for U_T is

$$U_T = 3\frac{\pi^4}{5}RT\left(\frac{T}{\Theta_D}\right)^3 + C \tag{40.15}$$

where C is a constant, and so the two theories agree for low temperatures, on account of the relation

$$\frac{1}{\Theta_l^3} + \frac{2}{\Theta_t^3} = \frac{3}{\Theta_D^3} \tag{40.16}$$

which is easily obtained from Eqs. (40.3), (40.4), and (39.17).

41. Thermal Expansion and Entropy of a Solid Body

We close our treatment of solids with a discussion of the entropy. To do this, we must take account of the radiation pressure due to elastic waves. The radiation pressure is due to deviations from Hooke's law and has been computed by Rayleigh and L. Brillouin:

$$p_m = \frac{U_m}{V}\left(\frac{1}{3} - \frac{V}{W_m}\frac{\partial W_m}{\partial V}\right) \tag{41.1}$$

where U_m denotes the total energy of the waves of type m. For electromagnetic radiation in vacuum,

$$p_m = \frac{1}{3}\frac{U_m}{V}$$

since in this case there is no $\dfrac{\partial W_m}{\partial V}$ term. Equation (41.1) may also be written in the form

$$p_m = -\frac{U_m}{\Theta_m}\frac{\partial \Theta_m}{\partial V} \tag{41.2}$$

since from Eq. (40.4)

$$\frac{\partial \log \Theta_m}{\partial V} = \frac{1}{\Theta_m}\frac{\partial \Theta_m}{\partial V} = \frac{\partial}{\partial V}\left(\log\frac{h}{k}W_m - \frac{1}{3}\log\frac{4\pi V}{3\mathfrak{N}}\right)$$
$$= \frac{1}{W_m}\frac{\partial W_m}{\partial V} - \frac{1}{3V}$$

or

$$-\frac{V}{\Theta_m}\frac{\partial \Theta_m}{\partial V} = \frac{1}{3} - \frac{V}{W_m}\frac{\partial W_m}{\partial V}$$

The external pressure must balance the internal pressure. The latter is given by the sum of the pressure due to the interactions of the molecules of the crystal and the radiation pressure.

$$p = f(V) + \sum_m p_m \tag{41.3}$$

If the external pressure is zero, then

$$f(V) = -\sum_m p_m$$

and we may think of the radiation pressure as doing work against the cohesive forces of the molecules during an expansion due to rise in temperature.

The total energy of the solid is

$$U = F(V) + U_l + U_{t_1} + U_{t_2} \tag{41.4}$$

where

$$F(V) = -\int f(V)dV$$

During a small expansion the work done is

$$\begin{aligned} dW = p\,dV &= f\,dV - \sum_m \frac{U_m}{\Theta_m}\frac{\partial\Theta_m}{\partial V}dV \\ &= f\,dV - RT\sum_m \left[D\left(\frac{\Theta_m}{T}\right)\frac{1}{\Theta_m}\frac{\partial\Theta_m}{\partial V}dV\right] \end{aligned} \tag{41.5}$$

where U_m is assumed to be given by Eq. (40.9). The change in energy is given by

$$\begin{aligned} dU = \frac{\partial U}{\partial V}dV + \frac{\partial U}{\partial T}dT &= -f\,dV + \sum_m \frac{\partial U_m}{\partial V}dV + \sum_m \frac{\partial U_m}{\partial T}dT \\ &= -f\,dV + R\sum_m \left[D'\left(\frac{\Theta_m}{T}\right)\frac{\partial\Theta_m}{\partial V}dV + D\,dT - \frac{\Theta_m}{T}D'\left(\frac{\Theta_m}{T}\right)dT\right] \end{aligned} \tag{41.6}$$

Now the heat change will be

$$dQ = dU + dW$$

and the change in entropy

$$dS = \frac{dQ}{T} = \frac{dU + dW}{T} \tag{41.7}$$

Substituting Eqs. (41.5) and (41.6) into Eq. (41.7) gives

$$dS = \frac{R}{T}\sum_m \left[D\,dT - D\frac{T}{\Theta_m}\frac{\partial\Theta_m}{\partial V}dV + D'\left(\frac{\partial\Theta_m}{\partial V}dV - \frac{\Theta_m}{T}dT\right)\right]$$

$$= R\sum_m \left(\frac{D'}{T} - \frac{D}{\Theta_m}\right)\left(d\Theta_m - \frac{\Theta_m}{T}dT\right)$$

on replacing $\frac{\partial\Theta_m}{\partial V}dV$ by $d\Theta_m$. If we let $X_m = \Theta_m/T$

$$dS = R\sum_m \left(D' - \frac{D}{X_m}\right)dX_m$$

and

$$\frac{dS}{dX_m} = R\left(D' - \frac{D}{X_m}\right) \tag{41.8}$$

We can write this as an explicit function of X_m by using Eq. (40.7)

$$D(X_m) = \frac{3}{X_m{}^3}\int_0^{X_m} \frac{\xi^3 d\xi}{e^\xi - 1} + \frac{3}{8}X_m$$

in Eq. (41.8), which then becomes

$$\frac{dS}{dX_m} = R\left(-\frac{9}{X_m{}^4}\int_0^{X_m}\frac{\xi^3 d\xi}{e^\xi - 1} + \frac{3}{e^{X_m} - 1} - \frac{3}{X_m{}^4}\int_0^{X_m}\frac{\xi^3 d\xi}{e^\xi - 1}\right)$$

$$= \frac{3R}{e^{X_m} - 1} - \frac{12R}{X_m{}^4}\int_0^{X_m}\frac{\xi^3 d\xi}{e^\xi - 1} \tag{41.9}$$

It is interesting to note that Eq. (41.9) agrees with the quantum mechanical result for the entropy of our system of harmonic oscillators. The quantum theory offers a possibility for a direct statistical computation of entropy. A distribution of n quanta $h\nu$ (total energy $nh\nu$) among g resonators is found to have an entropy

$$S = kg\left[\left(1 + \frac{n}{g}\right)\log\left(1 + \frac{n}{g}\right) - \frac{n}{g}\log\frac{n}{g}\right] \tag{41.10}$$

The most probable distribution corresponds to Planck's formula for the average energy per resonator.

$$u_\nu = \frac{nh\nu}{g} = \frac{h\nu}{e^{h\nu/kT} - 1} \qquad \xi = \frac{h\nu}{kT} \tag{41.11}$$

Hence

$$\frac{n}{g} = \frac{1}{e^\xi - 1} \qquad 1 + \frac{n}{g} = \frac{e^\xi}{e^\xi - 1}$$

On the other hand, we have obtained an expression (39.11) for the number of resonators of frequency $\nu(d\nu)$. Using this value for g,

$$g = V \frac{4\pi\nu^2 d\nu}{W^3} \qquad \text{wave type } m \tag{41.12}$$

and integrating on ν from 0 to the limit ν_m, we obtain the total entropy of the solid.

$$S = \sum_{m=l,t_1,t_2} S_m \tag{41.13}$$

$$S_m = 3\mathfrak{N}k \left(\frac{T}{\Theta_m}\right)^3 \int_0^{\Theta_m/T} \left(\frac{e^\xi}{e^\xi - 1} \log \frac{e^\xi}{e^\xi - 1} - \frac{1}{e^\xi - 1} \log \frac{1}{e^\xi - 1}\right) \xi^2 d\xi$$

The method followed for entropy is exactly the same as the one used for energy, in Eqs. (40.2) to (40.9). Some regrouping of terms and elementary transformations finally yields

$$S_m = \frac{3R}{X_m^3} \int_0^{X_m} \left[\frac{\xi e^\xi}{e^\xi - 1} - \log (e^\xi - 1)\right] \xi^2 d\xi \tag{41.14}$$

We may integrate by parts to eliminate the logarithmic term.

$$-\int_0^{X_m} \log (e^\xi - 1)\xi^2 d\xi = -\frac{X_m^3}{3} \log (e^{X_m} - 1) + \frac{1}{3} \int_0^{X_m} \frac{e^\xi}{e^\xi - 1} \xi^3 d\xi$$

so that

$$S = \sum_m \left[-R \log (e^{X_m} - 1) + \frac{4R}{X_m^3} \int_0^{X_m} \frac{e^\xi \xi^3 d\xi}{e^\xi - 1}\right] \tag{41.15}$$

Differentiation with respect to X_m yields

$$\begin{aligned}\frac{dS}{dX_m} &= -\frac{Re^{X_m}}{e^{X_m} - 1} - \frac{12R}{X_m^4} \int_0^{X_m} \frac{e^\xi \xi^3 d\xi}{e^\xi - 1} + \frac{4Re^{X_m}}{e^{X_m} - 1} \\ &= \frac{3Re^{X_m}}{e^{X_m} - 1} - \frac{12R}{X_m^4} \int_0^{X_m} \frac{e^\xi \xi^3 d\xi}{e^\xi - 1}\end{aligned} \tag{41.16}$$

This is easily seen to check with Eq. (41.9) by the following transformation:

$$\frac{dS}{dX_m} = 3R\left(\frac{1}{e^{X_m} - 1} + 1\right) - \frac{12R}{X_m^4} \int_0^{X_m} \left(\frac{1}{e^\xi - 1} + 1\right) \xi^3 d\xi$$

The (+1) term in the second bracket yields, after integration,

$$-\frac{12R}{X_m{}^4}\left|\frac{\xi^4}{4}\right|_0^{X_m} = -3R$$

which cancels the (+1) term in the first bracket and yields Eq. (41.9).

Thus the whole theory is proved to be entirely consistent. Debye's theory with its single characteristic temperature does not work, since it is not consistent with Eq. (41.2) for internal pressure.

Further details on the theory of solids and the direct computation of Eq. (41.1) for the radiation pressure can be found in the author's book, "Les Tenseurs en mécanique et en élasticité."[1] This short summary of the problem was intended to emphasize the connection of this problem with the theory of zones, as explained in Secs. 39 and 40, and to show the necessity of a correction to the original Debye theory involving the use of two characteristic temperatures, as pointed out by Born in his discussion of the theory of solids.

Selected References on Zones

Books

BRILLOUIN, L.: "Quantenstatistik," Springer, Berlin, 1931.
BRILLOUIN, L.: "Structure des corps solides," Hermann, Paris, 1937.
MOTT, N. F., and H. JONES: "Theory of Metals and Alloys," Oxford, New York, 1936.
SEITZ, F.: "The Modern Theory of Solids," McGraw-Hill, New York, 1940.

Original papers

BLOCH, F.: *Z. Physik*, **52**, 555 (1928).
MORSE, P. M.: *Phys. Rev.*, **35**, 1310 (1930).
PEIERLS, R.: *Ann. Physik*, **4**, 121 (1930).
BRILLOUIN, L.: *J. phys.*, **1**, 377 (1930); **3**, 565 (1932); **4**, 1, 333 (1933); **7**, 401 (1936).
JONES, H.: *Proc. Roy. Soc. (London)*, **A144**, 225 (1934); **A147**, 396 (1934).
JONES, H., N. F. MOTT, and H. W. B. SKINNER: *Phys. Rev.*, **45**, 379 (1934).
SLATER, J. C.: *Phys. Rev.*, **45**, 794 (1934).
HUND, F.: *Z. tech. Physik*, **16**, 331, 494 (1935). *Z. Physik*, **99**, 119 (1936).
PEIERLS, R.: *Ann. Inst. Henri Poincaré*, **5**, 177 (1935).
SEITZ, F.: *Ann. Math.*, **37**, 17 (1936).
BOUCKAERT, L. P., R. SMOLUCHOWSKI, and E. WIGNER: *Phys. Rev.*, **50**, 58 (1936).
HERRING, C.: *Phys. Rev.*, **52**, 361, 365 (1937).
CHODOROW, M. I., and M. F. MANNING: *Phys. Rev.*; **52**, 731 (1937).

[1] Masson, Paris, 1938.

HOUSTON, W. V.: *Rev. Mod. Phys.*, **20**, 161 (1948).

CHAPTER VIII

MATHIEU'S EQUATION AND RELATED PROBLEMS

42. Mathieu's Equation

The problem of the propagation of waves in a periodic continuous medium was discussed in Sec. 34, and there some general results were obtained on the type of the solution and its properties. Few examples of such problems have been completely discussed. Some of the best known relate to the one-dimensional problem. The general equation given in Eq. (34.1) reduces to

$$\left.\begin{aligned} \frac{\partial^2 \psi}{\partial x^2} + \omega^2 F(x)\psi &= 0 \\ \psi &= e^{i\omega t} u(x) \end{aligned}\right\} \qquad (42.1)$$

Mathieu's equation is obtained when the periodic function F (of period d in x) contains only one cosine term and the expansion (34.3) can be written

$$F(x) = C_0 + C_1 e^{2\pi i(x/d)} + C_1 e^{-2\pi i(x/d)} = C_0 + 2C_1 \cos \frac{2\pi x}{d} \qquad (42.2)$$

So far we have discussed equations of this type in detail only for very small C_1 (corresponding to a very small perturbation) when we assumed from Eqs. (35.1) and (35.3)

$$F = C_0 + \epsilon f \qquad \epsilon \text{ very small}$$

Now we wish to discuss the solutions for any arbitrary value of both C_0 and C_1. We may use the following notation to reduce the equation to standard type: We introduce a new variable

$$\xi = \frac{\pi x}{d} \qquad (42.3)$$

which has period π instead of d, and we obtain

$$\left.\begin{aligned} &\frac{\partial^2 u}{\partial \xi^2} + (\eta + \gamma \cos 2\xi)u = 0 \\ &\eta = \omega^2 \frac{d^2}{\pi^2} C_0 = 4\nu^2 d^2 C_0 \qquad \gamma = 8\nu^2 d^2 C_1 \end{aligned}\right\} \qquad (42.4)$$

This equation was first obtained by Mathieu in connection with the problem of vibrations of an elliptic membrane, and this is the reason for the choice of π as the period. The same equation is found for the oscillations of an elliptic lake, for the tides in an elliptic sea, and, in general, in all problems concerning waves or vibrations with an elliptic boundary, such as propagation of acoustic or electromagnetic waves along a pipe of elliptic cross section. We shall indicate in a later section some other interesting problems of physics and engineering where Mathieu's equation plays a major role.[1]

Floquet discovered that the general solution of the equation could be written

$$u = D_1 A(\xi) e^{\mu\xi} + D_2 B(\xi) e^{-\mu\xi} \tag{42.5}$$

with amplitudes A and B that are periodic functions of ξ with period π. This solution is thus a superposition of two waves propagated (or attenuated) in opposite directions. This is clearly seen if we retain the $e^{i\omega t}$ factor and write the original ψ function of Eq. (42.1). D_1 and D_2 are arbitrary constants. If we keep only *one* of those waves, we obtain

$$u = A(\xi) e^{\mu\xi} \qquad A(\xi) \text{ has period } \pi. \tag{42.6}$$

This corresponds exactly to our general solution (34.4).

In our previous discussion we assumed that we had to deal with *actual waves*, and we therefore took

$$\mu = i\beta = i\frac{k}{\pi}, \qquad \mu\xi = i\beta\xi = i\frac{kx}{d} = i2\pi a x$$

and determined afterwards the corresponding ω value and the frequency. Here the discussion is conducted in the opposite way. The frequency has been chosen as primary data, and the problem is to obtain μ, which may be

$$\left.\begin{array}{ll} \mu = i\beta & \text{pure imaginary, unattenuated sine waves} \\ \mu = \alpha + i\beta & \text{complex or real, attenuated motion} \end{array}\right\} \tag{42.7}$$

Both η and γ are proportional to ω^2 [from Eq. (42.4)], and hence increasing frequency means increasing η and γ. Their ratio is constant. The diagram in Fig. 42.1 summarizes the results.

[1] Different authors writing on Mathieu functions use widely different notations: this text, η, γ; Mathieu, R, $\pm 2h^2$; Strutt, λ, $2h^2$; Strutt and van der Pol, $4\omega^2$, $4\alpha^2$; Whittaker and Humbert, a, $16q$.

The coordinates are η and γ. The plain white regions correspond to (η,γ) values for which μ is complex or real and attenuation occurs. The shaded regions are those for which μ is pure imaginary and yields unattenuated waves. In the language of the engineers, blank regions mean absorption or stopping bands and shaded regions mean passing bands.

The two lines $\eta = \gamma$ and $\eta = -\gamma$ are drawn as guides. All the passing bands become straight lines parallel to $\eta = -\gamma$ at

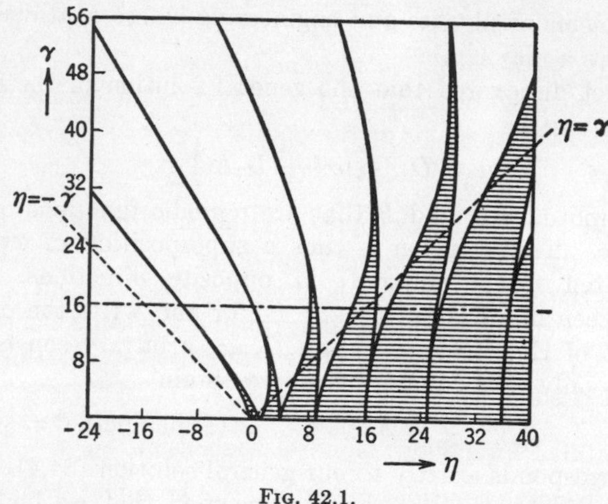

FIG. 42.1.

infinity. These lines intersect a line parallel to the η axis at the point given by

$$\eta = -\gamma + (2n + 1)\sqrt{2\gamma} \tag{42.8}$$

if the line is drawn sufficiently far above the η axis. Evidently, then, they also become parallel to one another at infinity.

There is no propagation for any value of $\eta < -\gamma$. We can make the following statements about the character of the waves:

1. $\eta < -\gamma$,	μ complex or real, absorption	(42.9)
2. $-\gamma < \eta < \gamma$	μ real or complex, broad absorption bands; μ pure imaginary, narrow transmission bands	
3. $\eta > \gamma$	μ real or complex, narrow absorption bands; μ pure imaginary, broad transmission bands	

The boundary between blank and shaded regions is the curve

$$\text{R.P. } \mu = 0 \qquad \text{(R.P. means "real part of.")} \tag{42.10}$$

The η axis corresponds to $\gamma = 0$ and hence to a continuous uniform medium with no periodic structure whatever. The entire positive part of the η axis lies inside the shaded region, since our definitions in Eq. (42.4) mean, in case of propagation,

$$C_0 = \frac{1}{V_0^2}, \qquad \eta = \frac{4\pi^2 d^2}{V_0^2} > 0 \tag{42.11}$$

A small perturbation is obtained when $\gamma << \eta$, *i.e.*, in the immediate neighborhood of the η axis. The boundary curves (42.10) leave the η axis at the points

$$\eta = n^2 \qquad n = \text{integer} \tag{42.12}$$

and have contacts of order $(n - 1)$ at these points:

$n = 1$, two curves crossing each other

$n = 2$, two curves with a common vertical tangent

$n = 3$, a common vertical tangent and the same curvature, etc.

These curves were very carefully computed by Mathieu himself and checked by later computations.

43. Mathieu Functions: General Discussion

The general solution, according to Floquet, was written in Eq. (42.5), and in this discussion emphasis can be laid either upon the imaginary exponentials [free waves as in Eq. (42.6)] or upon the real combinations that correspond to standing waves. This latter type of solution is the one mostly used by mathematicians who have computed the numerical solutions of Mathieu's equation. They start from the solution obtained along the η axis ($\gamma = 0$, no periodic perturbation), which they write

$$\cos m\xi, \qquad \sin m\xi, \qquad \mu_0 = im = i\sqrt{\eta} \tag{43.1}$$

In this case, $A(\xi)$ is a constant, and the correspondence with Eq. (42.5) is contained in the well-known relations

$$\cos m\xi = \tfrac{1}{2}(e^{im\xi} + e^{-im\xi}) \qquad D_1 = D_2 = \tfrac{1}{2}$$

$$\sin m\xi = \frac{1}{2i}(e^{im\xi} - e^{-im\xi}) \qquad D_1 = -D_2 = \frac{1}{2i}$$

For $\gamma \neq 0$, *Mathieu functions* have been defined:

$$Ce_m(\gamma,\xi) \qquad \text{and} \qquad Se_m(\gamma,\xi) \tag{43.2}$$

They are known as expansions in powers of γ, starting with either $\cos m\xi$ or $\sin m\xi$ as the independent term. Each of these functions corresponds to the same value of m, hence to the same μ.

$$\mu = im = f(\eta,\gamma), \qquad \gamma \rightarrow 0, \qquad m \rightarrow \sqrt{\eta} \tag{43.3}$$

Lines of given μ (or m) run through the shaded areas of Fig. 42.1, as schematically shown in Fig. 43.1. On each line, two functions Ce_m and Se_m may be computed, except on the boundaries of the shaded area. On these boundaries only one of the two functions

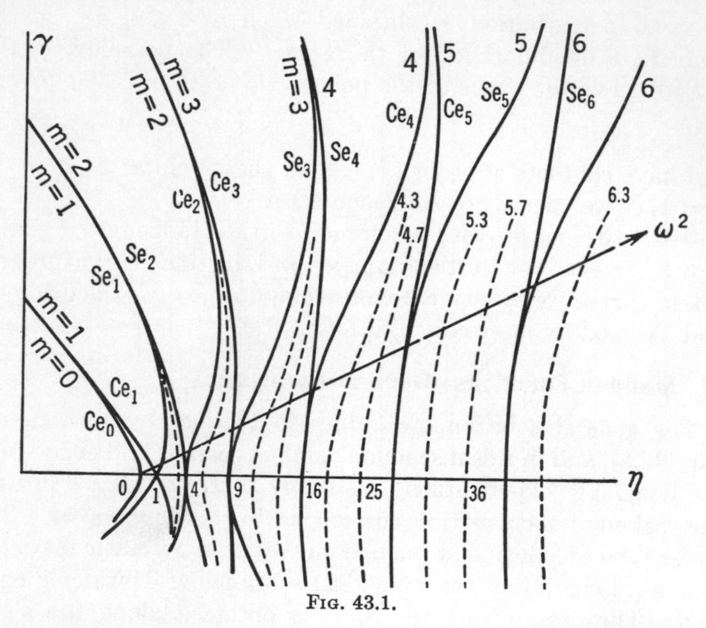

FIG. 43.1.

is obtained, as shown in Fig. 43.1. The boundaries correspond to integral values for m according to Eqs. (42.12) and (43.1) and start from the point $\eta = m^2 = 1, 4, 9, 16, \ldots$ on the η axis. Two m curves start from each of these points: one curve yields the function Se_m, and the other curve corresponds to Ce_m. On each curve there is an additional aperiodic solution.

From these diagrams we can see how to obtain information about waves propagating through a periodic medium. The medium is defined by two constant coefficients C_0 and C_1, and Eq. (42.4) yields η and γ each proportional to ν^2, with a fixed ratio

$$\frac{\eta}{\gamma} = \frac{C_0}{2C_1} \tag{43.4}$$

This means a straight line running from the origin as shown in Fig. 43.1. The line cuts the successive curves corresponding to different m values. The shaded area of Fig. 42.1 gives passing bands, and the blank areas give stopping bands. The correspondence with our former notation results from Eqs. (42.6) and (43.3).

$$i\mu = -k\frac{1}{\pi} = -m \tag{43.5}$$

Hence $+m\pi$ plays the same role as our former k. The type of the resulting (ν,m) curve is shown in Fig. 43.2. Here, again,

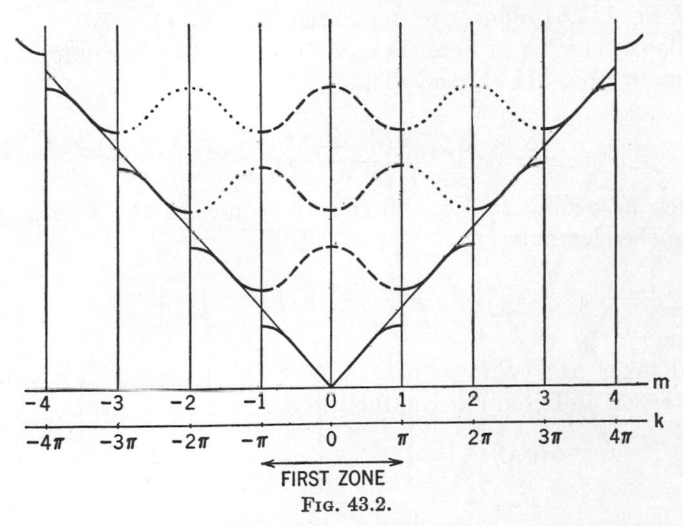

FIG. 43.2.

instead of choosing k (or m) values that insure continuity with the unperturbed uniform medium ($\gamma = 0$), we may select each time the smallest $|k|$ and reduce all curves inside the first zone $-\pi \leqq k \leqq \pi$. The important point is that *increased perturbation* (increased C_1) *does not modify the position* of the discontinuities but only *increases the magnitude* of the discontinuities.

The general theory of Mathieu's equation is very thoroughly discussed in Whittaker and Watson's "Modern Analysis,"[1] which contains some important results concerning the infinite determinants that we obtained in Sec. 34 in the preceding chap-

[1] Chap. IX, Sec. 19.41.

ter. Whittaker considers Hill's equation, which is a generalization of Mathieu's and which he writes as

$$\frac{d^2u}{dx^2} + J(x)u = 0 \tag{43.6}$$

where J is a periodic function (period π) of x. This is our general equation of Chap. VII, reduced to one dimension. The correspondence of notations is as follows:

$$\left.\begin{array}{llllll} \text{Brillouin:} & d & b = \dfrac{1}{d} & 2\pi a & \omega^2 C_n & \omega^2 F \\ \text{Whittaker and Watson:} & \pi & \dfrac{1}{\pi} & i\mu & \theta_n & J \end{array}\right\} \tag{43.7}$$

and Eq. (43.6) reduces to our former Eq. (42.1).

The discussion of Secs. 34 and 35 centered on the determinant given in Eqs. (34.14) and (34.15).

$$\Delta = |\Delta_{m,p}| = \left|\frac{C_{m-p}}{(a - mb)^2} - \frac{1}{\nu^2}\,\delta_{mp}\right| \tag{43.8}$$

which according to Eq. (43.7) corresponds to the determinant with the elements

$$\Delta_{m,p} = \frac{1}{\nu^2}\left[\frac{\omega^2 C_{m-p}}{(i\mu - 2m)^2} - \delta_{mp}\right] \tag{43.9}$$

Whittaker and Watson *assume* that the θ_n *series is absolutely convergent* and compute another determinant

$$\left.\begin{aligned} \Delta_1(i\mu) &= |B_{mp}| \\ B_{mp} &= -\frac{\theta_{m-p}}{(2m - i\mu)^2 - \theta_0} \qquad m \neq p \\ B_{mm} &= 1 \end{aligned}\right\} \tag{43.10}$$

These elements can be represented by the general formula

$$B_{mp} = \frac{-\theta_{m-p} + \delta_{mp}(2m - i\mu)^2}{-\theta_0 + (2m - i\mu)^2} = \nu^2 \Delta_{mp} \frac{(2m - i\mu)^2}{\omega^2 C_0 - (2m - i\mu)^2} \tag{43.11}$$

which gives the correspondence with our former notation. The determinant Δ_1 of Whittaker and Watson is shown to be equal to

$$\Delta_1(i\mu) = 1 + K\left[\cot\frac{\pi}{2}(i\mu + \sqrt{\theta_0}) - \cot\frac{\pi}{2}(i\mu - \sqrt{\theta_0})\right] \tag{43.12}$$

where the constant K can be obtained by computing $\Delta_1(0)$.

$$\Delta_1(i\mu) = 1 - K \frac{\sin \pi \sqrt{\theta_0}}{\sin \frac{\pi}{2} (i\mu + \sqrt{\theta_0}) \sin \frac{\pi}{2} (i\mu - \sqrt{\theta_0})}$$

$$\Delta_1(0) = 1 + 2K \cot \frac{\pi}{2} \sqrt{\theta_0},$$

$$K = \frac{\Delta_1(0) - 1}{2 \cot \frac{\pi}{2} \sqrt{\theta_0}} = \frac{\Delta_1(0) - 1}{2} \tan \frac{\pi}{2} \sqrt{\theta_0}$$

Hence

$$\Delta_1(i\mu) = 1 - [\Delta_1(0) - 1] \frac{\sin^2 \frac{\pi}{2} \sqrt{\theta_0}}{\sin \frac{\pi}{2} (i\mu + \sqrt{\theta_0}) \sin \frac{\pi}{2} (i\mu - \sqrt{\theta_0})} \tag{43.13}$$

This enables one to write the fundamental equation stating that the determinant is zero.

$$\sin \frac{\pi}{2} (i\mu + \sqrt{\theta_0}) \sin \frac{\pi}{2} (i\mu - \sqrt{\theta_0}) = [\Delta_1(0) - 1] \sin^2 \frac{\pi}{2} \sqrt{\theta_0} \tag{43.14}$$

or

$$-\cos^2 \left(\frac{\pi}{2} i\mu\right) + \cos^2 \left(\frac{\pi}{2} \sqrt{\theta_0}\right) = [\Delta_1(0) - 1] \sin^2 \frac{\pi}{2} \sqrt{\theta_0}$$

Hence

$$\sin^2 \left(\frac{\pi}{2} i\mu\right) = \Delta_1(0) \sin^2 \frac{\pi}{2} \sqrt{\theta_0} \tag{43.15}$$

which is Whittaker's result, except that he introduces another determinant $\Delta(i\mu)$ that is equal to $\Delta_1(0)$ for $\mu = 0$.

These relations are very interesting since they apply to Hill's general equation and not only to the Mathieu problem. An attempt to find an extension of these results for the three-dimensional problem of Sec. 34 would, if successful, be very important.

From our former notation, according to Eq. (43.7), Whittaker's equation (43.15) becomes

$$\sin^2 (\pi^2 a) = \Delta_1(0) \sin^2 \frac{\pi}{2} \omega \sqrt{C_0} = \Delta_1(0) \sin^2 \left(\frac{\pi^2 \nu}{V_0}\right) \tag{43.16}$$

and yields the general relation between wave number a and frequency ν for a one-dimensional lattice of period $d = \pi$ in x. The fact that ν appears as a periodic function of period $1/d = 1/\pi$ in a is obvious, as are the discontinuities in the $\nu(a)$ relation when $\Delta_1(0) > 1$. The similarity of this equation with those obtained in Chap. III is also very striking.

44. Hill's Equation with a Rectangular Curve

As already stated, Hill's equation is obtained when the cosine term in Mathieu's equation is replaced by an arbitrary periodic function of x. Let us write it as

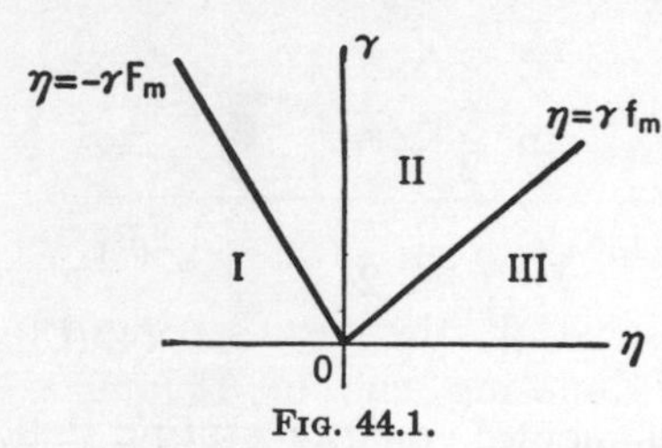

FIG. 44.1.

$$\frac{\partial^2 u}{\partial x^2} + [\eta + \gamma f(x)]u = 0 \qquad (44.1)$$

Strutt has shown that some general results about this equation can be obtained. Assuming the integral of f over a period to be zero so as to make

$$\bar{f} = 0$$

and calling f_M and $-f_m$ the maximum and minimum values of f, respectively, it is possible to show that the $\eta\gamma$ plane is again

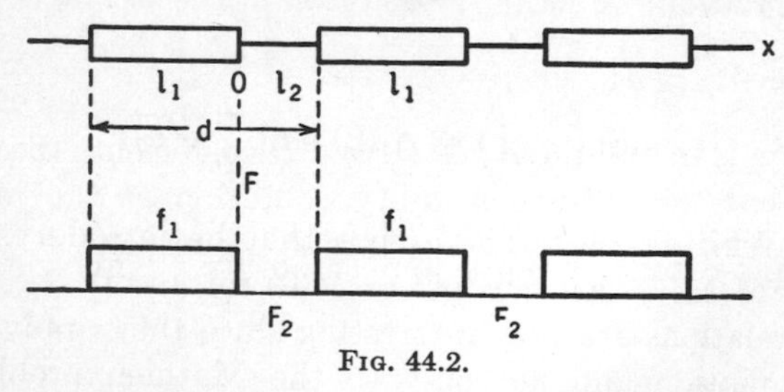

FIG. 44.2.

divided into three regions (Fig. 44.1) by the lines

$$\eta = -\gamma f_M, \qquad \eta = \gamma f_m \qquad (44.2)$$

In the first region μ is complex. In region II, μ is generally complex with some narrow bands where it becomes pure imaginary. In region III, μ is generally imaginary with some narrow bands where it is complex.

This may be shown in an example where the computations can be carried out explicitly. Let us assume a line built as shown in Fig. 44.2, with alternate portions of lengths l_1 and l_2 with values f_1 and f_2. This is obviously a special case of Eq. (44.1) with the function f represented by a rectangular curve.

$$\left.\begin{aligned} -l_1 < x < 0: \qquad & \eta + \gamma f_1 = \eta_1 = -\chi_1^2 \\ 0 < x < l_2: \qquad & \eta + \gamma f_2 = \eta_2 = -\chi_2^2 \end{aligned}\right\} \tag{44.3}$$

In the first interval we obtain a solution

$$-l_1 < x < 0: \qquad u = Ae^{\chi_1 x} + Be^{-\chi_1 x} \tag{44.4}$$

while in the next interval, the solution is

$$0 < x < l_2: \qquad u = Ce^{\chi_2 x} + De^{-\chi_2 x} \tag{44.5}$$

Furthermore, the entire solution must fit the form given by Floquet's theorem [Eq. (42.5)]. Choosing one of Floquet's exponentials, as in Eq. (42.6), we write

$$u = A(x)e^{\mu x} \tag{44.6}$$

where $A(x)$ has period d. This means, for instance,

$$u(x) = e^{\mu d}u(x - d) \tag{44.7}$$

Using this relation, we write the solution in the second l_1 interval

$$l_2 < x < l_1 + l_2 = d: \quad u(x) = Ae^{\mu d}e^{\chi_1(x-d)} + Be^{\mu d}e^{-\chi_1(x-d)} \tag{44.8}$$

The problem is to find the A, B, C, and D coefficients that satisfy these relations and the continuity condition at the junctions $(0,l_2)$, where u and $\dfrac{\partial u}{\partial x}$ must join smoothly. This yields four relations:

$$\left.\begin{aligned} x = 0: \quad & u: \quad A + B = C + D \\ & \frac{\partial u}{\partial x}: \quad A\chi_1 - B\chi_1 = C\chi_2 - D\chi_2 \\ x = l_2: \quad & u: \\ & Ae^{\mu d - \chi_1 l_1} + Be^{\mu d + \chi_1 l_1} = Ce^{\chi_2 l_2} + De^{-\chi_2 l_2} \\ & \frac{\partial u}{\partial x}: \\ & A\chi_1 e^{\mu d - \chi_1 l_1} - B\chi_1 e^{\mu d + \chi_1 l_1} = C\chi_2 e^{\chi_2 l_2} - D\chi_2 e^{-\chi_2 l_2} \end{aligned}\right\} \tag{44.9}$$

This set of four linear homogeneous equations in A, B, $-C$, and $-D$ can be solved only if its determinant is zero.

$$\Delta = \begin{vmatrix} 1 & 1 & 1 & 1 \\ \chi_1 & -\chi_1 & \chi_2 & -\chi_2 \\ e^{\mu d - \chi_1 l_1} & e^{\mu d + \chi_1 l_1} & e^{\chi_2 l_2} & e^{-\chi_2 l_2} \\ \chi_1 e^{\mu d - \chi_1 l_1} & -\chi_1 e^{\mu d + \chi_1 l_1} & \chi_2 e^{\chi_2 l_2} & -\chi_2 e^{-\chi_2 l_2} \end{vmatrix} = 0 \quad (44.10)$$

It is a matter of elementary computations to expand this determinant and to obtain the equation

$$Y^2 - 2Y\left[\cosh \chi_1 l_1 \cosh \chi_2 l_2 + \frac{1}{2}\left(\frac{\chi_1}{\chi_2} + \frac{\chi_2}{\chi_1}\right) \sinh \chi_1 l_1 \sinh \chi_2 l_2\right] + 1 = 0 \quad (44.11)$$

where $Y = e^{\mu d}$. This second-order equation has two solutions (Y_1, Y_2) whose product is unity

$$Y_1 = e^{\mu d}, \qquad Y_2 = e^{-\mu d}, \qquad Y_1 Y_2 = 1$$

and whose sum is twice the bracket in Eq. (44.11).

$$\left.\begin{aligned} Y_1 + Y_2 &= e^{\mu d} + e^{-\mu d} = 2 \cosh \mu d = 2[\cdot \ \cdot \ \cdot] \\ \cosh \mu d &= \cosh \chi_1 l_1 \cosh \chi_2 l_2 \\ &\qquad + \frac{1}{2}\left(\frac{\chi_1}{\chi_2} + \frac{\chi_2}{\chi_1}\right) \sinh \chi_1 l_1 \sinh \chi_2 l_2 \end{aligned}\right\} \quad (44.12)$$

To check this equation, let us take $\chi_1 = \chi_2$, a continuous line. Then $\mu d = \chi_1 l_1 + \chi_2 l_2$ is the obvious solution.

We shall discuss a whole class of problems of this type in Chap. X and develop a more direct and very powerful method for solving them. Equation (44.12) will appear as a special case of a more general equation. According to whether χ_1 and χ_2 are real or imaginary, some of the hyperbolic sines and cosines may become ordinary sines and cosines. For instance, van der Pol and Strutt consider the problem of equal sections. Let us take

$$l_1 = l_2 = \frac{\pi}{2} \qquad\qquad d = \pi$$

in order to obtain the same period π as occurs in Mathieu's equation,

$$\eta_1 = \eta + \gamma \qquad\qquad \eta_2 = \eta - \gamma$$

Case 1:

$$\left.\begin{aligned}
&\eta > \gamma > 0 \qquad\qquad \text{both } \eta_1 \text{ and } \eta_2 \text{ positive}\\
&\chi_1 l_1 = \frac{1}{2}\pi\chi_1 = \frac{\pi}{2}\sqrt{-\eta_1} = i\ x_1\\
&\qquad\qquad\qquad\qquad \mu = i\mu' = i2\pi a\\
&\chi_2 l_2 = \frac{1}{2}\pi\chi_2 = \frac{\pi}{2}\sqrt{-\eta_2} = i\ x_2
\end{aligned}\right\} \qquad (44.13)$$

Equation (44.12) becomes

$$\left.\begin{aligned}
&\cos \pi\mu' = \cos x_1 \cos x_2 - \frac{1}{2}\left(\frac{x_1}{x_2} + \frac{x_2}{x_1}\right) \sin x_1 \sin x_2\\
&\textit{Case 2:}\\
&\qquad \eta < \gamma, \qquad \gamma > 0 \qquad\qquad \eta_1 > 0, \qquad \eta_2 < 0\\
&\qquad \frac{\pi}{2}\chi_1 = \frac{\pi}{2}\sqrt{-\eta_1} = ix_1\\
&\qquad \frac{\pi}{2}\chi_2 = \frac{\pi}{2}\sqrt{-\eta_2} = x_3
\end{aligned}\right\} \qquad (44.14)$$

$$\cos \pi\mu' = \cos x_1 \cosh x_3 - \frac{1}{2}\left(\frac{x_1}{x_3} - \frac{x_3}{x_1}\right) \sin x_1 \sinh x_3 \qquad (44.15)$$

The problem is to follow the variation of expressions (44.12) or (44.14) and (44.15) in the $\eta\gamma$ plane and to distinguish between the regions giving μ real or complex. Three cases are obtained:

$$\left.\begin{aligned}
&A.\ \cosh \mu d \geqq 1 && \mu = \mu_0 \text{ real}\\
&B.\ -1 \leqq \cosh \mu d \leqq 1 && \mu = i\mu', \quad \mu' \text{ real}\\
&C.\ -1 \leqq \cosh \mu d && \mu = \mu_0 + i\pi
\end{aligned}\right\} \qquad (44.16)$$

Case B gives waves propagating through the whole line without attenuation, which means *passing bands*, and is represented in Fig. 44.3 by shaded regions. Both cases A and C yield waves attenuated exponentially either to the right or to the left [$e^{\pm\mu_0 x}$ factor in Eq. (44.6)] and differ only in the relative phases of oscillations in successive (l_1,l_2) sections. This means stopping bands and blank regions in Fig. 44.3.

The whole map in Fig. 44.3 is very similar to that in Fig. 42.1 for Mathieu functions, except for some intersections of boundary curves. The boundaries are obtained for $k = 0$ or $\mu = i\pi$. They are denoted by $C_0C_1C_2$ and $S_0S_1S_2$, these symbols corresponding to the Ce and Se Mathieu functions, respectively.

The discussion given by van der Pol and Strutt covers all cases

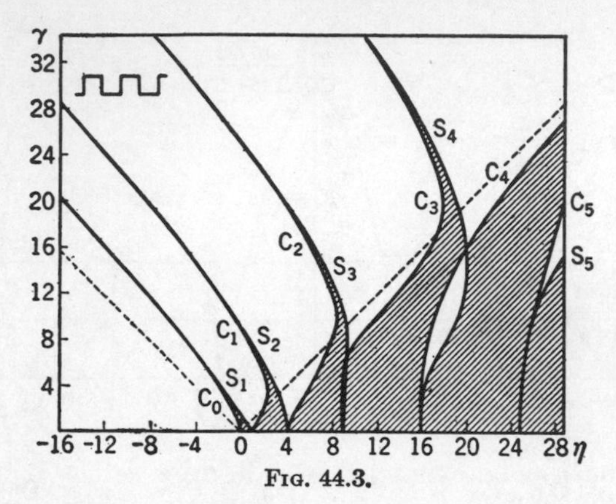

FIG. 44.3.

of (η,γ) variations. Kronig and Penney limited their discussion to the case of $(-\eta_1)$ very large and positive, with l_1 very small, while η_2 is positive and $l_2 \approx d$. The exact conditions assumed are

$$\chi_1 \to \sqrt{\frac{2c}{l_1 l_2}}, \qquad \chi_2 = i\alpha$$

where c is a constant. Then Eq. (44.12) yields

$$\cosh \mu d = \cosh \chi_1 l_1 \cos \alpha l_2 + \frac{\chi_1^2 - \alpha^2}{2\alpha\chi_1} \sinh \chi_1 l_1 \sin \alpha l_2 \tag{44.17}$$

According to these conditions

$$\cosh \chi_1 l_1 \to 1$$
$$\frac{\chi_1^2 - \alpha^2}{2\alpha\chi_1} \sinh \chi_1 l_1 \to \frac{l_1}{2\alpha} (\chi_1^2 - \alpha^2) = \frac{c}{\alpha l_2}$$

and we obtain

$$\cosh \mu d = \cos \alpha d + \frac{c}{\alpha d} \sin \alpha d \tag{44.18}$$

The variation of this expression is represented in Fig. 44.4 where the limits ± 1 corresponding to cases A, B, and C of Eq. (44.16) are clearly seen.

A general formula giving the relation between ν and a was obtained in Sec. 43 by using a result proved by Whittaker under the assumption that the coefficients $\theta_n = \omega^2 C_n$ of the Fourier expansion for the function J constituted an absolutely convergent series. This is not true of the step function used in this section.

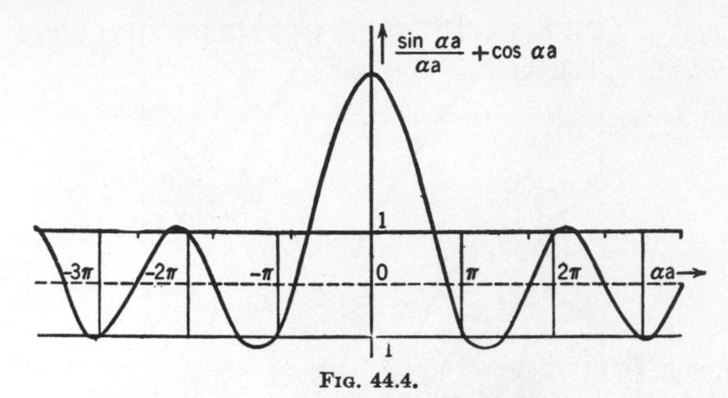

FIG. 44.4.

The function can be expanded in a Fourier series, but the convergence of the series of coefficients is not secured.

Equation (43.16) is

$$\sin^2 \pi a d = \Delta_1(0) \sin^2 \frac{\pi \nu d}{V_0} \tag{43.16}$$

where $\Delta_1(0)$ did not depend upon α or ν, and d was supposed equal to π, while

$$\frac{1}{V_0^2} = \overline{\left(\frac{1}{V^2}\right)} \qquad \text{average}$$

In the present section we obtained Eq. (44.14)

$$\cos 2\pi a d = \cos x_1 \cos x_2 - \frac{1}{2}\left(\frac{x_1}{x_2} + \frac{x_2}{x_1}\right) \sin x_1 \sin x_2 \tag{44.14}$$

with

$$x_1 = \frac{\omega d}{2V_1} = \frac{\pi \nu d}{V_1}, \qquad x_2 = \frac{\omega d}{2V_2} = \frac{\pi \nu d}{V_2} \qquad (d = \pi)$$

This equation can be written

$$\cos 2\pi a d = \cos (x_1 + x_2) + \left(1 - \frac{x_1^2 + x_2^2}{2x_1 x_2}\right) \sin x_1 \sin x_2$$

but

$$1 - \frac{x_1^2 + x_2^2}{2x_1 x_2} = -\frac{(x_1 - x_2)^2}{2x_1 x_2} = \frac{(V_2 - V_1)^2}{2V_1 V_2} \tag{44.19}$$

We may replace $\cos 2\varphi$ by $(1 - 2\sin^2 \varphi)$ and obtain

$$\sin^2 \pi a d = \sin^2 \left[\left(\frac{1}{V_1} + \frac{1}{V_2}\right)\frac{\pi \nu d}{2}\right] + \frac{(V_2 - V_1)^2}{4V_1 V_2} \sin \frac{\pi \nu d}{V_1} \sin \frac{\pi \nu d}{V_2} \tag{44.20}$$

which *does not reduce to the general type* (43.16). For *very small perturbations,* however, we may take

$$\frac{1}{V_1} = \frac{1}{V_0}(1 + \epsilon), \qquad \frac{1}{V_2} = \frac{1}{V_0}(1 - \epsilon),$$

$$\frac{(V_2 - V_1)^2}{4V_1V_2} = \epsilon^2 + \cdots$$

Hence

$$\sin^2 \pi a d = (1 + \epsilon^2 \cdots) \sin^2 \left(\frac{\pi \nu d}{V_0}\right) \tag{44.21}$$

dropping higher powers of ϵ. This equation, rather than the general one, is of the Whittaker type.

This example shows the limitations of the general equations of Sec. 43, which should not be used when the series of the Fourier coefficients θ_n (or C_n) does not converge absolutely.

45. The Self-excited Oscillator

A circuit containing only an inductance and a capacity will oscillate with frequency $1/\sqrt{LC}$, where L is the inductance and C the capacity. The equation of the circuit is

$$L\frac{d^2Q}{dt^2} + \frac{Q}{C} = 0 \tag{45.1}$$

If we vary the capacity periodically, the equation may be written in the form of Mathieu's equation.

$$\frac{1}{C} = A + B \cos \omega_1 t \tag{45.2}$$

where A and B are constants and ω_1 the frequency with which we vary the capacity. Equation (45.1) becomes

$$\frac{d^2Q}{dt^2} + \frac{1}{L}(A + B \cos \omega_1 t)Q = 0 \tag{45.3}$$

If we set

$$Q = u \qquad \text{and} \qquad \xi = \tfrac{1}{2}\omega_1 t$$

then Eq. (45.3) is

$$\frac{\partial^2 u}{\partial \xi^2} + (\eta + \gamma \cos 2\xi)u = 0 \tag{45.4}$$

where

$$\eta = \frac{4A}{L{\omega_1}^2}, \qquad \gamma = \frac{4B}{L{\omega_1}^2} \tag{45.5}$$

Equation (45.4) is Mathieu's equation and has solutions of the type (42.5)

$$u = D_1 A(\xi) e^{\mu\xi} + D_2 A(-\xi) e^{-\mu\xi} \tag{45.6}$$

where the exponent μ is pure imaginary in the shaded regions of Fig. 42.1 and real or complex in the blank regions. This means

Shaded regions: $\mu = i\beta$ *stable* oscillations of constant average amplitude
Blank regions: μ real or complex; *unstable* oscillations, one term increasing to infinity, the other term decreasing to zero (45.7)

Thus the map in Fig. 42.1 completely describes the situation. If the variation of capacity were stepwise instead of sinusoidal, we should use the map in Fig. 44.3.

An example of an electric circuit with variation of the capacity is shown in Fig. 45.1. This device was proposed in the last

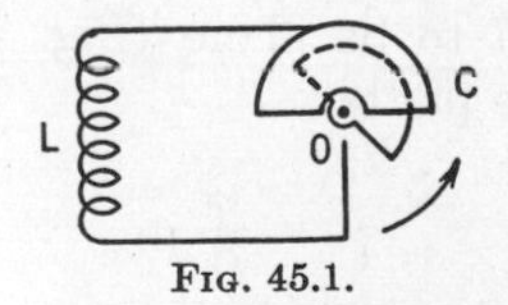

FIG. 45.1.

century as a self-excited high-frequency oscillator. A self-excited oscillator can also be built with a periodic variation of the self-inductance, such as a standard alternator with stator and rotor windings connected in series, and a fixed capacity. Self-excitation means unstable conditions, which yield oscillations of increasing amplitude: the amplitude would start from zero and continue to increase, finally reaching a constant value when some of the nonlinear terms omitted in the equation become sufficiently important; such terms might be sparks in the condenser or finite power of the engine turning the condenser.

In the *electric examples*, L and C are *always positive*, which means

$$\eta > \gamma > 0 \tag{45.8}$$

i.e., case 1 in Sec. 44 [Eq. (44.14)], which corresponds to region III in Figs. 42.1, 44.1, and 44.4, where stability is the rule and instability the exception. Looking at Fig. 42.1, we notice that the main region of instability (or *self-excitation*) is the V-shaped region near $\eta = 1$, which means, according to Eqs. (45.2) and (45.5),

$$\left.\begin{aligned} \frac{4A}{L\omega_1^2} = \frac{4}{LC_0\omega_1^2} = 4\frac{\omega_0^2}{\omega_1^2} \approx 1 \\ A = \frac{1}{C_0}, \quad \omega_0^2 = \frac{1}{LC_0}, \quad 2\omega_0 \approx \omega_1 \end{aligned}\right\} \tag{45.9}$$

ω_0 is the frequency of the circuit (L,C_0) and should be nearly equal to ½ the frequency of excitation ω_1.

This result was found by an elementary discussion, relating to the case of small excitation $(B << A)$ before the complete theory was developed. The situation is easier to explain if the

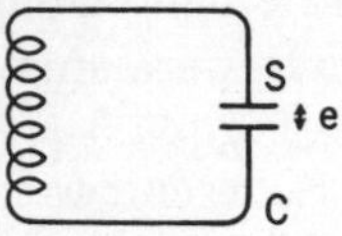

FIG. 45.2.

condenser is supposed to be plane (Fig. 45.2) with a varying distance e between the plates.

$$\frac{1}{C} = \frac{4\pi}{S} e \tag{45.10}$$

If the electric surface density on the condenser plates is $\sigma = Q/S$, then the force acting per unit area is $2\pi\sigma^2$, and the total force of attraction between the plates is

$$f = S2\pi\sigma^2 = \frac{2\pi}{S} Q^2 = \frac{Q^2}{2Ce} \tag{45.11}$$

The variation of capacity is obtained by varying the distance.

$$\left.\begin{aligned} e = e_0 + b \cos \omega_1 t \\ \frac{1}{C} = \frac{1}{C_0} + \frac{4\pi b}{S} \cos \omega_1 t \end{aligned}\right\} \tag{45.12}$$

For small perturbation, small b, the oscillations in the circuit will have a frequency very close to the proper frequency ω_0, and hence Q^2 will vary with twice this frequency.

$$\left.\begin{aligned} Q &= A \cos (\omega_0 t + \varphi) \\ Q^2 &= A^2 \cos^2 (\omega_0 t + \varphi) = \tfrac{1}{2}A^2[1 + \cos 2(\omega_0 t + \varphi)] \end{aligned}\right\} \tag{45.13}$$

The work done per oscillation by the engine operating the system is

$$W = \oint f\,de \approx \frac{-b\omega_1 A^2}{2Ce_0} \oint \cos^2 (\omega_0 t + \varphi) \sin \omega_1 t\, dt$$
$$= \frac{-b\omega_1 A^2}{4Ce_0} \oint \cos 2(\omega_0 t + \varphi) \sin \omega_1 t\, dt \quad (45.14)$$

This is zero unless $\omega_1 = 2\omega_0$ and may be positive or negative according to the phase φ. When the work done is positive, oscillations in the circuit increase in amplitude (instability and self-excitation). This is a crude explanation of the physical

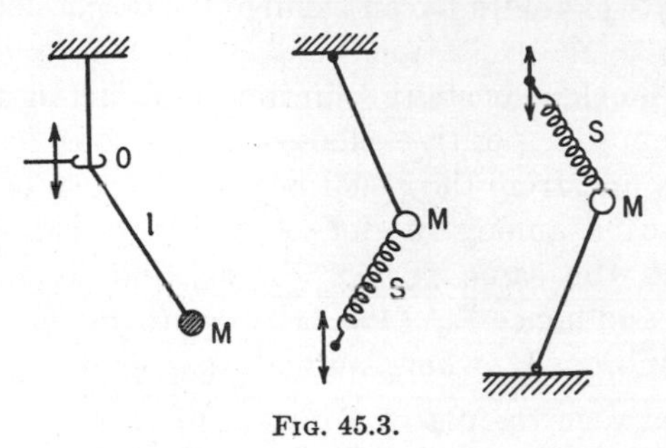

FIG. 45.3.

meaning of condition (45.9). The physical explanation for excitation near the points

$$\eta = 4, 9, \cdots, n^2$$

corresponding to

$$\frac{4A}{L_1\omega_1^2} = \frac{4}{LC_0\omega_1^2} = \frac{4\omega_0^2}{\omega_1^2} = n^2; \qquad 2\omega_0 = n\omega_1 \qquad (45.15)$$

is not so elementary and must be found in the harmonic content of oscillations in the circuit with varying capacity.

Mechanical oscillators can also be taken as examples, and some models are shown in Fig. 45.3. Here the mass M (replacing L) is always positive, but the A and B coefficients in the restoring force [replacing $1/C$, Eq. (45.2)] may become negative, as for a reversed pendulum or for a spring pushing the mass away instead of pulling it toward its equilibrium position. This means that the whole map of Fig. 42.1 or 44.3 can be used. Region II is very interesting: an unstable pendulum can be made stable by a periodic perturbation of appropriate frequency. Some other examples follow: the movement of a direct or reversed pendulum whose support is moved up and down with a frequency ω_1; oscillations along a string whose tension is varied periodically.

More detailed explanations and equations may be found in the paper by van der Pol and Strutt already quoted.

46. Free Electrons in Metals

According to wave mechanics, the motion of electrons in a potential field (x,y,z) is obtained from the solution of the Schroedinger wave equation:

$$\nabla^2\psi + k^2(E - P)\psi = 0, \qquad k^2 = \frac{8\pi^2 m}{h^2} \tag{46.1}$$

where h is Planck's constant. In a crystal lattice the potential P results from the positive charge of the ions located at the lattice points and from the equal negative charge of the electron cloud distributed among the ions. All this yields a periodic P function with the same periods $\mathbf{d}_1$, $\mathbf{d}_2$, and $\mathbf{d}_3$ as the crystal lattice itself, and hence Eq. (46.1) reduces to a type similar to the one studied in Sec. 34, where we had

$$\nabla^2\psi + H(\mathbf{r})\psi = 0 \tag{34.1}$$

$$H = \frac{\omega^2}{V^2} = \omega^2 F \tag{34.2}$$

while here the correspondence is

$$H = k^2[E - P(\mathbf{r})] \tag{46.2}$$

E is the energy of the electrons and $P(\mathbf{r})$ the periodic potential.

The whole theory of Sec. 34 applies directly to the problem of free electrons and yields the usual rules about zone structure. As a matter of fact, the *zone structure* is completely *independent of the special physical meaning* of the waves considered, and it must be the *same for elastic, electromagnetic, and Schroedinger electronic waves.* Some authors did not pay enough attention to this very general result and based their definitions of the zones on different criteria for different waves, thus obtaining discrepancies that are not consistent with the mathematical nature of the problem. As we emphasized in Secs. 26 and 31, another error to be avoided is an oversimplification of the problem, such as an assumption

$$P(\mathbf{r}) = P_1(x) + P_2(y) + P_3(z) \tag{46.3}$$

This is an academic problem of no actual interest whatever, since no crystal lattice is known that would give a field of the type (46.3), even as a first rough approximation. Such a structure would mean a disappearance of most Bragg spots in X rays except for the few reflections from planes parallel to coordinate planes, a circumstance never realized in any known crystal. Actual physical problems yield periodic potentials P with their complete set of $A_{m_1m_2m_3}$ coefficients in the triple Fourier expansion, which means a complete set of lattice planes with indices m_1, m_2, and m_3.

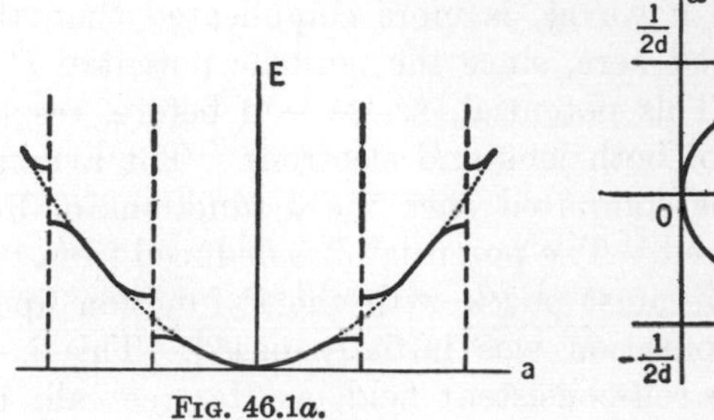

FIG. 46.1*a*.

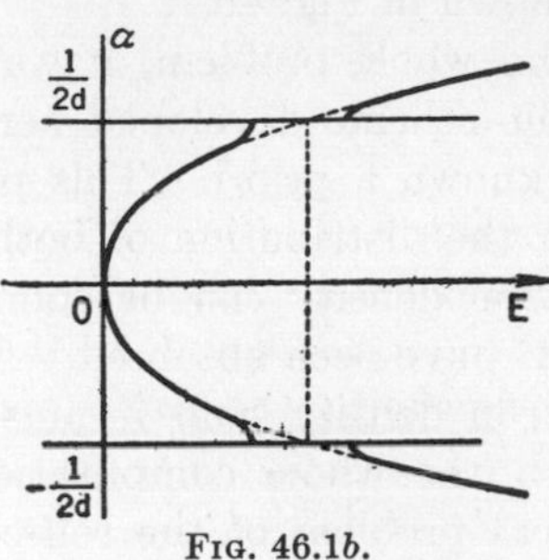

FIG. 46.1*b*.

The problem of a small perturbation for usual waves was discussed in Sec. 35 under the assumption

$$F = \frac{1}{V^2} = \frac{1}{V_0{}^2} + \epsilon f = C_{000} + \epsilon f, \qquad H = \frac{\omega^2}{V_0{}^2} + \epsilon\omega^2 f$$

In the electronic problem we may assume the average potential inside the crystal to be zero, since this merely means a special choice of the zero energy level, and we state

$$\left.\begin{aligned} P &= \epsilon\varphi \\ H &= k^2(E - \epsilon\varphi) \end{aligned}\right\} \tag{46.4}$$

Writing Planck's relation

$$E = h\nu \tag{46.5}$$

we define a frequency for the electron waves. The difference between the two problems results from a comparison of the equations

$$\text{Elastic waves } \frac{\omega^2}{V_0{}^2} = \omega^2 C_{000} = hk^2\nu \text{ electron waves} \tag{46.6}$$

The V-shaped curves obtained for unperturbed elastic waves with

$$\frac{\omega}{V_0} = 2\pi|a| \tag{46.7}$$

now result in parabolic curves for unperturbed electron waves with

$$hk^2\nu = 4\pi^2|a|^2 \tag{46.8}$$

and curves relating to a small perturbation differ from this parabola only in discontinuities on the boundaries of the zones, as shown in Fig. 46.1.

The whole problem, however, is more complicated than the simple scheme developed here, since the periodic potential P is not known a priori. This potential, as we said before, results from the distribution of both ions and electrons. The average electron density can be computed once the ψ functions of Eq. (46.1) have been obtained. The potential P is deduced from the electron density, and it must check with the P function upon which the whole computation was initially based. This is a typical problem of the self-consistent field, as Hartree calls it, and the solution of Eq. (46.1) represents only one step in a more complicated problem.

Selected References

Mathieu, P.: "Cours de Mathématique physique," p. 122, 1873.
Humbert, J.: "Fonctions de Lamé et Mathieu," G. Villars, Paris, 1926.
Whittaker and Watson: "Modern Analysis," p. 404, Cambridge, 1920.
Strutt, M. J. O.: *Ann. Physik*, **84**, 485 (1927); **85**, 129 (1928); **86**, 319 (1928).
van der Pol, B., and M. J. O. Strutt: *Phil. Mag.*, **5**, 18 (1928).
Brillouin, L.: "Quantenstatistik," p. 271, Springer, Berlin, 1931.
Kronig, R. de L., and W. G. Penney: *Proc. Roy. Soc.* (*London*), **130**, 499 (1931).
Stratton, J. A.: "Electromagnetic Theory," pp. 52–200, McGraw-Hill, New York, 1941.
Brillouin, L.: *Electrical Communications*, April, 1938.
Strutt, M. J. O.: *Math. Ann.*, **101**, 559 (1929).
Morse, P. M.: *Phys. Rev.*, **35**, 1310 (1930).

More recent references and discussions will be found in the following papers:

Brillouin, L.: *Quarterly of Applied Mathematics*, t.6, p. 167 (1948) and t.7, p. 364 (1950).

CHAPTER IX

MATRICES AND THE PROPAGATION OF WAVES ALONG AN ELECTRIC LINE

47. General Remarks

In the historical summary given in the first chapters, it was explained how the theory of wave propagation first started with the discussion of waves along a discontinuous string. Then followed the theory of waves in a continuous medium, and we emphasized the importance of some of Lord Kelvin's remarks on waves in a discontinuous structure and the existence of a cutoff frequency. Up to Kelvin's time only one type of wave had been discussed, *viz.*, elastic waves. Later electromagnetic waves and, still later, electron waves in wave mechanics were discovered, and the properties first obtained for elastic waves were immediately translated for these new waves. For instance, Lagrange's theory of how to pass from the discontinuous string to the limit of a continuous string was used by Pupin in his discussion of loaded telephonic cables. The deep discussion of Kelvin, related in Sec. 2, led him to imagine a new model for an optical medium. A similar mechanical model was built by Vincent and proved to have the properties of a mechanical band-pass filter. This model was translated into an electrical circuit by Campbell and was the point of departure for his invention of electric filters, of which he gave a number of important applications.

Hence, for scientists of the last century, it was common knowledge that the special nature of the waves did not matter and that the same general properties could be found for any type of waves. The general relations among the various types of waves seem to have been forgotten for some time. Physicists developed the theory of electromagnetic waves for optics and X rays. Then theoreticians discussed very carefully the properties of electron waves (wave mechanics) in crystals and too often did not pay attention to the fact that a great part of the work had already been done in the theory of X-ray propagation in crystals.

On the other hand, electrical engineers did a wonderful analysis on the theory of propagation of waves along lines, cables, filters, etc., but omitted to notice that many important facts had already been discovered by theoretical physicists (see Secs. 13 and 14). More recently, practical acoustics was revived, mostly by electrical engineers, who were especially well trained in electric-circuit theory and found it easier to translate mechanical problems into the equivalent electric circuits before discussion. These scientists at last rediscovered the similarity of all problems of vibration and wave propagation, but they did just the opposite of what their ancestors had done. Pupin and Campbell started from mechanical models to discuss electric lines and filters. A modern engineer, wishing to discuss wave propagation along a train of railway cars, translates the problem into an electrical one (an impulse propagating along a filter) and then translates the answer back into mechanical terms.

This explains why we want to include a general discussion of wave propagation along electric lines and filters in this book. Many modern theoretical physicists have hardly heard of these problems and do not realize the very great advance in the theory by this engineer's art. Engineers, on the other hand, have a tendency to imagine that any wave problem can be reduced to a problem in electric lines, and this is not entirely true. We have already discussed in Chap. V the importance and the limitations of the concept of *characteristic* or *surge impedance*. This concept is fundamental for one-dimensional structures such as mechanical or electric lines and filters. Its generalization for three dimensions is not so easy, and we noted that the definition of energy flow, exemplified by the Poynting vector for electromagnetic waves or similar definitions in wave mechanics, is better adapted to the three- or four-dimensional problems.

Recent developments in wave mechanics point to the importance of matrix calculus and its very close connection with a number of problems of wave propagation. It is very interesting to note that electrical engineers have independently come to the same conclusion. Matrix theory is now commonly used in the discussion of problems of waves in electric filters. Furthermore, these problems seem to represent the only classical example where some special matrices, of great importance for the theory of electron spin, appear for practical purposes, and we shall try in the next chapter to show the connection between the theory of electric filters and the Pauli-Dirac wave theory of the spinning electron.

The discussion in this chapter will be on the propagation of waves along electric lines. Let us, once for all, give the correlation between the electric quantities and the mechanical quantities arising in similar mechanical problems. This can be done in different ways, but the most direct translation is obtained by the use of the following glossary:

Electrical	*Mechanical*
Electric charge	Displacement or coordinate
Electric current	Velocity
Electric current, time derivative	Acceleration
Self-inductance	Mass
Mutual inductance	No direct equivalent; it appears, however, in problems with constraints, where generalized Lagrange coordinates are used
Magnetic energy	Kinetic energy
Electric energy	Potential energy
Capacity C	Elastic coefficient $= 1/C$
Voltage	Tension

We shall discuss in this chapter the propagation of electric disturbances along electric lines. This can be translated into a problem of mechanical disturbances propagating along a periodic mechanical line structure. Electric lines are schematically represented in Fig. 51.1 or 55.1, for instance. The same general scheme may be just as well interpreted in mechanical terms. A square box with four terminals is supposed to represent a certain electric circuit. Let us imagine the box to contain a given mechanical device. We have two terminals on the left for input current and voltage and the two others on the right for output current and voltage when we think of the box as containing an electric circuit. With a mechanical structure, we have only one connection on each side (a rod or a string going from one box to the next one), but we need two quantities to specify the connection: the *velocity* of the string motion (analogous to electric current) and the elastic tension along the string (analogous to the voltage). Hence the correlation is complete, and the glossary will help in translating from one problem to the other.

As noted earlier, there are, however, some cases where

difficulties are encountered: electrical mutual inductances between circuit elements have no direct counterpart in mechanical problems. However, a general expression for the kinetic energy was introduced long ago in analytical mechanics and has the same form as Eq. (48.2) of the next section. Such expressions are obtained in mechanical problems with constraints when generalized Lagrange coordinates must be used instead of the usual position coordinates of the mass points.

Other limitations refer to the range of possible values for some quantities. We have already pointed out in Secs. 11 and 12 the fact that capacities are always positive in electrical theory, while elastic coefficients may be either positive or negative in mechanics. Thus, if the general scheme and theory are common to all problems of wave propagation, there are restricting conditions or practical limitations for each separate class of problems, which should always be kept in mind.

The first sections of this chapter are devoted to essential definitions and to the systematic introduction of the matrix notation, visualizing elementary matrix computations by their equivalent circuit connections. Then we shall go on to a discussion of the role of characteristic impedance of the line and the propagation of waves. Finally, in the next chapter we shall let the elements of the line become infinitesimal and thus will be enabled to draw some analogies between the propagation of the waves and the quantum mechanical problem of electron spin.

The electric lines that we shall discuss are to consist of identical circuits connected together. Each circuit is an electric circuit, which may be as complicated as desired with the following restrictions. First, all circuit elements must be linear; *i.e.*, we allow resistances, self-inductances, mutual inductances, and capacities. Rectifiers, coils containing iron, and other nonlinear elements are excluded. Negative resistances are allowed if care is exercised in their use. They will appear in the mathematical equations, and, if they are to be used in an experiment, one must be sure that the linear portion of the characteristic curve is used. The second restriction is that no sources of current are to appear in the circuit. All electromotive forces will appear as external parts.

We shall represent the circuits composing the line as rectangles with pairs of terminals, as shown in Fig. 47.1. At present, we shall place no restriction on the number of terminals. The electromotive forces are to be applied to these terminals, which we number. Each electromotive force E_k will then give rise to a current i_k, both of the same frequency. For the present we shall choose the signs of E_k and i_k so that the product R.P. $E_k i_k^*$ is the power furnished to the circuit. We shall assume that the circuit is a simple circuit; *i.e.*, that it does not contain two or more circuits completely separate from one another. Further, we shall assume that the number of terminals is reduced to a minimum. For instance, if two or more pairs of terminals are

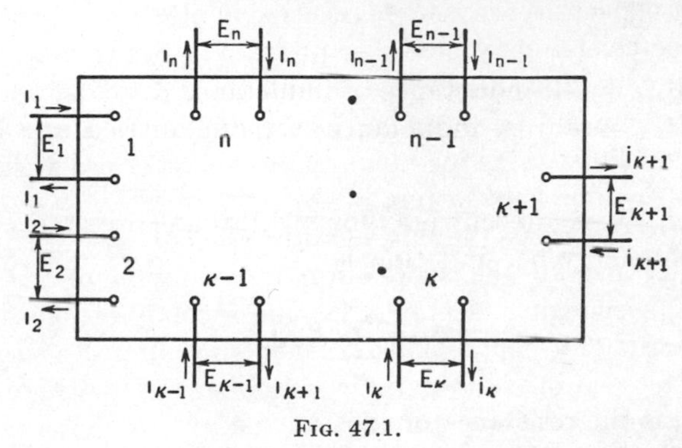

FIG. 47.1.

in series, they may be replaced by a single pair of terminals with an applied electromotive force equal to the sum of the separate electromotive forces.

48. Expressions for Energy

We shall assume that the minimum number of pairs of terminals is n. The kth pair of terminals will have an electromotive force E_k. The meaning of $E_k = 0$ is just that the kth pair of terminals is short-circuited. Each electromotive force E_k will furnish charge q_k to the pair of terminals across which it is connected. The q_k will form a complete set of independent variables for the system if there are n branches to the circuit. If there are more than n, then it is necessary to introduce more terminals with an applied electromotive force of zero at these additional terminals. We shall assume that this has been done.

There will be two types of energy present in the general circuit: electrostatic due to capacities, magnetic due to self-inductances and mutual inductances, and, in addition, dissipation of energy due to resistances. If we let Q_α be the charge on condenser α, then the electrostatic energy is given by

$$E_e = \frac{1}{2} \sum_\alpha \frac{Q_\alpha^2}{C_\alpha} \tag{48.1}$$

where C_α is the capacity of condenser α. Similarly, if $\dot{Q}_\alpha$ is the current in inductance α, the magnetic energy is

$$E_m = \frac{1}{2} \sum_\alpha L_\alpha \dot{Q}_\alpha^2 + \sum_{\alpha > \beta} M_{\alpha\beta} \dot{Q}_\alpha \dot{Q}_\beta = \frac{1}{2} \sum_{\alpha\beta} M_{\alpha\beta} \dot{Q}_\alpha \dot{Q}_\beta \tag{48.2}$$

where

$L_\alpha = M_{\alpha\alpha}$ = self-inductance of inductance α
$M_{\alpha\beta} = M_{\beta\alpha}$ = mutual inductance of inductances α and β when $\alpha \neq \beta$

Finally, if $\dot{Q}_\alpha$ is the current flowing through resistance α, the dissipated energy per unit time is

$$\phi = \sum_\alpha R_\alpha \dot{Q}_\alpha^2 \tag{48.3}$$

where R_α is the resistance of resistance α.

Now all of our circuit elements are to be linear and it follows that we may express the Q_α as a linear sum of the q_k defined in the first paragraph of this section; *i.e.*,

$$Q_\alpha = \sum_k a_{\alpha k} q_k \tag{48.4}$$

where the $a_{\alpha k}$ are constant coefficients. We may substitute Eq. (48.4) into Eqs. (48.1), (48.2), and (48.3) to obtain first

$$E_e = \frac{1}{2} \sum_\alpha \frac{1}{C_\alpha} \left(\sum_k a_{\alpha k} q_k \sum_j a_{\alpha j} q_j \right) = \frac{1}{2} \sum_{kj} c_{kj} q_k q_j \tag{48.5}$$

where

$$c_{kj} = \sum_\alpha \frac{a_{\alpha k} a_{\alpha j}}{C_\alpha} = c_{jk} \tag{48.6}$$

Next

$$E_m = \frac{1}{2} \sum_{\alpha\beta} M_{\alpha\beta} \sum_j a_{\alpha j} \dot{q}_j \sum_k a_{\beta k} \dot{q}_k = \frac{1}{2} \sum_{jk} m_{jk} \dot{q}_j \dot{q}_k \tag{48.7}$$

where

$$m_{jk} = \sum_{\alpha\beta} M_{\alpha\beta} a_{\alpha j} a_{\beta k} = m_{kj} \tag{48.8}$$

Finally,

$$\phi = \sum_{\alpha} R_{\alpha} \sum_{j} a_{\alpha j} \dot{q}_j \sum_{k} a_{\alpha k} \dot{q}_k = \sum_{jk} r_{jk} \dot{q}_j \dot{q}_k \tag{48.9}$$

where

$$r_{jk} = \sum_{\alpha} R_{\alpha} a_{\alpha j} a_{\alpha k} = r_{kj} \tag{48.10}$$

The coefficients c_{kj}, m_{kj}, and r_{kj} may be computed in terms of the circuit elements; they will be homogeneous in the C_α, $M_{\alpha\beta}$, and R_α, respectively. Furthermore, they are all symmetrical in k and j.

The general circuit equations may be written

$$E_k = \sum_{i} (m_{ki} \ddot{q}_i + r_{ki} \dot{q}_i + c_{ki} q_i) \tag{48.11}$$

where E_k is the electromotive force across the terminals k. The work furnished to the circuit in time dt is

$$\begin{aligned} dW &= \sum_{k} E_k \dot{q}_k \, dt = \sum_{k} \sum_{i} (m_{ki} \ddot{q}_i + r_{ki} \dot{q}_i + c_{ki} q_i) \dot{q}_k \, dt \\ &= \sum_{ik} (m_{ki} \dot{q}_k \, d\dot{q}_i + r_{ki} \dot{q}_i \dot{q}_k \, dt + c_{ki} q_i \, dq_k) \\ &= dE_m + dE_e + \phi \, dt \end{aligned}$$

This means that we have not omitted any energy from consideration.

We shall assume that all the applied electromotive forces have the same frequency ω. Then

$$i_k = \dot{q}_k = I_k e^{j\omega t}, \qquad E_k = V_k e^{j\omega t} \qquad (j = \sqrt{-1}) \tag{48.12}$$

and Eq. (48.11) may be written

$$V_k = \sum_{i} \zeta_{ki} I_i \tag{48.13}$$

where

$$\zeta_{ki} = m_{ki}j\omega + r_{ki} + \frac{c_{ki}}{j\omega} = \zeta_{ik} \tag{48.14}$$

from Eqs. (48.6), (48.8), and (48.10).

49. Definition of a Four-terminal and Equations for Its Circuit

A four-terminal is a special case of the circuits we have discussed in the previous sections. It is a circuit for which

$$E_k = 0 \qquad k \neq 1, 2 \tag{49.1}$$

For a four-terminal, Eq. (48.13) becomes

$$\left.\begin{aligned} &\sum_i \zeta_{1i}I_i = V_1 \\ &\sum_i \zeta_{2i}I_i = V_2 \\ &\sum_i \zeta_{ki}I_i = 0 \qquad k = 3, 4, \cdots, n \end{aligned}\right\} \tag{49.2}$$

where n is the number of branches. We may solve the equations (49.2) since the number of equations is equal to the number of independent variables I_i.

$$\left.\begin{aligned} I_1 &= \chi_{11}V_1 + \chi_{12}V_2 \\ I_2 &= \chi_{21}V_1 + \chi_{22}V_2 \\ I_k &= \chi_{k1}V_1 + \chi_{k2}V_2 \qquad k = 3, 4, \cdots, n \end{aligned}\right\} \tag{49.3}$$

It can be shown that $\chi_{ki} = \chi_{ik}$ follows from $\zeta_{ki} = \zeta_{ik}$. The first two relations are the only ones of interest. Solving them for V_1 and V_2 gives

$$\left.\begin{aligned} V_1 &= z_{11}I_1 + z_{12}I_2 \\ V_2 &= z_{21}I_1 + z_{22}I_2 \end{aligned}\right\} \qquad z_{21} = z_{12} \tag{49.4}$$

where the z_{ij} are constants of the circuit.

So far we have taken the V_i and I_i to have signs so that the product $E_i\dot{q}_i$ is the power furnished by the electromotive force. A different convention will be more useful in the discussion of electric lines since we shall regard the line as composed of a row of four-terminals each with a current flowing in one direction along one set of connections and in the opposite direction along the other set. This is shown in Fig. 49.1. If we consider four-terminal n, we have a potential difference E_1 at the left end and E_2 at the right end. The current I'_1 at the left end flows into the four-terminal, and I'_2 flows out of the right end. Then I' and I'_2 bear the following relation to I_1 and I_2:

$$I'_1 = I_1, \qquad I'_2 = -I_2 \tag{49.5}$$

Then Eq. (49.4) becomes on dropping the prime from I'_1 and I'_2

$$\left.\begin{aligned} V_1 &= z_{11}I_1 - z_{12}I_2 \\ V_2 &= z_{12}I_1 - z_{22}I_2 \end{aligned}\right\} \tag{49.6}$$

There is one further change in the equations to be made for convenience in discussing line problems. In general, we are

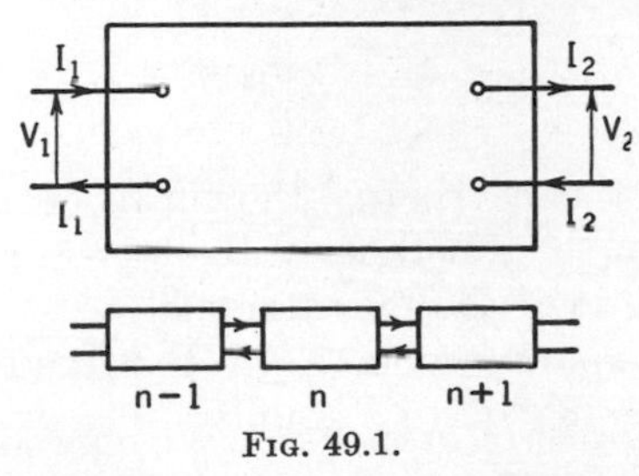

FIG. 49.1.

interested in comparing conditions at one end of the four-terminal with conditions at the other end, rather than currents with electromotive forces. This means that we should express V_1 and I_1 in terms of V_2 and I_2. Rearranging Eqs. (49.6) gives

$$\left.\begin{aligned} V_1 &= a_1V_2 + bI_2 \\ I_1 &= cV_2 + a_2I_2 \end{aligned}\right\} \tag{49.7}$$

where

$$\left.\begin{aligned} a_1 &= \frac{z_{11}}{z_{12}}, & a_2 &= \frac{z_{22}}{z_{12}} \\ b &= \frac{z_{11}z_{22} - z_{12}^2}{z_{12}}, & c &= \frac{1}{z_{12}} \end{aligned}\right\} \tag{49.8}$$

on taking account of the fact that $z_{12} = z_{21}$. The four constants are not independent, for it is obvious that

$$a_1a_2 - bc = 1 \tag{49.9}$$

50. Matrix Notation for a Four-terminal

We shall find it useful to regard the current and voltage at the exit of a four-terminal as two quantities that are transformed by a matrix to give the current and voltage at the entrance. The matrix will, of course, be the matrix of the coefficients in Eq. (49.7). From this point of view, it is convenient to change our notation as follows:

$$\left.\begin{array}{ll}\text{Electromotive force at entrance} & = V_1 = x_1 \\ \text{Electromotive force at exit} & = V_2 = x'_1 \\ \text{Current at entrance} & = I_1 = x_2 \\ \text{Current at exit} & = I_2 = x'_2\end{array}\right\} \quad (50.1)$$

Then Eq. (49.7) may be written

$$\left.\begin{array}{l} x_1 = a_{11}x'_1 + a_{12}x'_2 \\ x_2 = a_{21}x'_1 + a_{22}x'_2 \end{array}\right\} \quad (50.2)$$

where

$$\left.\begin{array}{ll} a_{11} = a_1, & a_{12} = b \\ a_{21} = c, & a_{22} = a_2 \end{array}\right\} \quad (50.3)$$

Then we may call the matrix (a_{ij}) the matrix of the four-terminal. It depends only on the constants of the four-terminal circuit and is thus characteristic of the four-terminal.

It follows immediately from Eqs. (49.9) and (49.3) that the determinant of the matrix (a_{ij}) is unity.

$$|a_{ij}| = \begin{vmatrix} a_{11} & a_{12} \\ a_{21} & a_{22} \end{vmatrix} = a_{11}a_{22} - a_{12}a_{21} = a_1a_2 - bc = 1 \quad (50.4)$$

Equation (50.2) may be solved for x'_1 and x'_2 in terms of x_1 and x_2.

$$\left.\begin{array}{l} x'_1 = b_{11}x_1 + b_{12}x_2 \\ x'_2 = b_{21}x_1 + b_{22}x_2 \end{array}\right\} \quad (50.5)$$

where

$$\left.\begin{array}{ll} b_{11} = \dfrac{a_{22}}{|a|} = a_{22}, & b_{12} = -\dfrac{a_{12}}{|a|} = -a_{12} \\ b_{21} = -\dfrac{a_{21}}{|a|} = -a_{21}, & b_{22} = \dfrac{a_{11}}{|a|} = a_{11} \end{array}\right\} \quad (50.6)$$

It is evident that the determinant of the matrix (b_{ij}) is unity. The matrix (b_{ij}) is the inverse of the matrix (a_{ij}), and we may write Eqs. (50.2) and (50.5) symbolically as follows:

$$\begin{pmatrix} x_1 \\ x_2 \end{pmatrix} = A \begin{pmatrix} x'_1 \\ x'_2 \end{pmatrix}; \quad \begin{pmatrix} x'_1 \\ x'_2 \end{pmatrix} = B \begin{pmatrix} x_1 \\ x_2 \end{pmatrix}; \quad B = A^{-1} \quad (50.7)$$

where A and B stand for the matrices (a_{ij}) and (b_{ij}), respectively.

Thus we see that there are two matrices, one the inverse of the other, that are of significance for a given four-terminal. One of these, A, would be used if we thought of a wave propagating through the four-terminal from right to left, and the other would be used for a wave propagating from left to right.

It should be noted that the elements of the matrices A and B are not all pure members; some have dimensions:

a_{11}, a_{22}, b_{11}, b_{22}	pure numbers
a_{12}, b_{12}	impedance
a_{21}, b_{21}	admittance (reciprocal of impedance)

51. Combination of Two Four-terminals; Multiplication of Matrices

In this and the following two sections, we shall illustrate various rules from the theory of matrices by means of four-terminals. First, we consider the effect of connecting two four-

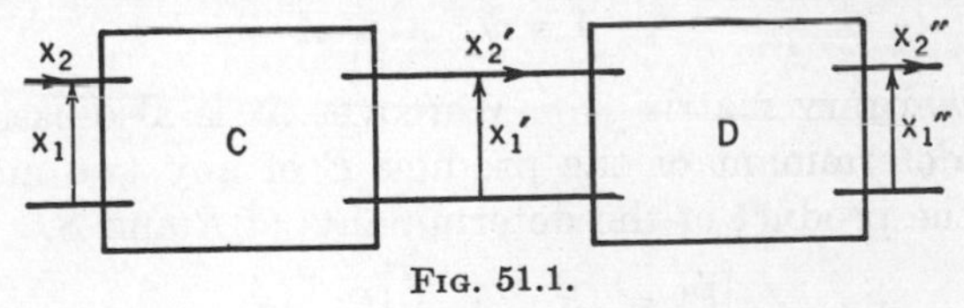

FIG. 51.1.

terminals in cascade, as in Fig. 51.1. These two four-terminals together constitute a composite four-terminal. We wish to find the matrix of the resultant four-terminal in terms of the matrices of the two component four-terminals.

If the matrix (b_{ij}) of the previous section is denoted by (c_{ij}) for the left-hand four-terminal and by (d_{ij}) for the right-hand four-terminal, then

$$\left.\begin{aligned} x''_i &= \sum_j d_{ij} x'_j = \sum_j d_{ij} \left(\sum_k c_{jk} x_k \right) \\ &= \sum_k \left(\sum_j d_{ij} c_{jk} \right) x_k = \sum_k f_{ik} x_k \end{aligned}\right\} \tag{51.1}$$

where the double-primed letters represent conditions at the exit (right end) of the right-hand four-terminal, the single-primed letters conditions between the two four-terminals, and the unprimed letters conditions at the entrance of the left-hand four-terminal.

Now

$$f_{ik} = \sum_j d_{ij}c_{jk} \qquad \text{or} \qquad F = D \cdot C \tag{51.2}$$

are the elements of a matrix (f_{ik}) that is the product of the matrices (d_{ij}) and (c_{ij}). The order in which the matrices appear makes a difference in the product except in certain cases. We shall have occasion to note some of these cases in later sections. In general, however,

$$\sum_j c_{ij}d_{jk} = C \cdot D \neq D \cdot C = \sum_j d_{ij}c_{jk} \tag{51.3}$$

In the previous section we noted that A and B were inverse matrices. It is readily verified by direct calculation that

$$A \cdot B = B \cdot A = \begin{pmatrix} 1 & 0 \\ 0 & 1 \end{pmatrix} = \delta \tag{51.4}$$

δ is called the unit matrix since it is evident that

$$A \cdot \delta = \delta \cdot A = A \tag{51.5}$$

for any arbitrary matrix A. Moreover, it is also easily shown that the determinant of the product P of any two matrices R and S is the product of the determinants of R and S.

$$|P| = |R \cdot S| = |R| \cdot |S| \tag{51.6}$$

52. Inverse and Reversed Four-terminals and Transformations

If two four-terminals, connected in cascade, produce no change in the electromotive force or in the current, then we say that one four-terminal is the *inverse* of the other; *i.e.*, if A is the matrix of the first and B the matrix of the second,

$$A \cdot B = \delta = B \cdot A \tag{52.1}$$

In this case, evidently, the order of the four-terminals with respect to the direction of propagation is immaterial.

Now making use of the fact that A and B each have determinant one and Eq. (50.6), we see that

$$\left.\begin{aligned} a_{11} &= b_{22} & a_{12} &= -b_{12} \\ a_{21} &= -b_{21} & a_{22} &= b_{11} \end{aligned}\right\} \tag{52.2}$$

Evidently to construct the four-terminal inverse to that with matrix A will require self and mutual inductances, capacities, and resistances that are the negatives of those occurring in four-terminal A. This is not always impossible, but often quite difficult to achieve experimentally.

By a *reversed four-terminal*, we mean one in which the sense of the current is changed and the entrance and exit are interchanged. This is, it should be noted, not the same as changing the direction of propagation of waves. The latter involves only interchanging the entrance and exit.

We shall denote the transformation of a four-terminal by B and the corresponding one for the reversed four-terminal by R. Then the direct four-terminal gives

$$x'_1 = b_{11}x_1 + b_{12}x_2$$
$$x'_2 = b_{21}x_1 + b_{22}x_2$$

Interchanging the entrance and exit requires us to use the matrix (a_{ij}) inverse to (b_{ij}).

$$x'_1 = a_{11}x_1 + a_{12}x_2$$
$$x'_2 = a_{21}x_1 + a_{22}x_2$$

and changing the sign of the currents (x_2 and x'_2) yields

$$x'_1 = a_{11}x_1 - a_{12}x_2$$
$$x'_2 = -a_{21}x_1 + a_{22}x_2$$

Therefore, the matrix $R = (r_{ij})$ is given by

$$\begin{pmatrix} r_{11} & r_{12} \\ r_{21} & r_{22} \end{pmatrix} = \begin{pmatrix} a_{11} & -a_{12} \\ -a_{21} & a_{22} \end{pmatrix} = \begin{pmatrix} b_{22} & b_{12} \\ b_{21} & b_{11} \end{pmatrix} \tag{52.3}$$

on making use of $|a| = 1$ and Eq. (50.6). Evidently,

$$|r_{ij}| = |a_{ij}| = |b_{ij}| = 1 \tag{52.4}$$

The elements of the matrix of the reversed four-terminal are equal to elements of the matrix of the direct four-terminal, so the construction of the reverse of a given four-terminal will not involve negative resistances except as they occur in the direct four-terminal.

We call a four-terminal *reversible* if it is identical with its reverse; *i.e.*, a four-terminal is reversible if

$$R = B \tag{52.5}$$

which yields

$$b_{11} = b_{22} \tag{52.6}$$

Since the determinant of B is unity,

$$b_{11} = b_{22} = \sqrt{1 + b_{12}b_{21}} \tag{52.7}$$

so that the matrix of a reversible four-terminal is

$$B = \begin{pmatrix} \sqrt{1 + b_{12}b_{21}} & b_{12} \\ b_{21} & \sqrt{1 + b_{12}b_{21}} \end{pmatrix} \tag{52.8}$$

53. Four-terminal Matrices and the Group C_2

The remarks that we have made in the previous sections are sufficient to show that the matrices arising in the theory of four-terminals form a group of two-rowed complex matrices of determinant one. The conditions that must be fulfilled in order for a set of matrices to form a group of the above type are

1. The matrices must be two-rowed complex matrices with determinant one (see Sec. 50).
2. Each matrix must possess an inverse matrix that is an element of the group. Evidently each four-terminal must have an inverse, since the number of equations involved is equal to the number of independent variables, and hence the matrix is non-singular and possesses an inverse (see Sec. 50).
3. Two matrices multiplied together must give a matrix in the group (see Sec. 51).
4. There is a unit matrix, *i.e.*, δ (see Sec. 51).

The group composed of matrices of four-terminals is at least a subgroup of the group C_2. The group C_2 is well known to mathematicians and is an integral part of the theory of electron spin and relativistic quantum mechanics. We shall find these matrices appearing in a similar fashion in the next chapter on the propagation of waves along lines composed of infinitesimal circuits.

Matrices have been introduced in the preceding sections in connection with the electrical problem of four-terminals. It is important to compare these definitions with the standard geometrical definitions given by mathematicians: In a plane, two coordinates x_1 and x_2 define a vector **P**, while x'_1 and x'_2 yield **P′**. The fundamental linear relations (50.7) show that the matrix A transforms any arbitrary **P′** vector into another **P**, while the inverse matrix B brings the transformed **P** back to **P′**.

This geometrical representation is perfectly adequate when

the x's are real numbers. In our electrical example, we always deal with complex numbers, and Fig. 53.1 must be considered only as a geometrical visualization of the matrix properties.

Multiplication of matrices was explained in Sec. 51 as representing the connection of two four-terminals in cascade. Looking at Eqs. (51.1) and (51.2), we notice that they represent two successive transformations of the vector **P** first from **P** to **P**′ by matrix C and then from **P**′ to **P**″ by matrix D.

The reversed four-terminal defined in Sec. 52 is typical of the electrical problem. Its geometrical counterpart was never considered in the theory of matrices. It can, however, be stated this way: We take $\mathbf{P}_1$ to be the reflection in the x_1 axis of **P**′,

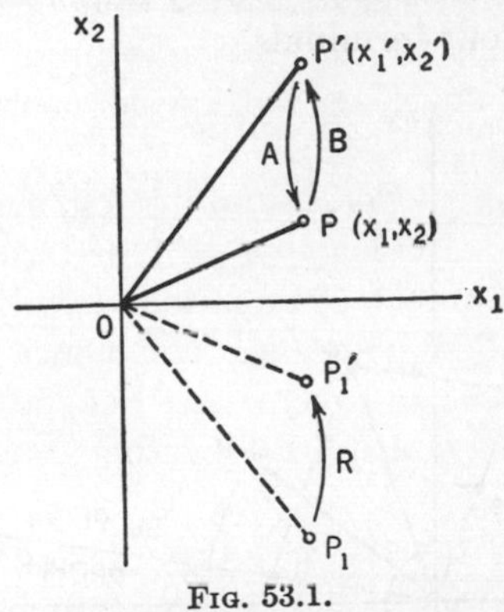

FIG. 53.1.

and $\mathbf{P'}_1$ the reflection in the x_1 axis of **P**. The R matrix (52.3) represents the transformation from $\mathbf{P}_1$ to $\mathbf{P'}_1$. A reversible four-terminal is represented by a matrix built in such a way that R is identical with B where R transforms $\mathbf{P}_1$ into $\mathbf{P'}_1$.

The next step in the geometrical description of matrices is to look for the *axes* of the matrix, which are defined by the condition that **P** and **P**′ lie in the same direction.

$$\left.\begin{aligned} \mathbf{P}' &= \xi\mathbf{P} \\ x'_1 &= \xi x_1 = b_{11}x_1 + b_{12}x_2 \\ x'_2 &= \xi x_2 = b_{21}x_1 + b_{22}x_2 \end{aligned}\right\} \tag{53.1}$$

These two linear equations can be solved only if their determinant is zero.

$$\begin{vmatrix} b_{11} - \xi & b_{12} \\ b_{21} & b_{22} - \xi \end{vmatrix} = 0 \tag{53.2}$$

This is known as the equation for the *proper values* of the matrix, and it yields two ξ coefficients, one corresponding to each of the axes of the matrix. The orientations of the axes are obtained when the ξ values of Eq. (53.2) are used in Eq. (53.1). Their slopes are given by the condition

$$S = \frac{x'_2}{x'_1} = \frac{x_2}{x_1}$$

$$S = \frac{b_{21} + b_{22}S}{b_{11} + b_{12}S} \tag{53.3}$$

$$b_{12}S^2 + (b_{11} - b_{22})S - b_{21} = 0 \tag{53.4}$$

We shall soon discover the physical meaning of these quantities and find that they correspond to very important definitions in the theory of electric four-terminals.

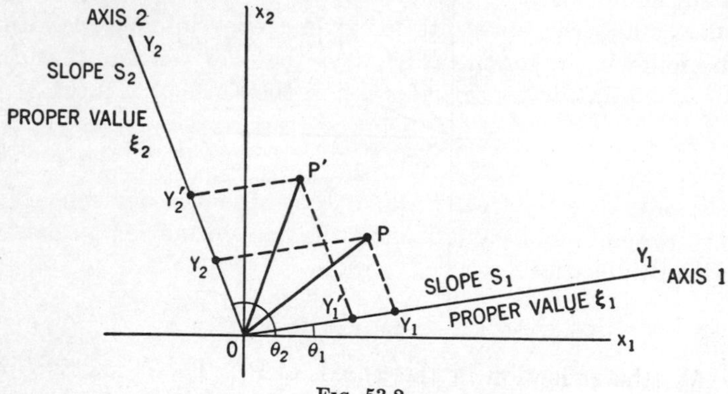

FIG. 53.2.

Once the axes of the matrix and the proper values have been determined, the matrix transformation acquires a simple geometrical meaning. A vector **P** is decomposed into its components Y_1 and Y_2 along the axes. Then each component is multiplied by the corresponding proper value, yielding

$$Y'_1 = \xi_1 Y_1, \qquad Y'_2 = \xi_2 Y_2 \tag{53.5}$$

which represent the components of the transformed vector **P′**, as shown in Fig. 53.2.

This was just explained for the matrix (b_{ij}), of which (a_{ij}) is the inverse matrix. Matrix (a_{ij}) has the same axes as (b_{ij}), but its proper values are ξ_1^{-1} and ξ_2^{-1}, and the (a_{ij}) transformation carries **P′** into **P**.

The relation between (Y_1,Y_2) and (x_1,x_2) is easily obtained. Let us state

$$S_1 = \tan\theta_1, \qquad S_2 = \tan\theta_2$$

Then

$$\left.\begin{aligned} x_1 &= Y_1 \cos\theta_1 + Y_2 \cos\theta_2 \\ x_2 &= Y_1 \sin\theta_1 + Y_2 \sin\theta_2 \end{aligned}\right\} \tag{53.6}$$

which we can also write

$$\left.\begin{aligned} x_2 &= y_1 + y_2, & y_1 &= Y_1 \sin\theta_1 \\ x_1 &= \frac{1}{S_1} y_1 + \frac{1}{S_2} y_2, & y_2 &= Y_2 \sin\theta_2 \end{aligned}\right\} \tag{53.7}$$

We shall use these last formulas for a comparison with the four-terminal problem.

The geometrical representation gives a very simple explanation of the following theorem, which says that *two matrices* C *and* D *whose axes coincide are commutative*, in the sense of Eq. (51.3).

$$C \cdot D = D \cdot C \tag{53.8}$$

This results directly from the fact that after the decomposition along the common Y_1 and Y_2 axes the transformation reduces to usual multiplication.

$$Y'_1 = \xi_C \xi_D Y_1 = \xi_D \xi_C Y_1$$

and the same is true for Y_2.

54. Surge, Iterative, or Characteristic Impedance of a Four-terminal

In Chap. V we discussed the characteristic impedance of a one-dimensional mechanical lattice in some detail. The characteristic impedance of the lattice was taken equal to the mechanical impedance offered by a single cell with its particles vibrating as if a single wave were propagating through an infinite lattice. We shall define the impedance of an electrical line composed of four-terminals in a similar fashion.

We take the impedance connected at the exit of a four-terminal to be z'; *i.e.*,

$$x'_1 = z'x'_2 \qquad z' = \text{output impedance} \tag{54.1}$$

Substitution of this relation in Eq. (50.2) yields

$$\left.\begin{aligned} x_1 &= (a_{11}z' + a_{12})x'_2 = (b_{22}z' - b_{12})x'_2 \\ x_2 &= (a_{21}z' + a_{22})x'_2 = (-b_{21}z' + b_{11})x'_2 \end{aligned}\right\} \tag{54.2}$$

upon making use of Eqs. (50.4) and (50.6). Now a four-terminal with its exit shunted by an impedance z' has an impedance z at the entrance given by

$$z = \frac{x_1}{x_2} = \frac{b_{22}z' - b_{12}}{-b_{21}z' + b_{11}} = \text{input impedance} \tag{54.3}$$

A similar calculation may be made for the reversed four-terminal. We take ζ and ζ' for the input and output impedances, respectively (Fig. 54.1).

$$\zeta = -\frac{b_{11}\zeta' - b_{12}}{b_{21}\zeta' - b_{22}} \tag{54.4}$$

from Eq. (52.3) for the matrix of a reversed four-terminal.

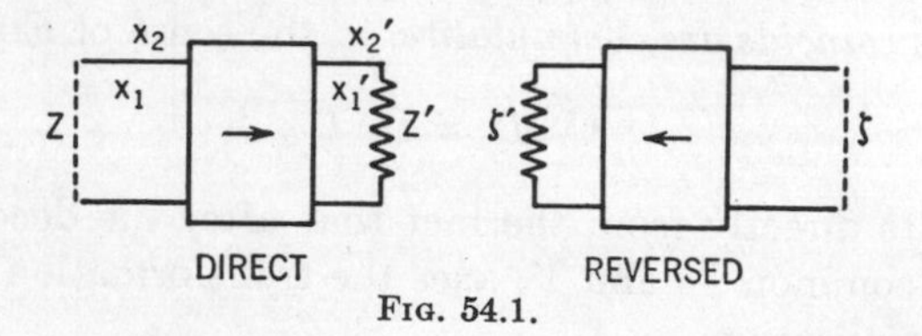

FIG. 54.1.

The four-terminal will have two iterative, surge, or characteristic impedances, obtained by the condition that

$$z = z' \qquad \text{or} \qquad \zeta = \zeta' \tag{54.5}$$

These two conditions are equivalent. The two roots of

$$b_{21}z^2 + (b_{22} - b_{11})z - b_{12} = 0 \tag{54.6}$$

are z and $-\zeta$. Equation (54.6) is obtained from Eq. (54.3). The analogous equation obtained from Eq. (54.4) has roots $-z$ and ζ.

Comparing Eq. (54.3) with Eq. (53.3), we note the relation

$$z = \frac{1}{S_1}, \qquad \zeta = -\frac{1}{S_2}$$

The characteristic impedance is the inverse of the slope of the axis of the matrix (Fig. 53.2). Equation (54.6) is thus similar to Eq. (53.4). The choice of z and $-\zeta$ as characteristic impedances would yield two positive numbers in our geometrical representation instead of a positive and a negative one. It is just a matter of conventions and is connected with the definition of the reversed four-terminal.

The two impedances z and ζ are called the *surge* or *characteristic* impedances in the direct and in the reverse senses, respectively. They are often denoted by k_1 and k_2. A *reversible four-terminal* is characterized by $b_{11} = b_{22}$ and hence

$$k_1 = k_2, \qquad z = \zeta \tag{54.7}$$

The axes in Fig. 53.2 are symmetrical with respect to the x_1 and x_2 coordinate axes in this case.

One of the characteristic impedances corresponds to the situation obtained in a row of identical four-terminals when a pure wave is propagating from left to right along the row. The

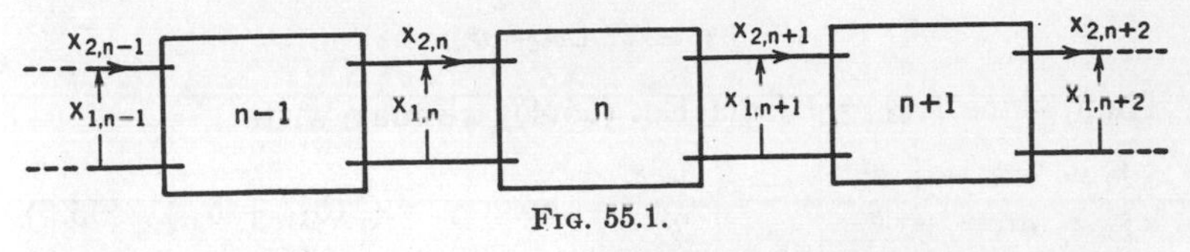

FIG. 55.1.

other characteristic impedance corresponds to a wave propagating from right to left. This will be explained in Sec. 55.

55. Propagation along a Line of Four-terminals

We start by assuming an infinite number of four-terminals connected in cascade, as in Fig. 55.1. Later we shall see how to terminate the line without disturbing the propagation of waves along it.

A single wave that propagates along this infinite line is characterized by the fact that the electromotive force and current are multiplied by the same complex factor ξ as the wave passes from four-terminal n to four-terminal $(n + 1)$.

$$\left.\begin{aligned} x_{1,n+1} &= \xi x_{1,n} \\ x_{2,n+1} &= \xi x_{2,n} \end{aligned}\right\} \tag{55.1}$$

Equation (55.1) together with Eq. (50.5) gives us two linear homogeneous equations in $x_{1,n}$ and $x_{2,n}$:

$$\left.\begin{aligned} \xi x_{1,n} &= b_{11}x_{1,n} + b_{12}x_{2,n} \\ \xi x_{2,n} &= b_{21}x_{1,n} + b_{22}x_{2,n} \end{aligned}\right\} \tag{55.2}$$

which can be solved only if the determinant of the coefficients vanishes.

$$\begin{vmatrix} b_{11} - \xi & b_{12} \\ b_{21} & b_{22} - \xi \end{vmatrix} = \xi^2 - (b_{11} + b_{22})\xi + 1 = 0 \qquad (55.3)$$

where we make use of the fact that the determinant $|b_{ij}| = 1$. Thus the complex factor ξ is determined by the constants of the four-terminal circuit.

The equation (55.3) is well known in the theory of matrices. The solutions for ξ are the *proper values* of the matrix (b_{ij}), or the diagonal elements if the matrix is reduced to diagonal form, as explained in Eq. (53.2). The two solutions are

$$\xi_{1_2} = \tfrac{1}{2}(b_{11} + b_{22}) \pm \sqrt{\tfrac{1}{4}(b_{11} + b_{22})^2 - 1} \qquad (55.4)$$

Let us take

$$\xi = e^{\gamma} = e^{\alpha + i\beta}$$

Then, since $\xi_1\xi_2 = 1$ from Eq. (55.4), we may write

$$\begin{aligned} \xi_1 &= e^{-\gamma} = e^{-\alpha - i\beta} \\ \xi_2 &= e^{\gamma} = e^{\alpha + i\beta} \end{aligned} \qquad \frac{\xi_1 + \xi_2}{2} = \cosh \gamma = \frac{1}{2}(b_{11} + b_{22}) \qquad (55.5)$$

If $\alpha = 0$, then $|\xi_1| = |\xi_2| = 1$ and

$$\xi_1 = e^{-i\beta}, \qquad \xi_2 = e^{i\beta} \qquad (55.6)$$

In this case one obtains propagation of waves without attenuation, and the two solutions given in Eq. (55.6) correspond to propagation in opposite directions: ξ_1 gives propagation to the right and ξ_2 to the left.

If $\alpha \neq 0$, attenuation is present. α is the attenuation constant and β the change in phase per four-terminal. When $\alpha > 0$, ξ_1 and ξ_2 give propagation to the right and left, respectively, as before.

Let us compute the ratio of electromotive force to current at the entrance to four-terminal n. From Eq. (55.2), we obtain

$$\frac{x_{1,n}}{x_{2,n}} = \frac{b_{12}}{\xi - b_{11}} = \frac{\xi - b_{22}}{b_{21}} \qquad (55.7)$$

which is a constant complex number that we may call z. There are two values of z, z_1 and z_2, corresponding to ξ_1 and ξ_2. A simple calculation shows that these two solutions are the two characteristic impedances corresponding to the directions of propagation associated with ξ_1 and ξ_2. Thus in the notation of the last paragraph of the previous section

$$z_1 = k_1, \qquad z_2 = -k_2 = -\zeta$$

We may ask how to terminate the line at four-terminal n in such a way as to avoid reflection of waves coming from the left. This is done by using an output impedance k_1 on the right side of four-terminal n. In the same way we terminate a line on the left side and prevent reflection for waves coming from the right by using an impedance k_2 on the left of the last four-terminal.

An arbitrary wave propagating along a line of four-terminals may be split up into a sum of two simple waves traveling in opposite directions. Evidently, from Eq. (55.1), the matrix of each four-terminal is diagonal for the simple waves. This procedure of splitting the vibration up into two waves is analogous to taking the principal axes for a transformation in matrix theory. Thus we may take the current to be y_1 for propagation to the right and y_2 for propagation to the left. Then the total electromotive force will be given by the sum of the electromotive forces z_1y_1 and z_2y_2 for the two currents, and the total current will be the sum of y_1 and y_2. We add a subscript n to the y's to indicate the four-terminal under consideration. Then if we take $n = 0$ for the first four-terminal,

$$x_{1,0} = z_1y_{1,0} + z_2y_{2,0}, \qquad x_{2,0} = y_{1,0} + y_{2,0} \tag{55.8}$$

These equations are identical with those for the reduction of the matrix to its axis, given in Eq. (53.7). Equation (55.8) holds for any n since we assume a stable condition in the line. Equation (55.8) may also be written in the form

$$\left.\begin{aligned} y_{1,0} &= \frac{x_{1,0} - z_2x_{2,0}}{z_1 - z_2} \\ y_{2,0} &= \frac{-x_{1,0} + z_1x_{2,0}}{z_1 - z_2} \end{aligned}\right\} \tag{55.9}$$

These equations will be of use shortly.

Now to obtain the current and electromotive force at four-terminal n, we merely note that

$$y_{1,n} = \xi_1{}^n y_{1,0}, \qquad y_{2n} = \xi_2{}^n y_{2,0} \tag{55.10}$$

where

$$\left.\begin{aligned} \xi_1{}^n &= e^{-n\gamma} = e^{-n(\alpha+j\beta)} \\ \xi_2{}^n &= e^{n\gamma} = e^{n(\alpha+j\beta)} \end{aligned}\right\} \tag{55.11}$$

We have taken α positive when the propagation to the right is represented by ξ_1. In this case $\xi_1{}^n$ becomes negligible for very large n while $\xi_2{}^n$ is large.

If we have an arbitrary impedance $\zeta_0 = -x_{1,0}/x_{2,0}$ placed at the beginning of the line, the impedance at the nth four-terminal will be, for very large n,

$$\zeta_n = -\frac{x_{1,n}}{x_{2,n}} \approx -\frac{z_2\xi_2{}^n y_{2,0}}{\xi_2{}^n y_{2,0}} = -z_2 \tag{55.12}$$

since from Eqs. (55.8) and (55.10) the exact solution is

$$\left.\begin{aligned} x_{1,n} &= z_1\xi_1{}^n y_{1,0} + z_2\xi_2{}^n y_{2,0} \\ x_{2,n} &= \xi_1{}^n y_{1,0} + \xi_2{}^n y_{2,0} \end{aligned}\right\} \tag{55.13}$$

and $\xi_1{}^n$ is negligible for very large n. This means that, except for the first few four-terminals, the impedance for very large n does not depend on the impedance at the end. This impedance is one of the characteristic impedances of the four-terminals that make up the line; the other one z_1 is obtained by reversing the condition.

Substitution of Eqs. (55.9) and (55.11) into Eq. (55.13) yields the relations

$$\left.\begin{aligned} x_{1,n} &= \frac{1}{z+\zeta}\left[(\zeta e^{n\gamma} + ze^{-n\gamma})x_{1,0} - 2\zeta z(\sinh n\gamma)x_{2,0}\right] \\ x_{2,n} &= \frac{1}{z+\zeta}\left[-2(\sinh n\gamma)x_{1,0} + (ze^{n\gamma} + \zeta e^{-n\gamma})x_{2,0}\right] \end{aligned}\right\} \tag{55.14}$$

where we have set

$$z_1 = z, \qquad z_2 = -\zeta \tag{55.15}$$

Equation (55.14) is called the canonical form of the line equations. They contain only three constants: the two characteristic impedances of the four-terminal and the propagation constant γ.

56. Application of the Theory to a Reversible Four-terminal

Equation (54.6) gives us the characteristic impedance of a four-terminal in terms of the constants of its circuit. A reversible four-terminal is characterized by the condition $b_{11} = b_{22}$; hence, for a reversible four-terminal we have

$$z = \zeta = \sqrt{\frac{b_{12}}{b_{21}}} \qquad (56.1)$$

This value is the geometric mean of the impedances of the four-terminal with open circuit and with short circuit. For the open circuit $z' = \infty$, and $z = -(b_{22}/b_{21})$, while for the short circuit $z' = 0$ and $z = -(b_{12}/b_{11})$ [Eq. (54.3)]. The impedances

$$z_{I_1} = \sqrt{\frac{b_{12}}{b_{21}}\frac{b_{22}}{b_{11}}} \quad \text{and} \quad z_{I_2} = \sqrt{\frac{b_{12}}{b_{21}}\frac{b_{11}}{b_{22}}} \qquad (56.2)$$

are called the *image impedances.* They are the geometric mean of the impedance z on open circuit and short circuit for the four-terminal and the reversed four-terminal, respectively. They

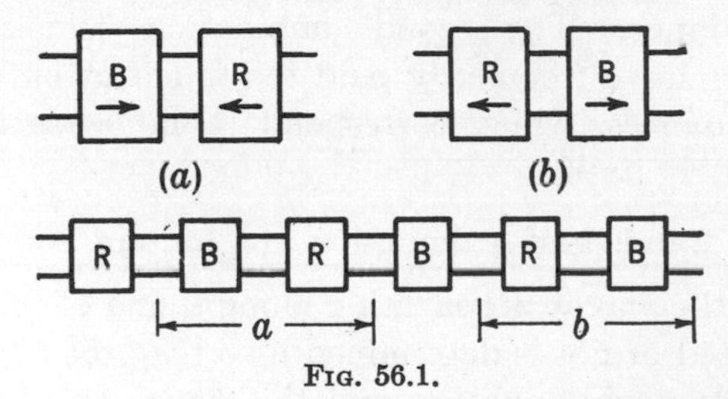

FIG. 56.1.

are the same and equal to the characteristic impedance in the case of a reversible four-terminal. This coincidence disappears for other cases.

Equation (55.14) becomes for a reversible four-terminal $(z = \zeta)$

$$\left.\begin{aligned} x_{1,n} &= (\cosh n\gamma)x_{1,0} - (z \sinh n\gamma)x_{2,0} \\ x_{2,n} &= \left(-\frac{1}{z}\sinh n\gamma\right)x_{1,0} + (\cosh n\gamma)x_{2,0} \end{aligned}\right\} \qquad (56.3)$$

The image impedances (56.2) are not directly connected with the properties of the row of similar four-terminals. This is better shown by proving that they represent the surge impedances of a row of symmetrical reversible four-terminals obtained by joining a given four-terminal B to its reverse R. Figure 56.1 shows a row of alternate R and B four-terminals. It can be considered either as a row of cells in the order (B,R) or as a row of cells in the order (R,B).

Let us take the first case and write down the corresponding

matrix [Eq. (51.2)], which is simply the product of R and B matrices in this order:

a. (B,R) four-terminal

$$\text{Matrix:} \qquad R \cdot B = \begin{pmatrix} r_{11}b_{11} + r_{12}b_{21} & r_{11}b_{12} + r_{12}b_{22} \\ r_{21}b_{11} + r_{22}b_{21} & r_{21}b_{12} + r_{22}b_{22} \end{pmatrix} \qquad (56.4)$$

When the r_{ik} coefficients from Eq. (52.3) are substituted,

$$R \cdot B = \begin{pmatrix} b_{11}b_{22} + b_{12}b_{21} & 2b_{12}b_{22} \\ 2b_{11}b_{21} & b_{11}b_{22} + b_{12}b_{21} \end{pmatrix} \qquad (56.5)$$

This represents a reversible four-terminal since the two diagonal elements are equal [Eq. (52.6)]. It has only *one* surge impedance, which, according to Eq. (56.1), is given by the square root of the ratio of the nondiagonal elements, and this is just z_{I_1}, the first image impedance. The second combination yields z_{I_2}. Electrical engineers have frequently paid too much attention to these image impedances, which correspond to no essential property of the B matrix itself.

57. Passing Bands and Attenuation in a Line of Four-terminals

Whether the waves propagating along a line of four-terminals are attenuated or not is determined by α [Eq. (55.5)]. If $\alpha = 0$, then there is no attenuation and the waves will be passed by the line. This condition yields

$$\xi_{\substack{1\\2}} = \cos\beta \pm j \sin\beta \qquad (57.1)$$

If we set $b = \frac{1}{2}(b_{11} + b_{22})$, then Eq. (55.4) becomes

$$\xi_{\substack{1\\2}} = b \pm \sqrt{b^2 - 1} = b \pm j\sqrt{1 - b^2} \qquad (57.2)$$

Comparison of Eqs. (57.1) and (57.2) shows that

$$\cos\beta = b \text{ real}, \qquad -1 < b < 1 \qquad (57.3)$$

This is the general *condition for propagation* of waves *without attenuation.* It can be obtained also from (55.5) since $\alpha = 0$ leaves us with

$$\cosh\gamma = \cos\beta = b = \tfrac{1}{2}(b_{11} + b_{22})$$

If our four-terminal circuits contain no resistance, the ζ_{ik} of Eq. (48.14) and the χ_{ik} and the z_{ik} of Eqs. (49.3) and (49.4) are all pure imaginary. It follows that a_1 and a_2 of Eq. (49.8) are real and b and c of Eq. (49.8) are pure imaginary. Hence, the matrix elements for a four-terminal without resistance are

$$\left.\begin{array}{ll} & b_{11}, b_{12}, b_{21}, b_{22} \\ \text{with} & b_{12} = j\beta_{12} \quad \text{and} \quad b_{21} = j\beta_{21} \end{array}\right\} \tag{57.4}$$

where b_{11}, b_{22}, β_{12}, and β_{21} are all real. Thus for this case the conditions that propagation without attenuation occur are

$$\left.\begin{array}{l} b_{11}, b_{22} \quad \text{real} \\ -2 \leqq b_{11} + b_{22} \leqq 2 \end{array}\right\} \tag{57.5}$$

If resistances are present, the first of these conditions is replaced by Eq. (57.3), which says that the sum of b_{11} and b_{22} shall be real, *i.e.*, that b_{11} and b_{22} be complex conjugates. This is equivalent to saying that, in general, we may have propagation without attenuation if $|b_{11} + b_{22}| \leqq 2$ and either the circuit contains zero resistance, or positive and negative resistances occur so that the net resistance is zero ($b_{11} = b_{22}^*$).

For a reversible four-terminal, the characteristic impedance is given by Eq. (55.7).

$$z = \frac{\xi - b_{22}}{b_{21}} = \frac{1}{b_{21}}\left[\frac{1}{2}(b_{11} - b_{22}) \pm j\sqrt{1 - \frac{1}{4}(b_{11} + b_{22})^2}\right] \tag{57.6}$$

on using Eq. (57.2). For a reversible four-terminal $b_{11} - b_{22} = 0$ and hence

$$z = \pm \frac{j\sqrt{1 - \frac{1}{4}(b_{11} + b_{22})^2}}{b_{21}} \tag{57.7}$$

If Eq. (57.3) is satisfied, both numerator and denominator of Eq. (57.7) are pure imaginary, which means that z is real. Thus z is real in a passing band and pure imaginary for other frequencies for a reversible four-terminal. The statement cannot, of course, be extended to nonreversible four-terminals.

58. Reflected Waves in a Line Terminated by an Impedance ζ_0

Let us assume z and ζ are the characteristic impedances of a line of four-terminals, and ζ_0 is the impedance at the left end, terminated by four-terminal 0. Then

$$-\zeta_0 = \frac{x_{1,0}}{x_{2,0}} \tag{58.1}$$

A wave propagated to the left will be partly reflected. With the notation of Sec. 55,

$$\rho = \text{coefficient of reflection} = \frac{y_{1,0}}{y_{2,0}}$$
$$= \frac{-x_{1,0} + z_2 x_{2,0}}{x_{1,0} - z_1 x_{2,0}} = \frac{z_2 + \zeta_0}{-\zeta_0 - z_1} = \frac{\zeta - \zeta_0}{\zeta_0 + z} \tag{58.2}$$

since $z_2 = -\zeta$. Evidently, if $\zeta_0 = \zeta$, there will be no reflection.

From this it follows that, to connect two lines of four-terminals without reflection, the characteristic impedances of the two must be equal. In all other cases there will be at least partial reflection (for frequencies in the passing band of the line that receives waves) and total reflection for waves in the stopping bands of the receiving line. The lack of reflection when the characteristic impedances are equal is very closely connected with the theorem explained at the end of Sec. 53 [Eq. (53.8)]. Four-terminals having the same characteristic impedances are represented by matrices whose axes have the same slope and coincide. Such matrices are commutative. This corresponds to the possibility of reversing the order of the four-terminals without changing the properties of the line. Now if the four-terminals C and D taken in either order, (C,D) or (D,C) give the same result, it certainly means that there is no reflection at their junction.

All these properties of four-terminal lines and their characteristic impedances represent a systematic generalization of the simple problems discussed in the first chapters.

59. A Continuous Line Loaded with Two-terminals

In this section we shall consider a line loaded with two-terminals as an example of the power of the matrix method.

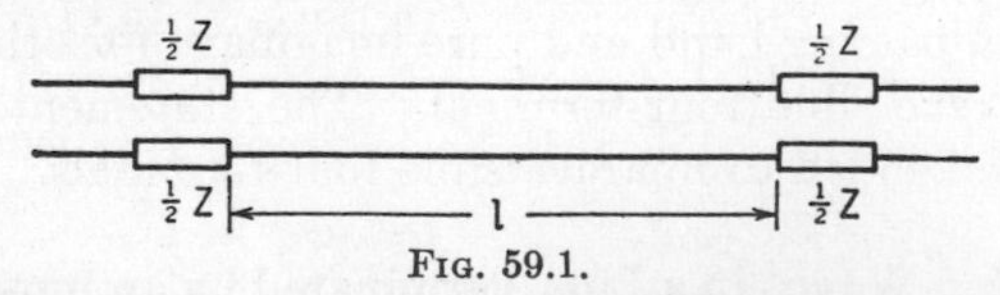

FIG. 59.1.

Such a line is shown in Fig. 59.1. The line consists of impedances $\frac{1}{2}z$ spaced a distance l from one another on each of the upper and lower wires of the line. This is very similar to the line loaded with uniformly spaced equal self-inductances discussed in Sec. 11. Here, however, we do not specify the elements contributing to the impedance $\frac{1}{2}z$ except to assume that there is no resistance; *i.e.*, z is pure imaginary.

$$z = jz', \qquad z' \text{ real} \tag{59.1}$$

The impedance z' of any arbitrary two-terminal can be shown to vary with the frequency according to the general law

$$z' = \frac{(\omega^2 - \omega_2^2)(\omega^2 - \omega_4^2)\ \cdots}{(\omega^2 - \omega_1)(\omega^2 - \omega_3^2)\ \cdots} L\omega \tag{59.2}$$

where $\omega = 2\pi\nu$ and $\omega_1 < \omega_2 < \omega_3 < \omega_4$. . . . Equation (59.2) is valid as long as the two-terminal contains only a finite number of circuit elements and no portions of a continuous line. A typical curve of z' as a function of ω is plotted in Fig. 59.2. The

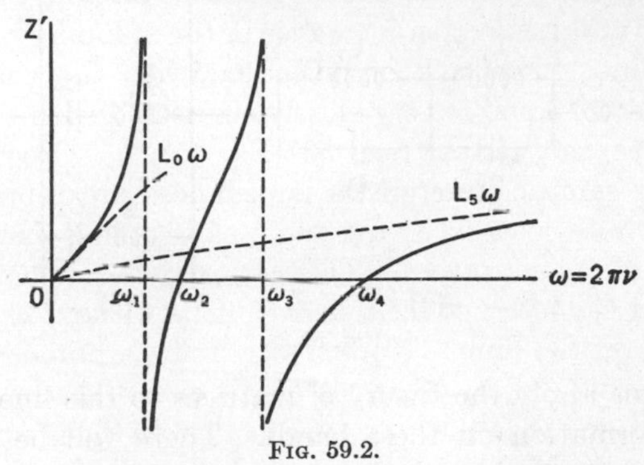

FIG. 59.2.

points ω_1 and ω_3 correspond to points of antiresonance, and ω_2 and ω_4 correspond to points of resonance. The number of such points can be increased at will by properly choosing the arrangement of the two-terminals, since this determines the number of branches in the (Z,ω) curve. An impedance law (59.2) can be obtained with a number of different circuits, some examples of which are shown on Fig. 59.3. In Fig. 59.3*a*, L_5 is the self-inductance at very high frequencies, and the circuit L_1C_1 has a proper frequency ω_1, while L_3C_3 has a proper frequency ω_3.

$$L_1C_1\omega_1^2 = 1 \qquad L_3C_3\omega_3^2 = 1$$

Frequencies ω_2 and ω_4 lie between ω_1 and ω_3 and above ω_3. Another type of circuit is shown on Fig. 59.3 where

$$L_0 = L_1 + L_3 + L_5, \qquad L_2C_2\omega_2^2 = 1, \qquad L_4C_4\omega_4^2 = 1$$

We shall find different types of passing and stopping bands in the continuous line loaded with two-terminals, some of them being characteristic of the two-terminal and some others of the loaded structure. The frequencies $\omega_1, \omega_2, \omega_3, \omega_4$ . . . are characteristic of the two-terminals used for loading. In the neighborhood of ω_2 and ω_4, $z' = 0$ and the line works as if it were not loaded at all; hence we find passing bands. In the neighborhood of ω_1 and ω_3 we find $z' = \infty$, hence stopping bands. These bands are referred to as *two-terminal bands.* In addition, the arrangement of the two-terminals may yield further bands, and these we refer to as *structure bands.* These latter bands depend principally on the distance of separation of the two-terminals.

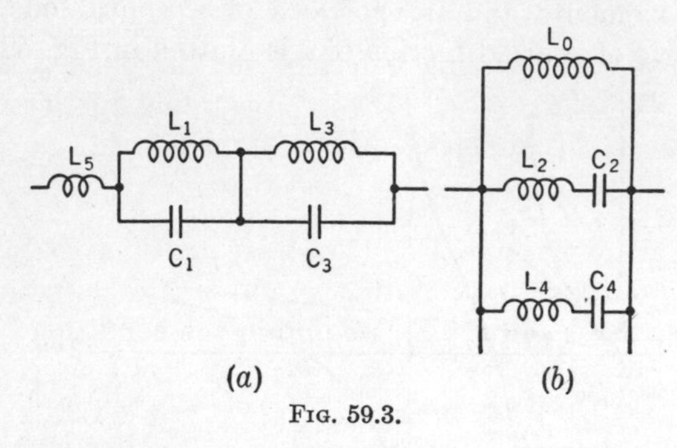

FIG. 59.3.

Now let us apply the theory of matrices to this line to obtain further information on these bands. There will be two parts of the line to be considered: the two-terminals themselves and the lines joining them. The matrix for the lines is obtained from Eq. (55.14) or (56.3). In this case the two values of the characteristic impedance ζ and z are to be set equal:

$$\zeta = z = k \tag{59.3}$$

and we assume zero resistance so that γ, the propagation constant per unit length, is given by

$$\gamma = j\beta \tag{59.4}$$

Then the matrix is obtained from Eq. (56.3), where we substitute l for n, assuming γ to correspond to a unit length of the line.

$$\begin{pmatrix} b_{11} & b_{12} \\ b_{21} & b_{22} \end{pmatrix} = \begin{pmatrix} \cosh \gamma l & -k \sinh \gamma l \\ -\dfrac{1}{k} \sinh \gamma l & \cosh \gamma l \end{pmatrix} \tag{59.5}$$

From inspection, we see that the matrix for the two-terminal itself is

$$\begin{pmatrix} b'_{11} & b'_{12} \\ b'_{21} & b'_{22} \end{pmatrix} = \begin{pmatrix} 1 & -z \\ 0 & 1 \end{pmatrix} \tag{59.6}$$

Then the matrix for a complete section of the line is given by

$$\begin{pmatrix} B_{11} & B_{12} \\ B_{21} & B_{22} \end{pmatrix} = \begin{pmatrix} b'_{11} & b'_{12} \\ b'_{21} & b'_{22} \end{pmatrix} \begin{pmatrix} b_{11} & b_{12} \\ b_{21} & b_{22} \end{pmatrix}$$

$$= \begin{pmatrix} \cosh \gamma l + \frac{z}{k} \sinh \gamma l & -z \cosh \gamma l - k \sinh \gamma l \\ -\frac{1}{k} \sinh \gamma l & \cosh \gamma l \end{pmatrix} \tag{59.7}$$

To investigate the passing bands of our line loaded with two-terminals, we refer to Eq. (57.5). According to this equation, the line will pass frequencies whenever

$$|B_{11} + B_{22}| \leqq 2 \tag{59.8}$$

The other conditions in Eq. (57.5) are automatically satisfied because of our assumption that z and γ are pure imaginary. Using Eqs. (59.7) and (59.8), we obtain the condition

$$|\cos B| = \left|\cosh \gamma l + \frac{z}{2k} \sinh \gamma l\right| = \left|\cos \beta l - \frac{z'}{2k} \sin \beta l\right| \leqq 1 \tag{59.9}$$

The limits of the passing bands are given by

$$|\cos B| = \left|\cos \beta l - \frac{z'}{2k} \sin \beta l\right| = 1 \tag{59.10}$$

There are two cases to be considered, corresponding to the two types of bands mentioned earlier:

1. *Two-terminal Bands.*—Two-terminal bands contain the point $z' = 0$, since for this case Eq. (59.9) is always satisfied. There will be a certain range of values for z' including the point $z' = 0$ for which Eq. (59.9) is satisfied, and this range comprises the two-terminal passing band.

2. *Structure Bands.*—A structure passing band will have for one of its limits

$$\beta l = \frac{\omega l}{W} = N\pi \qquad \text{where } \beta = \frac{\omega}{W}$$

since this gives

$$\sin \beta l = 0, \qquad \cos \beta l = \pm 1 \tag{59.11}$$

and condition (59.10) is satisfied. The width of the band can be obtained in the following way: If one limit of the band corresponds to $\cos B_1 = \pm 1$ (when $B_1 = N\pi$), the other limit is found for $\cos B_2 = \mp 1$ and $B_2 = (N + 1)\pi$. Let us assume, for instance, $|z'| >> k$; the second limit is obtained for

$$\beta l = N\pi + \epsilon \qquad \epsilon \text{ small}$$

$$\cos (N+1)\pi = -\cos N\pi = \cos \beta l - \frac{z'}{2k} \sin \beta l$$
$$= \cos (N\pi + \epsilon) - \frac{z'}{2k} \sin (N\pi + \epsilon)$$
$$\approx \cos N\pi - \frac{z'}{2k} \cos N\pi \cdot \epsilon$$

Hence

$$\epsilon = \frac{4k}{z'} \tag{59.12}$$

This gives the width of narrow bands, assuming that z' is approximately constant throughout this passing band, and $|z'| >> k$.

Let us apply this theory to two simple cases: a line loaded with inductances, and a line loaded with capacitances.

a. A line loaded with inductances.—In this case

$$z' = L_0\omega$$

where L_0 is the value of the inductances. $z' = 0$ only for $\omega = 0$. The corresponding two-terminal passing band is the well-known low-frequency band. The structure passing bands are found for high frequencies. One of the band limits is

$$\omega = \frac{N\pi W}{l} \tag{59.13}$$

and the band width is given by

$$\epsilon = \frac{4k}{L_0\omega} = \frac{4kl}{L_0 N\pi W} = \frac{4}{N\pi}\frac{L_s}{L_0} \tag{59.14}$$

since, if L_s and C_s are the inductance and capacity per section l of the line,

$$k = \sqrt{\frac{L_s}{C_s}}, \qquad W = \frac{l}{\sqrt{L_s C_s}} \tag{59.15}$$

Figure 59.4 shows the curve of ω vs.

$$B = \cos^{-1} \left| \cos \beta l - \frac{z'}{2k} \sin \beta l \right|.$$

b. A line loaded with condensers.—In this case we obtain

$$z' = -\frac{1}{C_0\omega}, \qquad \epsilon = \frac{4k}{z'} = -4kC_0\omega \tag{59.16}$$

where C_0 is the capacity of the condensers and ϵ the width of the

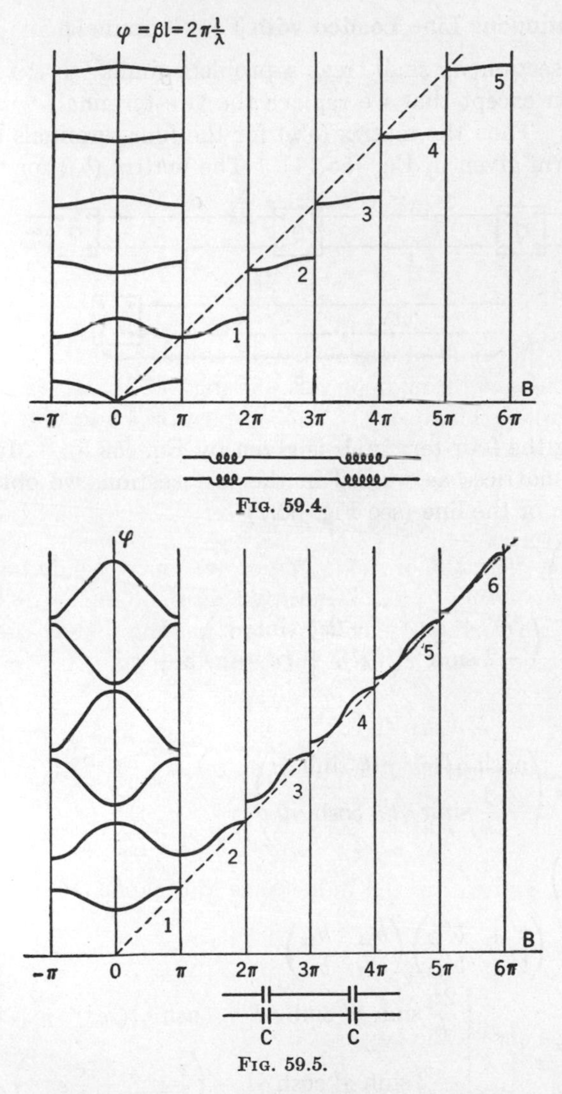

FIG. 59.4.

FIG. 59.5.

structure bands. The two-terminal band disappears since $z' = 0$ only for $\omega = \infty$. The upper limits of the structure bands again appear at

$$\omega = \frac{N\pi W}{l} \tag{59.17}$$

Figure 59.5 shows the frequency as a function of B.

60. A Continuous Line Loaded with Four-terminals

In this section we shall treat a problem similar to that of the last section except that we replace the two-terminals with four-terminals. Then the matrix (b'_{ij}) for the four-terminals has the general form given in Eq. (55.14). The matrix (b_{ij}) for the line

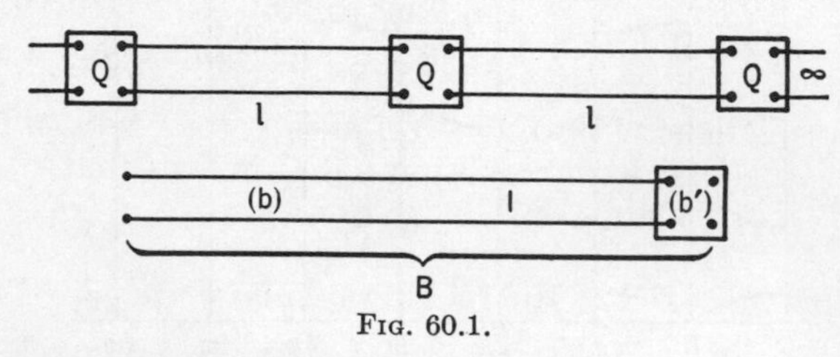

FIG. 60.1.

connecting the four-terminals is given by Eq. (59.5). Multiplying these matrices as we did in the last section, we obtain for one section of the line (see Fig. 60.1)

$$\begin{pmatrix} b'_{11} & b'_{12} \\ b'_{21} & b'_{22} \end{pmatrix} = \begin{pmatrix} \zeta e^{\gamma'} + ze^{-\gamma'} & -2z\zeta \sinh \gamma' \\ -2 \sinh \gamma' & ze^{\gamma'} + \zeta e^{-\gamma'} \end{pmatrix} \frac{1}{z + \zeta} \tag{60.1}$$

$$\begin{pmatrix} b_{11} & b_{12} \\ b_{21} & b_{22} \end{pmatrix} = \begin{pmatrix} \cosh \gamma l & -k \sinh \gamma l \\ -\frac{1}{k} \sinh \gamma l & \cosh \gamma l \end{pmatrix} \tag{60.2}$$

$$\begin{pmatrix} B_{11} & B_{12} \\ B_{21} & B_{22} \end{pmatrix} = \begin{pmatrix} b'_{11} & b'_{12} \\ b'_{21} & b'_{22} \end{pmatrix} \begin{pmatrix} b_{11} & b_{12} \\ b_{21} & b_{22} \end{pmatrix}$$
$$= \frac{1}{z + \zeta} \begin{bmatrix} \frac{2z\zeta}{k} \sinh \gamma' \sinh \gamma l + \cosh \gamma l (ze^{-\gamma'} + \zeta e^{\gamma'}) & -k \sinh \gamma l (ze^{-\gamma'} + \zeta e^{\gamma'}) - 2z\zeta \sinh \gamma' \cosh \gamma l \\ -2 \sinh \gamma' \cosh \gamma l - \left(\frac{z}{k} e^{-\gamma'} + \frac{\zeta}{k} e^{-\gamma'}\right) \sinh \gamma l & 2k \sinh \gamma' \sinh \gamma l + \cosh \gamma l (ze^{\gamma'} + \zeta e^{-\gamma'}) \end{bmatrix} \tag{60.3}$$

where k is the characteristic impedance and γ the propagation constant of the line net unit length, z and ζ are the characteristic impedances, γ' is the propagation constant of the four-terminal, and l is the distance between four-terminals.

We assume that the four-terminals contain no resistance that gives the condition

$$\left.\begin{array}{ll} b'_{11}, b'_{22} & \text{real} \\ b'_{12}, b'_{21} & \text{pure imaginary} \end{array}\right\} \tag{60.4}$$

In a passing band of the four-terminals, $\gamma' = j\beta'$ is pure imaginary, and this together with condition (60.4) tells us that

$$z = \zeta^* \tag{60.5}$$

In a stopping band of the four-terminals

$$\gamma' = \alpha' \text{ real}, \qquad z \text{ and } \zeta \text{ pure imaginary} \tag{60.6}$$

If the four-terminal is reversible, we know that z and ζ are equal and hence real in the passing bands, a result obtained in Eq. (57.7).

Now the condition for a passing band in the line as a whole is given by

$$\begin{aligned} |\cos B| &= \frac{1}{2}|B_{11} + B_{22}| \\ &= \left|\cosh \gamma' \cosh \gamma l + \frac{k + (z\zeta/k)}{z + \zeta} \sinh \gamma' \sinh \gamma l\right| \leqq 1 \end{aligned} \tag{60.7}$$

Again we shall find that we can divide the passing bands into two classes: (1) *four-terminal bands* due to the four-terminals, and (2) *structure bands* due to the spacing of the four-terminals.

To obtain the four-terminal bands we must consider frequencies in the passing bands of the four-terminal. Both $\gamma = j\beta$ and $\gamma' = j\beta'$ must be pure imaginary. We set

$$\left.\begin{aligned} z &= z_r + jz_i \\ \zeta &= z_r - jz_i \end{aligned}\right\} \tag{60.8}$$

on using Eq. (60.5). z_r and z_i are the real and imaginary parts, respectively, of z and ζ. This gives on referring to Eq. (60.7)

$$|\cos B| = \left|\cos \beta' \cos \beta l - \frac{k^2 + z_r^2 + z_i^2}{2kz_r} \sin \beta' \sin \beta l\right| \leqq 1 \tag{60.9}$$

Passing bands will include points for which

$$\frac{k^2 + z_r^2 + z_i^2}{2kz_r} = \pm 1 \qquad \cos B = \cos(\beta' \pm \beta l) \tag{60.10}$$

holds. To obtain further results, we must know the characteristic impedances of the four-terminal as functions of the frequency. If the four-terminal is reversible, $z_i = 0$, and condition (60.10) reduces to

$$z_r = \pm k \tag{60.11}$$

The condition (60.11) means that the loaded line has passing bands containing all frequencies (in the passing bands of the four-terminals) for which the characteristic impedance of the four-terminal equals that of the line (no reflection at their junction). For frequencies in a stopping band of the four-terminal,

$$z = jz', \qquad \zeta = j\zeta' \tag{60.12}$$

Equation (60.7) becomes

$$|\cos B| = \left|\cosh \alpha' \cos \beta l + \frac{k^2 - z'\zeta'}{k(z' + \zeta')} \sinh \alpha' \sin \beta l\right| \leqq 1 \tag{60.13}$$

In general, Eq. (60.13) is not satisfied. However, there will be a structure passing band around the frequency for which the cos B is zero. This is given by

$$\cot \beta l = \frac{z'\zeta' - k^2}{k(z' + \zeta')} \tanh \alpha' \tag{60.14}$$

In connection with this problem it is interesting to note that the matrix method greatly simplifies some of the computations discussed in Chap. VIII. For a reversible four-terminal, Eq. (60.7) becomes

$$\left|\cosh \gamma' \cosh \gamma l + \frac{1}{2}\left(\frac{k}{z} + \frac{z}{k}\right) \sinh \gamma' \sinh \gamma l\right| \leqq 1 \tag{60.15}$$

since $z = \zeta$. This problem corresponds exactly to the one discussed in Sec. 44, and if we set

$$\left.\begin{array}{ll} \gamma' = \chi_1 l_1, & \gamma l = \chi_2 l_2 \\ k = \chi_1, & z = \chi_2 \end{array}\right\} \tag{60.16}$$

we obtain Eq. (44.12). The direct computation given in Sec. 44 led to a fourth-order determinant that is equivalent to the determinant of the matrix in Eq. (60.3). The theory developed in this chapter thus appears as an important generalization of the problem of Sec. 44.

Selected References

BRILLOUIN, L.: *Rev. gén. élec.*, **39**, 3–16 (Jan. 4, 1936); **42**, 771–778, (Dec. 18, 1937); **42**, 803–816 (Dec. 23, 1937).

PIPES, L. A.: *El. Eng.*, t. 56, p. 1177 (1937).

CHAPTER X

CONTINUOUS ELECTRIC LINES

61. Transition from a Line of Four-terminals to a Continuous Line

In the previous sections we discussed lines composed of four-terminals. Each four-terminal was characterized by a matrix that produced finite changes in the current and electromotive force. We may think of these four-terminals as becoming very small so that their matrices produce very small changes and in the limit these changes will be zero. Thus, if dz is an infinitesimal portion of the line, we may take the matrix (b_{ij}) to be

$$(b_{ij}) = \begin{pmatrix} 1 + \epsilon_{11}\,dz & \epsilon_{12}\,dz \\ \epsilon_{21}\,dz & 1 + \epsilon_{22}\,dz \end{pmatrix} \tag{61.1}$$

which differs very little from the unit matrix. Equation (61.1) may be written

$$(b_{ij}) = e^{(\epsilon_{ij})dz} = 1 + (\epsilon_{ij})dz + \cdots \tag{61.2}$$

where we neglect terms in dz higher that the first and

$$(\epsilon_{ij}) = \begin{pmatrix} \epsilon_{11} & \epsilon_{12} \\ \epsilon_{21} & \epsilon_{22} \end{pmatrix}$$

Now the determinant of (b_{ij}) must be equal to one. This condition is fulfilled to the first order in dz by setting

$$\epsilon_{11} = -\epsilon_{22} \tag{61.3}$$

Since our transformation is now an infinitesimal transformation, it follows that

$$\left.\begin{aligned} x'_1 &= b_{11}x_1 + b_{12}x_2 = x_1 + dx_1 = x_1 + (\epsilon_{11}x_1 + \epsilon_{12}x_2)dz \\ x'_2 &= b_{21}x_1 + b_{22}x_2 = x_2 + dx_2 = x_2 + (\epsilon_{21}x_1 + \epsilon_{22}x_2)dz \end{aligned}\right\} \tag{61.4}$$

from which we obtain

$$\left.\begin{aligned} \frac{dx_1}{dz} &= \epsilon_{11}x_1 + \epsilon_{12}x_2 \\ \frac{dx_2}{dz} &= \epsilon_{21}x_1 + \epsilon_{22}x_2 \end{aligned}\right\} \qquad \epsilon_{22} = -\epsilon_{11} \tag{61.5}$$

For the special case of a reversible four-terminal, $b_{11} = b_{22}$ or $\epsilon_{11} = \epsilon_{22}$. This result combined with Eq. (61.3) yields

$$\epsilon_{11} = \epsilon_{22} = 0 \tag{61.6}$$

An example is given by a telegraphic cable. Let the cable have series resistance, series self-inductance, shunt conductance, and shunt capacity per unit length given by R, L, G, and C, respectively. Then

$$dV = (R + i\omega L)dzI, \qquad dI = (G + i\omega C)dzV$$

which in the usual notation becomes

$$\frac{dx_1}{dz} = \epsilon_{12}x_2, \qquad \frac{dx_2}{dz} = \epsilon_{21}x_1 \tag{61.7}$$

where

$$\epsilon_{11} = \epsilon_{22} = 0, \qquad \left.\begin{aligned} \epsilon_{12} &= R + i\omega L \\ \epsilon_{21} &= G + i\omega C \end{aligned}\right\} \tag{61.8}$$

The first of Eqs. (61.8) shows that the cable is composed of reversible four-terminals. The four-terminals are, of course, infinitesimal.

We may obtain equations for the propagation of waves along a line composed of nonreversible infinitesimal four-terminals by splitting the waves up into two simple waves propagating in opposite directions, as before. If we let γ be the propagation constant (attenuation and phase shift) per unit length of the line, a single wave propagating in a given direction is represented by

$$\frac{dx_1}{dz} = \gamma x_1, \qquad \frac{dx_2}{dz} = \gamma x_2 \tag{61.9}$$

Combining Eq. (61.5) with Eq. (61.9), we obtain

$$\left.\begin{aligned} (\epsilon_{11} - \gamma)x_1 + \epsilon_{12}x_2 &= 0 \\ \epsilon_{21}x_1 - (\gamma + \epsilon_{11})x_2 &= 0 \end{aligned}\right\} \tag{61.10}$$

The condition that Eq. (61.10) be soluble for x_1 and x_2 is that the determinant of the coefficients vanish. The resulting equation for γ is

$$\gamma^2 - \epsilon_{11}^2 - \epsilon_{12}\epsilon_{21} = 0$$

or

$$\gamma = \pm \sqrt{\epsilon_{11}^2 + \epsilon_{12}\epsilon_{21}} \qquad (61.11)$$

The values of γ given by Eq. (61.11) are the proper values of the matrix (ϵ_{ij}). They are, in general, complex. For the case of reversible four-terminals

$$\gamma = \pm \sqrt{\epsilon_{12}\epsilon_{21}}$$

and

$$\frac{x_1}{x_2} = k = \frac{\epsilon_{12}}{\gamma} = \pm \sqrt{\frac{\epsilon_{12}}{\epsilon_{21}}} \qquad (61.12)$$

k is the characteristic impedance of the line and has the same value for the two directions of propagation given by $\pm\gamma$. The characteristic impedances in the general case are different.

$$\left.\begin{matrix} k_1 \\ -k_2 \end{matrix}\right\} = \frac{x_1}{x_2} = \frac{\epsilon_{12}}{\pm\gamma - \epsilon_{11}} = \frac{\pm\gamma + \epsilon_{11}}{\epsilon_{21}} \qquad (61.13)$$

62. Examples of Four-terminal Representation of Continuous Lines

A line of infinitesimal four-terminals may be used to represent certain continuous lines. In this section we shall discuss some particular examples of this.

1. *A Line with Coefficients Varying Exponentially.*—In a number of practical problems (exponential electric line, exponential horn for a loud speaker, etc.) one has to deal with continuous lines whose coefficients vary exponentially with the distance. There is a close connection between such exponential lines and our general type of (ϵ_{ij}) line. Let us start from the equations of Sec. 61 and make the following transformation:

$$X_1 = x_1 e^{-\epsilon_{11}z}, \qquad x_1 = X_1 e^{\epsilon_{11}z}, \qquad x_2 = X_2 e^{-\epsilon_{11}z}, \qquad X_2 = x_2 e^{\epsilon_{11}z} \qquad (62.1)$$

$$A_{12} = \epsilon_{12}e^{-2\epsilon_{11}z}, \qquad A_{21} = \epsilon_{21}e^{2\epsilon_{11}z}$$

Then our general equations (61.5) yield

$$\left.\begin{aligned} \frac{dX_1}{dz} &= e^{-\epsilon_{11}z}\left(\frac{dx_1}{dz} - \epsilon_{11}x_1\right) = \epsilon_{12}x_2e^{-\epsilon_{11}z} = A_{12}X_2 \\ \frac{dX_2}{dz} &= e^{\epsilon_{11}z}\left(\frac{dx_2}{dz} + \epsilon_{11}x_2\right) = \epsilon_{21}x_1e^{\epsilon_{11}z} = A_{21}X_1 \end{aligned}\right\} \qquad (62.2)$$

These are the equations of propagation of X_1 and X_2 along the exponential line characterized by A_{12} and A_{21}.

The solution obtained in Eq. (61.9) for a wave (x_1,x_2) on the (ϵ_{ij}) line was

$$x_1 = x_{1,0}e^{\pm \gamma z}, \qquad x_2 = x_{2,0}e^{\pm \gamma z}$$

where γ is the propagation constant (61.11); hence the solution for the exponential line is

$$X_1 = X_{1,0}e^{(-\epsilon_{11} \pm \gamma)z}, \qquad X_2 = X_{2,0}e^{(\epsilon_{11} \pm \gamma)z} \tag{62.3}$$

The plus and minus signs before γ correspond to the two directions of propagation. Thus a finite length of exponential line behaves as a finite length of (ϵ) line terminated by a transformer of ratio $e^{-2\epsilon_{11}z}$.

As an instance of an exponential line, let us consider an electric line with the following values of L and C per unit length:

$$L = L_0e^{-2\epsilon_{11}z}, \qquad C = C_0e^{2\epsilon_{11}z}$$

where ϵ_{11} is any real number. Calling X_1 the voltage amplitude and X_2 the current amplitude and dropping the common $e^{i\omega t}$, we obtain the usual line equations

$$\frac{dX_1}{dz} = i\omega LX_2, \qquad \frac{dX_2}{dz} = i\omega CX_1$$

which are similar to Eq. (61.7) when $R = G = 0$. These equations of the exponential line have exactly the same form as Eq. (62.2) and possess solutions of the type (62.3). Substituting Eq. (62.3) in the line equations gives

$$\begin{aligned} (-\epsilon_{11} \pm \gamma)X_1 &= i\omega LX_2 \\ i\omega CX_1 &= (\epsilon_{11} \pm \gamma)X_2 \end{aligned}$$

which are two simultaneous linear equations whose determinant must be zero in order to yield a nontrivial solution; hence

$$\gamma^2 = \epsilon_{11}^2 - \omega^2LC = \epsilon_{11}^2 - \omega^2L_0C_0 \tag{62.4}$$

which is exactly the same as Eq. (61.11). The interesting point here is the frequency dependence. The *exponential line* behaves like a *high-pass filter* with a lower cutoff frequency at ω_0.

$$L_0C_0\omega_0^2 = \epsilon_{11}^2$$

since

$$\omega < \omega_0, \qquad \gamma^2 = L_0C_0(\omega_0{}^2 - \omega^2), \qquad \gamma \text{ real: attenuation}$$

$$\omega > \omega_0,\ \gamma^2 = -L_0C_0(\omega^2 - \omega_0{}^2),\ \gamma \text{ pure imaginary: propagation}$$

This result is familiar to electrical engineers and was given here as an example of the general theory. The characteristic impedance of the line varies exponentially as $e^{-2\epsilon_{11}z}$. The phase velocity above cutoff is $1/\sqrt{L_0C_0(1 - \omega_0{}^2/\omega^2)}$.

2. $\epsilon_{11}, \epsilon_{12}, \epsilon_{21}$ *Arbitrary Functions of z.*—As in the first example, we express x_1 and x_2 in terms of ϵ_{11}:

$$x_1 = X_1e^{\varphi}, \qquad x_2 = X_2e^{-\varphi} \tag{62.5}$$

where

$$\varphi = \int_0^z \epsilon_{11}\,dz \tag{62.6}$$

The coefficients A_{12} and A_{21} become

$$A_{12} = \epsilon_{12}e^{-2\varphi}, \qquad A_{21} = \epsilon_{21}e^{2\varphi} \tag{62.7}$$

and Eq. (61.5) yields

$$\frac{dX_1}{dz} = A_{12}(z)X_2, \qquad \frac{dX_2}{dz} = A_{21}(z)X_1 \tag{62.8}$$

To obtain a four-terminal corresponding to a finite length of the line, we write

$$x_i(z) = b_{i_1}(z)x_1(0) + b_{i_2}(z)x_2(0) \qquad i = 1, 2 \tag{62.9}$$

Increasing the length of dz yields (from the rule for the multiplication of matrices to obtain the effective four-terminal resulting from two four-terminals connected in cascade)

$$b(z + dz) = b(z)b(dz) = [1 + (\epsilon)dz]b(z) \tag{62.10}$$

on substitution of Eq. (61.2). Equation (62.10) may be written explicitly

$$\left.\begin{aligned} \frac{db_{11}}{dz} &= \epsilon_{11}b_{11} + \epsilon_{12}b_{21}, & \frac{db_{12}}{dz} &= \epsilon_{11}b_{12} + \epsilon_{12}b_{22} \\ \frac{db_{21}}{dz} &= \epsilon_{21}b_{11} + \epsilon_{22}b_{21}, & \frac{db_{22}}{dz} &= \epsilon_{21}b_{12} + \epsilon_{22}b_{22} \end{aligned}\right\} \tag{62.11}$$

Equations (62.11) consist of two sets of equations of the type (61.5). The four-terminal equivalent to a length z of the line is obtained by integrating these equations.

3. *A Line with Constant ϵ Coefficients.*—We have already seen that such a line gives propagation with the propagation constant γ of Eq. (61.11) and the characteristic impedances k_1 and k_2 of Eq. (61.13). Then the matrix (b_{ij}) at $z = 0$ is just the unit matrix

$$b(0) = \begin{pmatrix} 1 & 0 \\ 0 & 1 \end{pmatrix}$$

The matrix elements

$$\left.\begin{aligned} b_{11} &= \frac{1}{k_1 + k_2} (k_2 e^{\gamma z} + k_1 e^{-\gamma z}), \\ b_{12} &= \frac{-k_1 k_2}{k_1 + k_2} (e^{\gamma z} - e^{-\gamma z}) \\ b_{21} &= \frac{-1}{k_1 + k_2} (e^{\gamma z} - e^{-\gamma z}), \\ b_{22} &= \frac{1}{k_1 + k_2} (k_1 e^{\gamma z} + k_2 e^{-\gamma z}) \end{aligned}\right\} \qquad (62.12)$$

satisfy the initial conditions and the relation (61.13). Further, (b_{ij}) has determinant one and, in general, represents a finite nonreversible four-terminal. The matrix (ϵ_{ij}) may be found by taking the z derivatives of the matrix (b_{ij}) at $z = 0$.

$$\left.\begin{aligned} \epsilon_{11} &= \frac{k_2 - k_1}{k_2 + k_1} \gamma, & \epsilon_{21} &= \frac{-k_1 k_2}{k_1 + k_2} 2\gamma \\ \epsilon_{12} &= \frac{-1}{k_1 + k_2} 2\gamma, & \epsilon_{22} &= \frac{k_1 - k_2}{k_1 + k_2} \gamma = -\epsilon_{11} \end{aligned}\right\} \qquad (62.13)$$

If $k_1 = k_2$, we have $\epsilon_{11} = 0$, which means that the four-terminal is reversible. The line will have zero resistance if

$$\epsilon_{11} \text{ is real}; \qquad \epsilon_{12}, \epsilon_{21} \text{ pure imaginary} \qquad (62.14)$$

Equation (62.12) is identical with Eq. (55.14) of Chap. IX.

63. Application of Hill's Equation to a Continuous Line

The most general example of a continuous periodic line is given by assuming ϵ_{11}, ϵ_{12}, and ϵ_{21} periodic functions of z, with a common period L. The general wave solution is given by a superposition of the two particular solutions (Floquet's theorem):

$$\left.\begin{aligned} x_1(z) &= e^{\pm \gamma z} f_1(z) \\ x_2(z) &= e^{\pm \gamma z} f_2(z) \end{aligned}\right\} \qquad (63.1)$$

where f_1 and f_2 are two periodic function, each with period L. Equations (63.1) are of the same form as the solutions for Mathieu's and Hill's equations, discussed in Chap. VIII. Hill's equation is the appropriate one if we take

$$\begin{pmatrix} \epsilon_{11} & \epsilon_{12} \\ \epsilon_{21} & \epsilon_{22} \end{pmatrix} = \begin{pmatrix} 0 & c \\ \frac{1}{c}F(z) & 0 \end{pmatrix} \tag{63.2}$$

where $F(z)$ is periodic in z with period L. Mathieu's equation is obtained by taking $F(z)$ a sine or cosine function. Equation (61.5) then becomes

$$\frac{dx_1}{dz} = cx_2, \qquad \frac{dx_2}{dz} = \frac{1}{c}F(z)x_1$$

so that

$$\frac{d^2x_1}{dz^2} = F(z)x_1 \qquad \text{(Hill)} \tag{63.3}$$

Equation (63.2) implies, evidently, that we are dealing with reversible circuits that may, if desired, contain positive and negative resistance, since $\epsilon_{11} = \epsilon_{22} = 0$ but ϵ_{12} is not pure imaginary. Resistances are avoided by taking $c = i$.

We may reduce more general examples to Hill's equation. To do this, we set, as in Eq. (62.5) to Eq. (62.8)

$$\left.\begin{aligned} \varphi &= \int \epsilon_{11} dz, & \frac{dX_1}{dz} &= A_{12}X_2 \\ A_{12} &= \epsilon_{12}e^{-2\varphi}, & \frac{dX_2}{dz} &= A_{21}X_1 \\ A_{21} &= \epsilon_{21}e^{2\varphi}, \end{aligned}\right\} \tag{63.4}$$

where ϵ_{11}, ϵ_{12}, and ϵ_{21} are assumed periodic with period L in z. Increasing the length of the line by L gives

$$\varphi(z + L) = \varphi(z) + I \qquad \text{where } I = \int_0^L \epsilon_{11}\,dz \tag{63.5}$$

where I will be zero only if ϵ_{11} has an average value of zero. A_{12} and A_{21} will be multiplied by e^{-2I} and e^{2I}, respectively. Then Eqs. (63.4) become

$$\frac{dX_2}{dz} = \frac{d}{dz}\left(\frac{1}{A_{12}}\frac{dX_1}{dz}\right) = A_{21}X_1$$

and if we set

$$z' = \int A_{12}\,dz \tag{63.6}$$

we obtain

$$\frac{d^2X_1}{dz'^2} = \frac{A_{21}}{A_{12}} X_1 \tag{63.7}$$

Equation (63.7) is Hill's equation if

$$F = \frac{A_{21}}{A_{12}} = \frac{\epsilon_{21}}{\epsilon_{12}} e^{4\varphi} \tag{63.8}$$

is periodic. This is the case only if I is zero; *i.e.*, only if ϵ_{11} has an average of zero. This means that we may reduce the equations for a periodic line of nonreversible infinitesimal four-terminals to Hill's form only if a section L as a whole appears as a reversible four-terminal. If this is the case, the corresponding continuous periodic line may be reduced to a line of identical reversible four-terminals.

64. Normalization of the Matrix (ε_{ij}) and the Pauli Matrices

We have been led in the study of continuous lines to introduce matrices of the form

$$(\epsilon_{ij}) = \begin{pmatrix} \epsilon_{11} & \epsilon_{12} \\ \epsilon_{21} & \epsilon_{22} \end{pmatrix} = \begin{pmatrix} \epsilon_{11} & \epsilon_{12} \\ \epsilon_{21} & -\epsilon_{11} \end{pmatrix} \tag{64.1}$$

The square of the matrix (ϵ_{ij}) is diagonal.

$$(\epsilon_{ij})^2 = \begin{pmatrix} \epsilon_{11}{}^2 + \epsilon_{12}\epsilon_{21} & 0 \\ 0 & \epsilon_{11}{}^2 + \epsilon_{12}\epsilon_{21} \end{pmatrix} = \begin{pmatrix} -|\epsilon_{ij}| & 0 \\ 0 & -|\epsilon_{ij}| \end{pmatrix} \tag{64.2}$$

where $|\epsilon_{ij}|$ is the determinant of (ϵ_{ij}). We may introduce a normalization factor $E(z)$ so that the square of (ϵ_{ij}) is 1. Assuming this to be done, we may write

$$(\epsilon_{ij})^2 = \begin{pmatrix} 1 & 0 \\ 0 & 1 \end{pmatrix}, \qquad |\epsilon_{ij}| = -1,$$

$$(\epsilon_{ij}) = \begin{pmatrix} \sqrt{1 - \epsilon_{12}\epsilon_{21}} & \epsilon_{12} \\ \epsilon_{21} & -\sqrt{1 - \epsilon_{12}\epsilon_{21}} \end{pmatrix} \tag{64.3}$$

If we assume (ϵ_{ij}) to be normalized, the factor $E(z)$ will appear explicitly in the other equations.

$$\left. \begin{aligned} \frac{dx_1}{dz} &= E(z)(\epsilon_{11}x_1 + \epsilon_{12}x_2) \\ \frac{dx_2}{dz} &= E(z)(\epsilon_{21}x_1 - \epsilon_{11}x_2) \end{aligned} \right\} \tag{64.4}$$

If we let x represent a column matrix, with elements x_1 and x_2, we may write Eq. (64.4) symbolically as follows:

$$\frac{dx}{dz} = E(z)(\epsilon_{ij})x \tag{64.5}$$

From Eq. (64.3) it follows that

$$(\epsilon_{ij})^2 = 1; \qquad (\epsilon_{ij}) = (\epsilon_{ij})^{-1} \tag{64.6}$$

Hence Eq. (64.5) becomes

$$\frac{1}{E(z)}(\epsilon_{ij})\frac{dx}{dz} = x \tag{64.7}$$

or

$$\left.\begin{aligned} \frac{1}{E(z)}\left(\epsilon_{11}\frac{dx_1}{dz} + \epsilon_{12}\frac{dx_2}{dz}\right) = x_1 \\ \frac{1}{E(z)}\left(\epsilon_{21}\frac{dx_1}{dz} - \epsilon_{11}\frac{dx_2}{dz}\right) = x_2 \end{aligned}\right\} \tag{64.8}$$

From Eq. (64.7) it follows that we may write the operator equation

$$\frac{1}{E}(\epsilon_{ij})\frac{d}{dz} = 1 \tag{64.9}$$

If we now assume E and the ϵ_{ij} to be constant and not to depend upon z, the matrix operator (ϵ_{ij}) and the differential operator d/dz become independent and hence commute on squaring Eq. (64.9).

$$\left[\frac{1}{E}(\epsilon_{ij})\frac{d}{dz}\right]\left[\frac{1}{E}(\epsilon_{ij})\frac{d}{dz}\right] = \frac{1}{E^2}(\epsilon_{ij})^2\frac{d^2}{dz^2} = \frac{1}{E^2}\frac{d^2}{dz^2} \tag{64.10}$$

Then

$$\frac{1}{E^2}\frac{d^2x}{dz^2} = x \tag{64.11}$$

which is the usual wave equation after the time-dependent part of the solution has been separated out. We assume x_1 and x_2 both periodic in t with the same frequency ω.

We may now *generalize* to the *three-dimensional wave equation.* We take the three space variables to be z_1, z_2, and z_3 and introduce the three constant matrices $(\epsilon)_1$, $(\epsilon)_2$, and $(\epsilon)_3$ and a constant E such that

$$\sum_i (\epsilon)_i \frac{\partial x}{\partial z_i} = Ex \tag{64.12}$$

The operator equation analogous to Eq. (64.9) is

$$\sum_i (\epsilon)_i \frac{\partial}{\partial z_i} = E$$

and squaring yields

$$\sum_i \frac{\partial^2}{\partial z_i{}^2} = E^2 \tag{64.13}$$

provided that

$$(\epsilon)_i{}^2 = \delta; \qquad (\epsilon)_i(\epsilon)_k + (\epsilon)_k(\epsilon)_i = 0, \qquad i \neq k \tag{64.14}$$

The first set of conditions is analogous to the normalization condition (64.3) for one dimension. The second set requires that the matrices anticommute. Three solutions satisfy Eq. (64.14) and are the Pauli matrices

$$(\epsilon)_1 = \begin{pmatrix} 0 & i \\ -i & 0 \end{pmatrix}, \qquad (\epsilon)_2 = \begin{pmatrix} 0 & 1 \\ 1 & 0 \end{pmatrix}, \qquad (\epsilon)_3 = \begin{pmatrix} -1 & 0 \\ 0 & 1 \end{pmatrix} \tag{64.15}$$

It can be shown that any other set of solutions is reducible to a linear combination of the solutions (64.15).

The Pauli matrices are Hermitian symmetrical, a type that we encounter for the first time in this discussion. The *first two* matrices are *reversible*, and the *third is not*. This corresponds to the fact in the Pauli theory of electron spin that these matrices refer to the magnetic moment of an electron having its spin directed along the z_3 axis, a special feature that introduces an asymmetry along the z_3 axis.

The method that we have employed is based on Dirac's method for the linearization of the relativistic wave equation of the electron. Dirac's problem involves four-rowed matrices instead of the two-rowed matrices that we have so far encountered. In the next section we discuss a problem closely connected with Dirac's.

65. Three-phase and Polyphase Lines

Matrices with more than two rows occur in polyphase lines. For instance, a six-terminal inserted in a three-phase line, as in Fig. 65.1, will have four variables at the entrance and an equal number at the exit. We let

$$\left.\begin{array}{ll} x_1 = v & x'_1 = v' \\ x_2 = i & x'_2 = i' \\ x_3 = V & x'_3 = V' \\ x_4 = I & x'_4 = I' \end{array}\right\} \tag{65.1}$$

where the variables are as in Fig. 65.1. Then the matrix for the six-terminal will have four rows and four columns. The elements will be defined by

$$x'_i = \sum_k b_{ik} x_k \tag{65.2}$$

It is a general rule that a $4n$-terminal in $(n + 1)$ parallel lines will require a matrix with $2n$ rows and $2n$ columns.

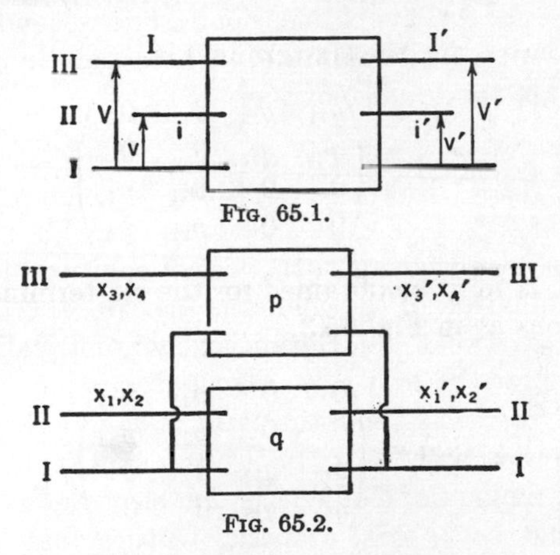

FIG. 65.1.

FIG. 65.2.

The determinant of the matrix (b_{ij}) for the six-terminal is no longer unity as for the four-terminal. There are six conditions resulting from the circuit theory, and their form is quite different and leads to consequences different from the four-terminal.

The diagonal form of the matrix (b_{ij}) corresponds to the superposition of two simple waves traveling in opposite directions for the four-terminal. The same general statement is true for the six-terminal except that there will be four simple waves to be superposed instead of two. It does not appear possible, in general, to obtain a simple relation among these four waves.

We shall consider a particular type of six-terminal, built up out of two four-terminals as in Fig. 65.2. Then we may

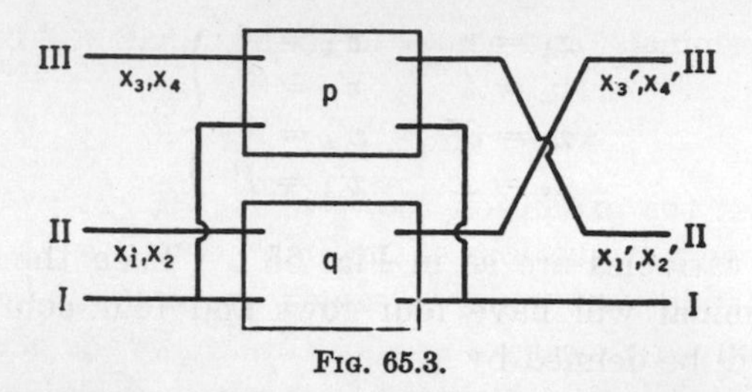

FIG. 65.3.

write Eq. (65.2) in terms of the matrices of the component four-terminals.

$$\left.\begin{aligned} x'_1 &= q_{11}x_1 + q_{12}x_2 \qquad & x'_3 &= p_{11}x_3 + p_{12}x_4 \\ x'_2 &= q_{21}x_1 + q_{22}x_2 \qquad & x'_4 &= p_{21}x_3 + p_{22}x_4 \end{aligned}\right\} \tag{65.3}$$

so that the matrix for the six terminal is

$$(b_{ij}) = \begin{pmatrix} q_{11} & q_{12} & 0 & 0 \\ q_{21} & q_{22} & 0 & 0 \\ 0 & 0 & p_{11} & p_{12} \\ 0 & 0 & p_{21} & p_{22} \end{pmatrix} \tag{65.4}$$

Another matrix may be obtained for the six-terminal by making the connections as in Fig. 65.3.

$$(b_{ij}) = \begin{pmatrix} 0 & 0 & p_{11} & p_{12} \\ 0 & 0 & p_{21} & p_{22} \\ q_{11} & q_{12} & 0 & 0 \\ q_{21} & q_{22} & 0 & 0 \end{pmatrix} \tag{65.5}$$

If we let the four-terminals making up the six-terminal become infinitesimal, we have

$$\begin{pmatrix} p_{11} & p_{22} \\ p_{21} & p_{22} \end{pmatrix} = \begin{pmatrix} 1 + \pi_{11}\,dz & \pi_{12}\,dz \\ \pi_{21}\,dz & 1 + \pi_{22}\,dz \end{pmatrix},$$
$$\begin{pmatrix} q_{11} & q_{12} \\ q_{21} & q_{22} \end{pmatrix} = \begin{pmatrix} 1 + \chi_{11}\,dz & \chi_{12}\,dz \\ \chi_{21}\,dz & 1 + \chi_{22}\,dz \end{pmatrix} \tag{65.6}$$

so that Eq. (65.4) becomes

$$(b_{ij}) = \begin{pmatrix} 1 & 0 & 0 & 0 \\ 0 & 1 & 0 & 0 \\ 0 & 0 & 1 & 0 \\ 0 & 0 & 0 & 1 \end{pmatrix} + dz \begin{pmatrix} \chi_{11} & \chi_{12} & 0 & 0 \\ \chi_{21} & \chi_{22} & 0 & 0 \\ 0 & 0 & \pi_{11} & \pi_{12} \\ 0 & 0 & \pi_{21} & \pi_{22} \end{pmatrix} \tag{65.7}$$

The four-terminals (and hence the six-terminal) will be reversible if

$$\chi_{11} = \pi_{11} = \chi_{22} = \pi_{22} = 0 \tag{65.8}$$

We may use the expansion (65.7) in Eq. (65.2) to obtain four linear differential equations of the first order for x_1, x_2, x_3, and x_4. These four equations are of the same form as the Dirac equations for the relativistic electron provided we make the generalization to three dimensions. A set of four-rowed matrices will occur in the theory. There are four possible independent choices for these matrices, and all these matrices are made up of the Pauli matrices. All the matrices are Hermitian and have the following diagonal form:

$$\begin{pmatrix} \gamma_1 & 0 & 0 & \cdot & \cdot & \cdot\ \cdot\ \cdot\ \cdot \\ 0 & \gamma_2 & 0 & \cdot & \cdot & \cdot\ \cdot\ \cdot\ \cdot \\ 0 & 0 & \gamma_3 & \cdot & \cdot & \cdot\ \cdot\ \cdot\ \cdot \\ \cdot & \cdot & \cdot & \cdot & \cdot & \cdot\ \cdot\ \cdot\ \cdot \\ \cdot & \cdot & \cdot & -\gamma_1 & 0 & 0\ \cdot\ \cdot\ \cdot \\ \cdot & \cdot & \cdot & 0 & -\gamma_2 & 0\ \cdot\ \cdot\ \cdot \\ \cdot & \cdot & \cdot & 0 & 0 & -\gamma_3\ \cdot\ \cdot\ \cdot \\ \cdot & \cdot & \cdot & \cdot & \cdot & \cdot\ \cdot\ \cdot\ \cdot \end{pmatrix} \tag{65.9}$$

In other words, for each wave with propagation constant γ_i, there is a wave with propagation constant $-\gamma_i$. These two waves will propagate in opposite senses.[1]

[1] BRILLOUIN, L., *J. phys.*, **7**, 401 (1936).

APPENDIX

The reader must be aware of the fact that the whole discussion of wave propagation in periodic structures rests on a general Theorem which was first stated for one-dimensional problems on p. 17, then generalized for two dimensions (pp. 103-104) and finally for three dimensions (pp. 137-144), with the help of the reciprocal lattice.

Most of the examples discussed in this book are dissipationless. There are usually no losses or very small ones in crystal lattices and it is a reasonable approximation to ignore these losses in a first discussion. In technical problems of filters, the losses cannot be ignored since their contribution to the attenuation factor is of importance. Losses have been considered in the discussion of Chap. IX and it should be emphasized that losses can be included without disturbing the general theorem stated above. The vector k is complex in these problems, but it is still determined only with modulus 2π along each of its components, and the frequency ν of a wave must always be a periodic function of the vector k with periods 2π. The importance of the reciprocal lattice and the role played by the zones still retains its value even in the case of dissipation.

A great many examples could now be added to the special ones discussed in this book. The invention of linear accelerators lead to the discussion of a variety of structures yielding a low velocity of propagation for electromagnetic waves. Most of these structures are periodical and represent direct examples of our general theory. See, for instance:

Chu, E. L., and W. W. Hansen: *J App. Phys.*, **18**, 996 (1947), **20**, 280 (1949).

Brillouin, L.: *J. App. Phys.*, **19**, 1023 (1948).

Slater, J. C.: *Rev. Modern Phys.*, **20**, 473 (1948).

(A rather complete bibliography is found in this paper.)

Cohn, S. B.: Harvard Ph. D. Thesis (1948).

Three-dimensional lattices with metallic obstacles or metallic strips have been used to build artificial media that would propagate electromagnetic waves in space, with a low velocity. These structures represent actual large scale models of crystal lattices, and should be discussed according to the general rules of our Chap. VII. These "artificial dielectrics" were applied to build lenses for electromagnetic waves. See:

KOCK, W. E.: Metallic Delay Lenses *Bell Syst. Techn. J.*, **27**, 58 (1948).
COHN, S. B.: *J. App. Phys.*, **20**, 257 (1949), **21**, 674 (1950), **22**, 628 (1951).
BROWN, J.: *J. I. El. E.*, **97** (III), 45 (1950).
WICHER, E. R.: *J. App. Phys.*, **22**, 1327 (1951).

In our discussions we mostly considered wave propagation in an infinite medium. The problem of reflexions on a boundary was investigated in Chap. V, in connection with the definition of a characteristic impedance. We also discussed in Chap. VII Bragg's reflexions and their relation to the theory of zones.

Oscillations on a finite line of coupled circuits were discussed in a very elegant way by M. Parodi [*Memorial des Sc. Physiques*, **47** Gauthier-Villars, Paris (1944)], who was able to solve directly the complete system of simultaneous equations and to obtain the whole set of proper vibrations for a finite line of circuits.

Applying his very powerful method to electric filters, M. Parodi showed the connection with the usual definition of characteristic impedance along the line.

We explained (p. 158, 159) the difficulties of reflexion problems in three dimensions and introduced the very useful method of "cyclic boundary conditions" of M. Born. A few simple examples may be in order, and help visualize the physical meaning of these cyclic conditions. Let us consider an electric filter comprising n similar cells with the output terminals directly connected back to the input terminals. This is a typical case of cyclic structure. For instance, we might investigate a closed circuit with all the coils of the stator of an alternator connected in series. Oscillations in such a circuit would be given by cyclic conditions. A similar example is found in the oscillation of a cold magnetron with n cavities. The rising sun magnetron is a case similar to a NaCl one-dimensional lattice (Chap. IV) with cyclic conditions. A mechanical problem leading to similar results is found in connection with the natural frequencies of turbine blades, or the oscillations in a merry-go-round. All these examples could serve as typical problems of wave propagation in a periodic structure with cyclic conditions.

The *theory of the zones* obtains very important applications in the theory of metals, alloys and semi-conductors. In the case of alloys, it yields a very direct explanation of the Hume-Rothery rule [Hume-Rothery, "The Metallic State," Oxford, (1931)]. These problems are very carefully discussed in the book of Mott and Jones (see Preface). Modern developments were recently analyzed by L. Pauling and F. J. Ewing in a paper on the role of valence electrons in metals and intermetallic compounds (*Rev. Mod. Phys.*, **20**, 112 (1948)).

As for the theory of semi-conductors, the reader will find it brilliantly presented in the book of W. Shockley, "Electrons and Holes in Semi-Conductors," Van Nostrand, New York (1950).

Some interesting problems resulting in splitting the zones have been discussed by Slater:

SLATER, J. C.: *Phys. Rev.*, **84**, 179 (1951).
KATZ, E.: *Phys. Rev.*, **85**, 495 (1952).

The actual basic cell of a crystal lattice may happen to be an integral multiple of the "naive" basic cell. This is the case if certain refinements in the law of interaction between atoms are taken into account, as for instance spin coupling. Doubling the size of the lattice cell means dividing by two the volume of the zone and splitting in two the energy bands. This is the type of problem investigated by Slater, who discussed some interesting applications of this remark. We now want to conclude with a few words on the *theory of the zones* and its connection with group theory. This discussion contains the proof of the statement given on p. 107, that the volume of each zone must be equal to the volume of the elementary cell in the reciprocal lattice. We shall be satisfied with a summary of the problem, which the reader will find completely discussed in the following papers:

BOUCKAERT, L. P., R. SMOLUCHOWSKI and E. WIGNER: "Theory of Brillouin Zones and Symmetry Properties of Wave Functions in Crystals," *Phys. Rev.*, **50**, 58 (1936).
BIEBERBACH, L.: "Ueber die Inhaltsgleichheit der Brillouinsche Zonen," *Monatshefte für Math. und Physik*, **48**, 509 (1939).

I owe to G. Deschamps the principle of the following discussion. Let us consider a problem in two dimensions. The extension to three dimensions offers no special difficulty. The reciprocal lattice in the plane is defined by two non-parallel translations T_1 and

T_2, corresponding to the two vectors b_1 and b_2 of Chap. VII. All the translations

$$T = T_1^n T_2^p \tag{A.1}$$

where n, p are positive or negative integers, constitute a free abelian group G. When these translations are applied to the point O at the origin, one obtains a point lattice R which is the reciprocal lattice.

In order to obtain the zones around point O, we draw the perpendicular bisectors on all the vectors joining O to the successive points of the lattice R. Some points in the plane can be reached from O in a continuous way without crossing any perpendicular bisector. These points belong to the first zone. The second zone contains all the points that can be reached after crossing only one bisector. If two bisectors have to be crossed, the points belong to the third zone, and so on. These definitions correspond to the drawing shown on Fig. 27.4 (p. 106). We now want to specify the properties of points belonging to the successive zones or to their boundaries. Let us choose an arbitrary point M in the plane and a certain point P of the reciprocal lattice. We define two functions $j_P(M)$ and $k_P(M)$ in the following way: we draw a circle (M) of center M passing through the lattice point P. This circle contains $j - 1$ points of the reciprocal lattice R and there are $k + 1$ points of this lattice R lying exactly on the circle (M).

We now consider first the functions $j_0(M)$ and $k_0(M)$ attached to the origin O of the lattice R. It is obvious that $k_0(M)$ represents the number of bisectors upon which point M happens to be. It is zero within a zone, and equal to 1 if M is on one bisector, 2 if M is at the intersection of two bisectors and so on. In general, $k_0(M)$ is different from zero when point M is on a boundary line between zones.

The j_0 function can vary only when one or more points of lattice R enter into the circle (M) or get out of it, which means that M crosses one or many bisectors. More precisely, j_0 increases by a number of units exactly equal to the number of bisectors crossed by M when moving radially away from O. Since j_0 equals 1 in the first zone, we see that $j_0(M)$ simply yields the number of the zone where M happens to be (provided of course M is within a zone and not on a boundary, $k_0(M)$ being zero). If

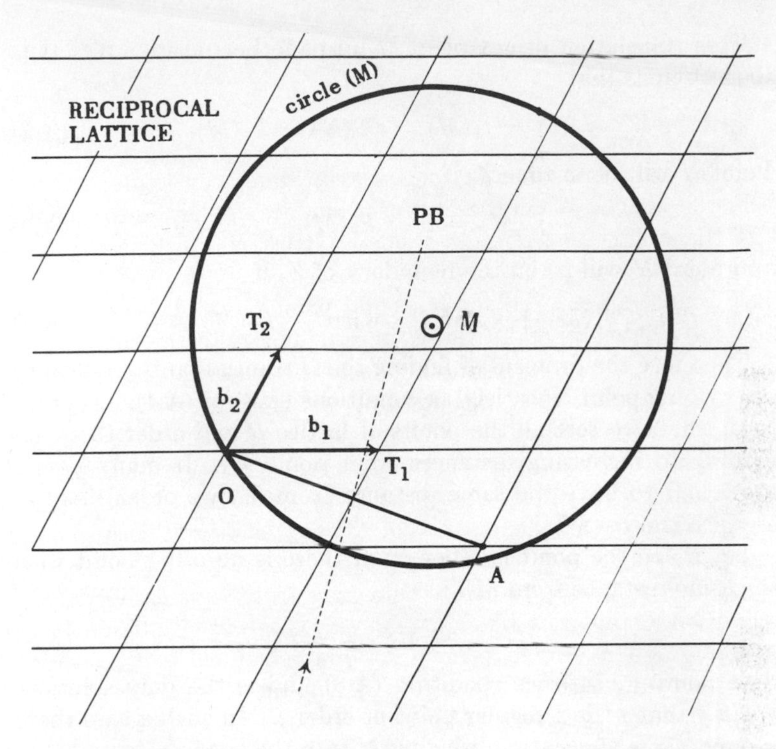

PB, perpendicular bisector on OA

j_o(M) = 12
k_o(M) = 0
k_o(M) would be 1 if circle (M) happened to pass on A and M would be on bisector PB.

$k_0(M) \neq 0$, it is easy to see that M is on the boundary of all zones

$$j, j+1, j+2, \cdots, j+k$$

We now prove the following *Theorem*:
Any point M can be brought into a certain zone Z_i or on its boundary, by a G translation (A.1). In the first case there is only one possible translation, in the second case there are at least two possible translations.

Let us define the G translation by a vector $\overrightarrow{PO}$ where P is a point of the reciprocal lattice R.

This translation brings point M into another position N. It is then obvious that

$$j_0(N) = j_P(M) \qquad k_0(N) = k_P(M) \tag{A.2}$$

Point N will be in zone Z_i if

$$j_P(M) = i \qquad k_P(M) = 0 \tag{A.3}$$

and point N will be on the boundary of Z_i if

$$j_P(M) \leq i \leq j_P(M) + k_P(M) \qquad \text{with} \qquad k_P(M) \neq 0 \tag{A.4}$$

Therefore the problem of finding the G translation is reduced to discovering points P satisfying conditions (A.3) or (A.4). In order to do that, we sort all the points of lattice R and order them according to increasing distances from point M. If many points are found to have the same distance from M, we order them in any arbitrary way.

Let P_i be the point number i. If there is no other point with the same distance from M,

$$MP_{i-1} < MP_i < MP_{i+1} \tag{A.5}$$

then point P_i satisfies condition (A.3) and is the only solution. We say that M is a regular point of order i. In such a case there is only one G translation bringing M into the zone Z_i.

Another case obtains when P_i is in a set of $k + 1$ equivalent points with equal distances from M

$$MP_{j-1} < MP_j = MP_{j+1} \cdots = MP_{j+k} < MP_{j+k+1} \tag{A.6}$$

with $j \leq i \leq j + k$

Here we have

$$j_P(M) = j \qquad k_P(M) = k$$

for every point P of this set. This is equivalent to conditions (A.4). We say that point M is a singular point of order i. There are exactly $k + 1$ translations of group G bringing point M on the boundary of the Z_i zone.

We may now consider an elementary cell D of the lattice R, for instance the cell of the parallelogram built on the two vectors $b_1 b_2$ originating in O. The cell includes the parallelogram and its boundary lines. Any point in the plane can be brought, by a G

translation back into the cell D. This applies for instance to the points of the Z_i zone. Vice versa, according to our theorem, any point of cell D, if regular of order i, can be brought into Z_i by a certain G translation. There is a one to one correspondence between the points in the Z_i zone and the regular points of order i in the cell D.

Let us now discuss the case of singular points of order i in the cell D. They are distributed along a finite number of segments of straight lines belonging to perpendicular bisectors on couples of points of the lattice R. These straight segments divide the cell D into a finite number of polygonal areas containing regular points. Each one of these regular areas can be translated as a whole in the Z_i zone by a given G translation, since point P_i of order i associated to M cannot change unless M becomes singular.

This proves that the areas of the Z_i zone and of the elementary cell D must be equal, Q. E. D.

We may describe the results in a slightly different language. Let us define the *distance* (PM) between an arbitrary point M in the plane and a certain lattice point P. The definition of distance will be based upon the functions $j_P(M)$ and $k_P(M)$. If P is the only lattice point on circle (M), we take

$$k_P(M) = 0 \qquad (PM) = j_P(M)$$

and $(PM) - 1$ is the number of lattice points inside the circle. But, in addition to P, we may have $k_P(M)$ other points lying just on the circumference of the circle (M).

In such a case we say that (PM) is a multi-valued function.

$$k_P(M) \neq 0 \qquad (PM) = j_P(M), j_P(M) + 1 \cdots j_P(M) + k_P(M)$$

With these definitions, the zone Z_i of order i is simply the set of all points which are at the "distance" i from the origin

$$(OM) = j_0(M) = i$$

(OM) is single-valued for the points M which are within a zone and multi-valued for the points on the boundary of a zone: double-valued if the point is on a perpendicular bisector, triple-valued at the intersection of two bisectors &. In the discussion of the Theorem, we simply sorted all the points P of the lattice R according to increasing distances (PM) from point M and we used the vector $\overrightarrow{PO}$ to bring the point M into the zone, or on the border of the zone if (PM) be multi-valued. As for the elementary cell D of the lattice R, it represents a fundamental domain for the group G, and any point M in the plane can be brought, by one and only one G translation, back into the cell D.

INDEX

T

U

V

W

X

Z

CATALOG OF DOVER BOOKS

BOOKS EXPLAINING SCIENCE AND MATHEMATICS

THE COMMON SENSE OF THE EXACT SCIENCES, W. K. Clifford. Introduction by James Newman, edited by Karl Pearson. For 70 years this has been a guide to classical scientific and mathematical thought. Explains with unusual clarity basic concepts, such as extension of meaning of symbols, characteristics of surface boundaries, properties of plane figures, vectors, Cartesian method of determining position, etc. Long preface by Bertrand Russell. Bibliography of Clifford. Corrected, 130 diagrams redrawn. 249pp. 5⅜ x 8.
T61 Paperbound **$1.60**

SCIENCE THEORY AND MAN, Erwin Schrödinger. This is a complete and unabridged reissue of SCIENCE AND THE HUMAN TEMPERAMENT plus an additional essay: "What is an Elementary Particle?" Nobel Laureate Schrödinger discusses such topics as nature of scientific method, the nature of science, chance and determinism, science and society, conceptual models for physical entities, elementary particles and wave mechanics. Presentation is popular and may be followed by most people with little or no scientific training. "Fine practical preparation for a time when laws of nature, human institutions . . . are undergoing a critical examination without parallel," Waldemar Kaempffert, N. Y. TIMES. 192pp. 5⅜ x 8.
T428 Paperbound **$1.35**

PIONEERS OF SCIENCE, O. Lodge. Eminent scientist-expositor's authoritative, yet elementary survey of great scientific theories. Concentrating on individuals—Copernicus, Brahe, Kepler, Galileo, Descartes, Newton, Laplace, Herschel, Lord Kelvin, and other scientists—the author presents their discoveries in historical order adding biographical material on each man and full, specific explanations of their achievements. The clear and complete treatment of the post-Newtonian astronomers is a feature seldom found in other books on the subject. Index. 120 illustrations. xv + 404pp. 5⅜ x 8.
T716 Paperbound **$1.50**

THE EVOLUTION OF SCIENTIFIC THOUGHT FROM NEWTON TO EINSTEIN, A. d'Abro. Einstein's special and general theories of relativity, with their historical implications, are analyzed in non-technical terms. Excellent accounts of the contributions of Newton, Riemann, Weyl, Planck, Eddington, Maxwell, Lorentz and others are treated in terms of space and time, equations of electromagnetics, finiteness of the universe, methodology of science. 21 diagrams. 482pp. 5⅜ x 8.
T2 Paperound **$2.00**

THE RISE OF THE NEW PHYSICS, A. d'Abro. A half-million word exposition, formerly titled THE DECLINE OF MECHANISM, for readers not versed in higher mathematics. The only thorough explanation, in everyday language, of the central core of modern mathematical physical theory, treating both classical and modern theoretical physics, and presenting in terms almost anyone can understand the equivalent of 5 years of study of mathematical physics. Scientifically impeccable coverage of mathematical-physical thought from the Newtonian system up through the electronic theories of Dirac and Heisenberg and Fermi's statistics. Combines both history and exposition; provides a broad yet unified and detailed view, with constant comparison of classical and modern views on phenomena and theories. "A must for anyone doing serious study in the physical sciences," JOURNAL OF THE FRANKLIN INSTITUTE. "Extraordinary faculty . . . to explain ideas and theories of theoretical physics in the language of daily life," ISIS. First part of set covers philosophy of science, drawing upon the practice of Newton, Maxwell, Poincaré, Einstein, others, discussing modes of thought, experiment, interpretations of causality, etc. In the second part, 100 pages explain grammar and vocabulary of mathematics, with discussions of functions, groups, series, Fourier series, etc. The remainder is devoted to concrete, detailed coverage of both classical and quantum physics, explaining such topics as analytic mechanics, Hamilton's principle, wave theory of light, electromagnetic waves, groups of transformations, thermodynamics, phase rule, Brownian movement, kinetics, special relativity, Planck's original quantum theory, Bohr's atom, Zeeman effect, Broglie's wave mechanics, Heisenberg's uncertainty, Eigen-values, matrices, scores of other important topics. Discoveries and theories are covered for such men as Alembert, Born, Cantor, Debye, Euler, Foucault, Galois, Gauss, Hadamard, Kelvin, Kepler, Laplace, Maxwell, Pauli, Rayleigh, Volterra, Weyl, Young, more than 180 others. Indexed. 97 illustrations. ix + 982pp. 5⅜ x 8.
T3 Volume 1, Paperbound **$2.00**
T4 Volume 2, Paperbound **$2.00**

CONCERNING THE NATURE OF THINGS, Sir William Bragg. Christmas lectures delivered at the Royal Society by Nobel laureate. Why a spinning ball travels in a curved track; how uranium is transmuted to lead, etc. Partial contents: atoms, gases, liquids, crystals, metals, etc. No scientific background needed; wonderful for intelligent child. 32pp. of photos, 57 figures. xii + 232pp. 5⅜ x 8.
T31 Paperbound **$1.35**

THE UNIVERSE OF LIGHT, Sir William Bragg. No scientific training needed to read Nobel Prize winner's expansion of his Royal Institute Christmas Lectures. Insight into nature of light, methods and philosophy of science. Explains lenses, reflection, color, resonance, polarization, x-rays, the spectrum, Newton's work with prisms, Huygens' with polarization, Crookes' with cathode ray, etc. Leads into clear statement of 2 major historical theories of light, corpuscle and wave. Dozens of experiments you can do. 199 illus., including 2 full-page color plates. 293pp. 5⅜ x 8.
S538 Paperbound **$1.85**

PHYSICS, THE PIONEER SCIENCE, L. W. Taylor. First thorough text to place all important physical phenomena in cultural-historical framework; remains best work of its kind. Exposition of physical laws, theories developed chronologically, with great historical, illustrative experiments diagrammed, described, worked out mathematically. Excellent physics text for self-study as well as class work. Vol. 1: Heat, Sound: motion, acceleration, gravitation, conservation of energy, heat engines, rotation, heat, mechanical energy, etc. 211 illus. 407pp. 5⅜ x 8. Vol. 2: Light, Electricity: images, lenses, prisms, magnetism, Ohm's law, dynamos, telegraph, quantum theory, decline of mechanical view of nature, etc. Bibliography. 13 table appendix. Index. 551 illus. 2 color plates. 508pp. 5⅜ x 8.
Vol. 1 S565 Paperbound **$2.00**
Vol. 2 S566 Paperbound **$2.00**
The set **$4.00**

FROM EUCLID TO EDDINGTON: A STUDY OF THE CONCEPTIONS OF THE EXTERNAL WORLD, Sir Edmund Whittaker. A foremost British scientist traces the development of theories of natural philosophy from the western rediscovery of Euclid to Eddington, Einstein, Dirac, etc. The inadequacy of classical physics is contrasted with present day attempts to understand the physical world through relativity, non-Euclidean geometry, space curvature, wave mechanics, etc. 5 major divisions of examination: Space; Time and Movement; the Concepts of Classical Physics; the Concepts of Quantum Mechanics; the Eddington Universe. 212pp. 5⅜ x 8. T491 Paperbound **$1.35**

THE STORY OF ATOMIC THEORY AND ATOMIC ENERGY, J. G. Feinberg. Wider range of facts on physical theory, cultural implications, than any other similar source. Completely non-technical. Begins with first atomic theory, 600 B.C., goes through A-bomb, developments to 1959. Avogadro, Rutherford, Bohr, Einstein, radioactive decay, binding energy, radiation danger, future benefits of nuclear power, dozens of other topics, told in lively, related, informal manner. Particular stress on European atomic research. "Deserves special mention . . . authoritative," Saturday Review. Formerly "The Atom Story." New chapter to 1959. Index. 34 illustrations. 251pp. 5⅜ x 8. T625 Paperbound **$1.45**

THE STRANGE STORY OF THE QUANTUM, AN ACCOUNT FOR THE GENERAL READER OF THE GROWTH OF IDEAS UNDERLYING OUR PRESENT ATOMIC KNOWLEDGE, B. Hoffmann. Presents lucidly and expertly, with barest amount of mathematics, the problems and theories which led to modern quantum physics. Dr. Hoffmann begins with the closing years of the 19th century, when certain trifling discrepancies were noticed, and with illuminating analogies and examples takes you through the brilliant concepts of Planck, Einstein, Pauli, de Broglie, Bohr, Schroedinger, Heisenberg, Dirac, Sommerfeld, Feynman, etc. This edition includes a new, long postscript carrying the story through 1958. "Of the books attempting an account of the history and contents of our modern atomic physics which have come to my attention, this is the best," H. Margenau, Yale University, in "American Journal of Physics." 32 tables and line illustrations. Index. 275pp. 5⅜ x 8. T518 Paperbound **$1.45**

SPACE AND TIME, Emile Borel. An entirely non-technical introduction to relativity, by world-renowned mathematician, Sorbonne Professor. (Notes on basic mathematics are included separately.) This book has never been surpassed for insight, and extraordinary clarity of thought, as it presents scores of examples, analogies, arguments, illustrations, which explain such topics as: difficulties due to motion; gravitation a force of inertia; geodesic lines; wave-length and difference of phase; x-rays and crystal structure; the special theory of relativity; and much more. Indexes. 4 appendixes. 15 figures. xvi + 243pp. 5⅜ x 8.
T592 Paperbound **$1.45**

THE RESTLESS UNIVERSE, Max Born. New enlarged version of this remarkably readable account by a Nobel laureate. Moving from sub-atomic particles to universe, the author explains in very simple terms the latest theories of wave mechanics. Partial contents: air and its relatives, electrons & ions, waves & particles, electronic structure of the atom, nuclear physics. Nearly 1000 illustrations, including 7 animated sequences. 325pp. 6 x 9.
T412 Paperbound **$2.00**

SOAP SUBBLES, THEIR COLOURS AND THE FORCES WHICH MOULD THEM, C. V. Boys. Only complete edition, half again as much material as any other. Includes Boys' hints on performing his experiments, sources of supply. Dozens of lucid experiments show complexities of liquid films, surface tension, etc. Best treatment ever written. Introduction. 83 illustrations. Color plate. 202pp. 5⅜ x 8. T542 Paperbound **95¢**

SPINNING TOPS AND GYROSCOPIC MOTION, John Perry. Well-known classic of science still unsurpassed for lucid, accurate, delightful exposition. How quasi-rigidity is induced in flexible and fluid bodies by rapid motions; why gyrostat falls, top rises; nature and effect on climatic conditions of earth's precessional movement; effect of internal fluidity on rotating bodies, etc. Appendixes describe practical uses to which gyroscopes have been put in ships, compasses, monorail transportation. 62 figures. 128pp. 5⅜ x 8. T416 Paperbound **$1.00**

MATTER & LIGHT, THE NEW PHYSICS, L. de Broglie. Non-technical papers by a Nobel laureate explain electromagnetic theory, relativity, matter, light and radiation, wave mechanics, quantum physics, philosophy of science. Einstein, Planck, Bohr, others explained so easily that no mathematical training is needed for all but 2 of the 21 chapters. Unabridged. Index. 300pp. 5⅜ x 8. T35 Paperbound **$1.60**

BRIDGES AND THEIR BUILDERS, David Steinman and Sara Ruth Watson. Engineers, historians, everyone who has ever been fascinated by great spans will find this book an endless source of information and interest. Dr. Steinman, recipient of the Louis Levy medal, was one of the great bridge architects and engineers of all time, and his analysis of the great bridges of history is both authoritative and easily followed. Greek and Roman bridges, medieval bridges, Oriental bridges, modern works such as the Brooklyn Bridge and the Golden Gate Bridge, and many others are described in terms of history, constructional principles, artistry, and function. All in all this book is the most comprehensive and accurate semipopular history of bridges in print in English. New, greatly revised, enlarged edition. 23 photographs, 26 line drawings. Index. xvii + 401pp. 5⅜ x 8. T431 Paperbound **$2.00**

FADS AND FALLACIES IN THE NAME OF SCIENCE, Martin Gardner. Examines various cults, quack systems, frauds, delusions which at various times have masqueraded as science. Accounts of hollow-earth fanatics like Symmes; Velikovsky and wandering planets; Hoerbiger; Bellamy and the theory of multiple moons; Charles Fort; dowsing, pseudoscientific methods for finding water, ores, oil. Sections on naturopathy, iridiagnosis, zone therapy, food fads, etc. Analytical accounts of Wilhelm Reich and orgone sex energy; L. Ron Hubbard and Dianetics; A. Korzybski and General Semantics; many others. Brought up to date to include Bridey Murphy, others. Not just a collection of anecdotes, but a fair, reasoned appraisal of eccentric theory. Formerly titled IN THE NAME OF SCIENCE. Preface. Index. x + 384pp. 5⅜ x 8. T394 Paperbound **$1.50**

See also: **A PHILOSOPHICAL ESSAY ON PROBABILITIES, P. de Laplace; ON MATHEMATICS AND MATHEMATICIANS, R. E. Moritz; AN ELEMENTARY SURVEY OF CELESTIAL MECHANICS, Y. Ryabov; THE SKY AND ITS MYSTERIES, E. A. Beet; THE REALM OF THE NEBULAE, E. Hubble; OUT OF THE SKY, H. H. Nininger; SATELLITES AND SCIENTIFIC RESEARCH, D. King-Hele; HEREDITY AND YOUR LIFE, A. M. Winchester; INSECTS AND INSECT LIFE, S. W. Frost; PRINCIPLES OF STRATIGRAPHY, A. W. Grabau; TEACH YOURSELF SERIES.**

HISTORY OF SCIENCE AND MATHEMATICS

DIALOGUES CONCERNING TWO NEW SCIENCES, Galileo Galilei. This classic of experimental science, mechanics, engineering, is as enjoyable as it is important. A great historical document giving insights into one of the world's most original thinkers, it is based on 30 years' experimentation. It offers a lively exposition of dynamics, elasticity, sound, ballistics, strength of materials, the scientific method. "Superior to everything else of mine," Galileo. Trans. by H. Crew, A. Salvio. 126 diagrams. Index. xxi + 288pp. 5⅜ x 8.
S99 Paperbound **$1.65**

A DIDEROT PICTORIAL ENCYCLOPEDIA OF TRADES AND INDUSTRY, Manufacturing and the Téchnical Arts in Plates Selected from "L'Encyclopédie ou Dictionnaire Raisonné des Sciences, des Arts, et des Métiers" of Denis Diderot. Edited with text by C. Gillispie. This first modern selection of plates from the high point of 18th century French engraving is a storehouse of valuable technological information to the historian of arts and science. Over 2000 illustrations on 485 full page plates, most of them original size, show the trades and industries of a fascinating era in such great detail that the processes and shops might very well be reconstructed from them. The plates teem with life, with men, women, and children performing all of the thousands of operations necessary to the trades before and during the early stages of the industrial revolution. Plates are in sequence, and show general operations, closeups of difficult operations, and details of complex machinery. Such important and interesting trades and industries are illustrated as sowing, harvesting, beekeeping, cheesemaking, operating windmills, milling flour, charcoal burning, tobacco processing, indigo, fishing, arts of war, salt extraction, mining, smelting, casting iron, steel, extracting mercury, zinc, sulphur, copper, etc., slating, tinning, silverplating, gilding, making gunpowder, cannons, bells, shoeing horses, tanning, papermaking, printing, dyeing, and more than 40 other categories. Professor Gillispie, of Princeton, supplies a full commentary on all the plates, identifying operations, tools, processes, etc. This material, presented in a lively and lucid fashion, is of great interest to the reader interested in history of science and technology. Heavy library cloth. 920pp. 9 x 12. T421 Two volume set **$18.50**

DE MAGNETE, William Gilbert. This classic work on magnetism founded a new science. Gilbert was the first to use the word "electricity", to recognize mass as distinct from weight, to discover the effect of heat on magnetic bodies; invent an electroscope, differentiate between static electricity and magnetism, conceive of the earth as a magnet. Written by the first great experimental scientist, this lively work is valuable not only as an historical landmark, but as the delightfully easy to follow record of a perpetually searching, ingenious mind. Translated by P. F. Mottelay. 25 page biographical memoir. 90 figures. lix + 368pp. 5⅜ x 8.
S470 Paperbound **$2.00**

CHARLES BABBAGE AND HIS CALCULATING ENGINES, edited by P. Morrison and E. Morrison. Babbage, leading 19th century pioneer in mathematical machines and herald of modern operational research, was the true father of Harvard's relay computer Mark I. His Difference Engine and Analytical Engine were the first machines in the field. This volume contains a valuable introduction on his life and work; major excerpts from his autobiography, revealing his eccentric and unusual personality; and extensive selections from "Babbage's Calculating Engines," a compilation of hard-to-find journal articles by Babbage, the Countess of Lovelace, L. F. Menabrea, and Dionysius Lardner. 8 illustrations, Appendix of miscellaneous papers. Index. Bibliography. xxxviii + 400pp. 5⅜ x 8. T12 Paperbound **$2.00**

A HISTORY OF ASTRONOMY FROM THALES TO KEPLER, J. L. E. Dreyer. (Formerly A HISTORY OF PLANETARY SYSTEMS FROM THALES TO KEPLER.) This is the only work in English to give the complete history of man's cosmological views from prehistoric times to Kepler and Newton. Partial contents: Near Eastern astronomical systems, Early Greeks, Homocentric Spheres of Eudoxus, Epicycles, Ptolemaic system, medieval cosmology, Copernicus, Kepler, etc. Revised, foreword by W. H. Stahl. New bibliography. xvii + 430pp. 5⅜ x 8. S79 Paperbound **$1.98**

A SHORT HISTORY OF ANATOMY AND PHYSIOLOGY FROM THE GREEKS TO HARVEY, Charles Singer. Corrected edition of THE EVOLUTION OF ANATOMY, classic work tracing evolution of anatomy and physiology from prescientific times through Greek & Roman periods, Dark Ages, Renaissance, to age of Harvey and beginning of modern concepts. Centered on individuals, movements, periods that definitely advanced anatomical knowledge: Plato, Diocles, Aristotle, Theophrastus, Herophilus, Erasistratus, the Alexandrians, Galen, Mondino, da Vinci, Linacre, Sylvius, others. Special section on Vesalius; Vesalian atlas of nudes, skeletons, muscle tabulae. Index of names, 20 plates. 270 extremely interesting illustrations of ancient, medieval, Renaissance, Oriental origin. xii + 209pp. 5⅜ x 8. T389 Paperbound **$1.75**

FROM MAGIC TO SCIENCE, Charles Singer. A great historian examines aspects of medical science from the Roman Empire through the Renaissance. Includes perhaps the best discussion of early herbals, and a penetrating physiological interpretation of "The Visions of Hildegarde of Bingen." Also examined are Arabian and Galenic influences; the Sphere of Pythagoras; Paracelsus; the reawakening of science under Leonardo da Vinci, Vesalius; the Lorica of Gildas the Briton; etc. Frequent quotations with translations. New Introduction by the author. New unabridged, corrected edition. 158 unusual illustrations from classical and medieval sources. Index. xxvii + 365pp. 5⅜ x 8. T390 Paperbound **$2.00**

HISTORY OF MATHEMATICS, D. E. Smith. Most comprehensive non-technical history of math in English. Discusses lives and works of over a thousand major and minor figures, with footnotes supplying technical information outside the book's scheme, and indicating disputed matters. Vol I: A chronological examination, from primitive concepts through Egypt, Babylonia, Greece, the Orient, Rome, the Middle Ages, the Renaissance, and up to 1900. Vol 2: The development of ideas in specific fields and problems, up through elementary calculus. Two volumes, total of 510 illustrations, 1355pp. 5⅜ x 8. Set boxed in attractive container. T429, 430 Paperbound, the set **$5.00**

A SHORT ACCOUNT OF THE HISTORY OF MATHEMATICS, W. W. R. Ball. Most readable non-technical history of mathematics treats lives, discoveries of every important figure from Egyptian, Phoenician mathematicians to late 19th century. Discusses schools of Ionia, Pythagoras, Athens, Cyzicus, Alexandria, Byzantium, systems of numeration; primitive arithmetic; Middle Ages, Renaissance, including Arabs, Bacon, Regiomontanus, Tartaglia, Cardan, Stevinus, Galileo, Kepler; modern mathematics of Descartes, Pascal, Wallis, Huygens, Newton, Leibnitz, d'Alembert, Euler, Lambert, Laplace, Legendre, Gauss, Hermite, Weierstrass, scores more. Index. 25 figures. 546pp. 5⅜ x 8. S630 Paperbound **$2.00**

A SOURCE BOOK IN MATHEMATICS, D. E. Smith. Great discoveries in math, from Renaissance to end of 19th century, in English translation. Read announcements by Dedekind, Gauss, Delamain, Pascal, Fermat, Newton, Abel, Lobachevsky, Bolyai, Riemann, De Moivre, Legendre, Laplace, others of discoveries about imaginary numbers, number congruence, slide rule, equations, symbolism, cubic algebraic equations, non-Euclidean forms of geometry, calculus, function theory, quaternions, etc. Succinct selections from 125 different treatises, articles, most unavailable elsewhere in English. Each article preceded by biographical, historical introduction. Vol. I: Fields of Number, Algebra. Index. 32 illus. 338pp. 5⅜ x 8. Vol. II: Fields of Geometry, Probability, Calculus, Functions, Quaternions. 83 illus. 432pp. 5⅜ x 8.
Vol. 1: S552 Paperbound **$1.85**
Vol. 2: S553 Paperbound **$1.85**
2 vol. set, boxed **$3.50**

A HISTORY OF THE CALCULUS, AND ITS CONCEPTUAL DEVELOPMENT, Carl B. Boyer. Provides laymen and mathematicians a detailed history of the development of the calculus, from early beginning in antiquity to final elaboration as mathematical abstractions. Gives a sense of mathematics not as a technique, but as a habit of mind, in the progression of ideas of Zeno, Plato, Pythagoras, Eudoxus, Arabic and Scholastic mathematicians, Newton, Leibnitz, Taylor, Descartes, Euler, Lagrange, Cantor, Weierstrass, and others. This first comprehensive critical history of the calculus was originally titled "The Concepts of the Calculus." Foreword by R. Courant. Preface. 22 figures. 25-page bibliography. Index. v + 364pp. 5⅜ x 8. S509 Paperbound **$2.00**

A CONCISE HISTORY OF MATHEMATICS, D. Struik. Lucid study of development of mathematical ideas, techniques from Ancient Near East, Greece, Islamic science, Middle Ages, Renaissance, modern times. Important mathematicians are described in detail. Treatment is not anecdotal, but analytical development of ideas. "Rich in content, thoughtful in interpretation," U.S. QUARTERLY BOOKLIST. Non-technical; no mathematical training needed. Index. 60 illustrations, including Egyptian papyri, Greek mss., portraits of 31 eminent mathematicians. Bibliography. 2nd edition. xix + 299pp. 5⅜ x 8. T255 Paperbound **$1.75**

See also: **NON-EUCLIDEAN GEOMETRY, R. Bonola; THEORY OF DETERMINANTS IN HISTORICAL ORDER OF DEVELOPMENT, T. Muir; HISTORY OF THE THEORY OF ELASTICITY AND STRENGTH OF MATERIALS, I. Todhunter and K. Pearson; A SHORT HISTORY OF ASTRONOMY, A. Berry; CLASSICS OF SCIENCE.**

PHILOSOPHY OF SCIENCE AND MATHEMATICS

FOUNDATIONS OF SCIENCE: THE PHILOSOPHY OF THEORY AND EXPERIMENT, N. R. Campbell. A critique of the most fundamental concepts of science in general and physics in particular. Examines why certain propositions are accepted without question, demarcates science from philosophy, clarifies the understanding of the tools of science. Part One analyzes the presuppositions of scientific thought: existence of the material world, nature of scientific laws, multiplication of probabilities, etc.: Part Two covers the nature of experiment and the application of mathematics: conditions for measurement, relations between numerical laws and theories, laws of error, etc. An appendix covers problems arising from relativity, force, motion, space, and time. A classic in its field. Index. xiii + 565pp. 5⅝ x 8⅜. S372 Paperbound **$2.95**

WHAT IS SCIENCE?, Norman Campbell. This excellent introduction explains scientific method, role of mathematics, types of scientific laws. Contents: 2 aspects of science, science & nature, laws of science, discovery of laws, explanation of laws, measurement & numerical laws, applications of science. 192pp. 5⅜ x 8. S43 Paperbound **$1.25**

THE VALUE OF SCIENCE, Henri Poincaré. Many of the most mature ideas of the "last scientific universalist" covered with charm and vigor for both the beginning student and the advanced worker. Discusses the nature of scientific truth, whether order is innate in the universe or imposed upon it by man, logical thought versus intuition (relating to math, through the works of Weierstrass, Lie, Klein, Riemann), time and space (relativity, psychological time, simultaneity), Hertz's concept of force, interrelationship of mathematical physics to pure math, values within disciplines of Maxwell, Carnot, Mayer, Newton, Lorentz, etc. Index. iii + 147pp. 5⅜ x 8. S469 Paperbound **$1.35**

SCIENCE AND METHOD, Henri Poincaré. Procedure of scientific discovery, methodology, experiment, idea-germination—the intellectual processes by which discoveries come into being. Most significant and most interesting aspects of development, application of ideas. Chapters cover selection of facts, chance, mathematical reasoning, mathematics, and logic; Whitehead, Russell, Cantor; the new mechanics, etc. 288pp. 5⅜ x 8. S222 Paperbound **$1.35**

SCIENCE AND HYPOTHESIS, Henri Poincaré. Creative psychology in science. How such concepts as number, magnitude, space, force, classical mechanics were developed, and how the modern scientist uses them in his thought. Hypothesis in physics, theories of modern physics. Introduction by Sir James Larmor. "Few mathematicians have had the breadth of vision of Poincaré, and none is his superior in the gift of clear exposition," E. T. Bell. Index. 272pp. 5⅜ x 8. S221 Paperbound **$1.35**

PHILOSOPHY AND THE PHYSICISTS, L. S. Stebbing. The philosophical aspects of modern science examined in terms of a lively critical attack on the ideas of Jeans and Eddington. Discusses the task of science, causality, determinism, probability, consciousness, the relation of the world of physics to that of everyday experience. Probes the philosophical significance of the Planck-Bohr concept of discontinuous energy levels, the inferences to be drawn from Heisenberg's Uncertainty Principle, the implications of "becoming" involved in the 2nd law of thermodynamics, and other problems posed by the discarding of Laplacean determinism. 285pp. 5⅜ x 8. T480 Paperbound **$1.65**

EXPERIMENT AND THEORY IN PHYSICS, Max Born. A Nobel laureate examines the nature and value of the counterclaims of experiment and theory in physics. Synthetic versus analytical scientific advances are analyzed in the work of Einstein, Bohr, Heisenberg, Planck, Eddington, Milne, and others by a fellow participant. 44pp. 5⅜ x 8. S308 Paperbound **60¢**

THE NATURE OF PHYSICAL THEORY, P. W. Bridgman. Here is how modern physics looks to a highly unorthodox physicist—a Nobel laureate. Pointing out many absurdities of science, and demonstrating the inadequacies of various physical theories, Dr. Bridgman weighs and analyzes the contributions of Einstein, Bohr, Newton, Heisenberg, and many others. This is a non-technical consideration of the correlation of science and reality. Index. xi + 138pp. 5⅜ x 8. S33 Paperbound **$1.25**

THE PHILOSOPHY OF SPACE AND TIME, H. Reichenbach. An important landmark in the development of the empiricist conception of geometry, covering the problem of the foundations of geometry, the theory of time, the consequences of Einstein's relativity, including: relations between theory and observations; coordinate and metrical properties of space; the psychological problem of visual intuition of non-Euclidean structures; and many other important topics in modern science and philosophy. The majority of ideas require only a knowledge of intermediate math. Introduction by R. Carnap. 49 figures. Index. xviii + 296pp. 5⅜ x 8. S443 Paperbound **$2.00**

MATTER & MOTION, James Clerk Maxwell, This excellent exposition begins with simple particles and proceeds gradually to physical systems beyond complete analysis: motion, force, properties of centre of mass of material system, work, energy, gravitation, etc. Written with all Maxwell's original insights and clarity. Notes by E. Larmor. 17 diagrams. 178pp. 5⅜ x 8. S188 Paperbound **$1.35**

THE ANALYSIS OF MATTER, Bertrand Russell. How do our senses concord with the new physics? This volume covers such topics as logical analysis of physics, prerelativity physics, causality, scientific inference, physics and perception, special and general relativity, Weyl's theory, tensors, invariants and their physical interpretation, periodicity and qualitative series. "The most thorough treatment of the subject that has yet been published," THE NATION. Introduction by L. E. Denonn. 422pp. 5⅜ x 8. T231 Paperbound **$1.95**

SUBSTANCE AND FUNCTION, & EINSTEIN'S THEORY OF RELATIVITY, Ernst Cassirer. Two books bound as one. Cassirer establishes a philosophy of the exact sciences that takes into consideration newer developments in mathematics, and also shows historical connections. Partial contents: Aristotelian logic, Mill's analysis, Helmholtz & Kronecker, Russell & cardinal numbers, Euclidean vs. non-Euclidean geometry, Einstein's relativity. Bibliography. Index. xxi + 465pp. 5⅜ x 8. T50 Paperbound **$2.00**

PRINCIPLES OF MECHANICS, Heinrich Hertz. This last work by the great 19th century physicist is not only a classic, but of great interest in the logic of science. Creating a new system of mechanics based upon space, time, and mass, it returns to axiomatic analysis, to understanding of the formal or structural aspects of science, taking into account logic, observation, and a priori elements. Of great historical importance to Poincaré, Carnap, Einstein, Milne. A 20-page introduction by R. S. Cohen, Wesleyan University, analyzes the implications of Hertz's thought and the logic of science. Bibliography. 13-page introduction by Helmholtz. xlii + 274pp. 5⅜ x 8. S316 Clothbound **$3.50**
S317 Paperbound **$1.85**

THE PHILOSOPHICAL WRITINGS OF PEIRCE, edited by Justus Buchler. (Formerly published as THE PHILOSOPHY OF PEIRCE.) This is a carefully balanced exposition of Peirce's complete system, written by Peirce himself. It covers such matters as scientific method, pure chance vs. law, symbolic logic, theory of signs, pragmatism, experiment, and other topics. Introduction by Justus Buchler, Columbia University. xvi + 368pp. 5⅜ x 8. T217 Paperbound **$1.95**

ESSAYS IN EXPERIMENTAL LOGIC, John Dewey. This stimulating series of essays touches upon the relationship between inquiry and experience, dependence of knowledge upon thought, character of logic; judgments of practice, data and meanings, stimuli of thought, etc. Index. viii + 444pp. 5⅜ x 8. T73 Paperbound **$1.95**

LANGUAGE, TRUTH AND LOGIC, A. Ayer. A clear introduction to the Vienna and Cambridge schools of Logical Positivism. It sets up specific tests by which you can evaluate validity of ideas, etc. Contents: Function of philosophy, elimination of metaphysics, nature of analysis, a priori, truth and probability, etc. 10th printing. "I should like to have written it myself," Bertrand Russell. Index. 160pp. 5⅜ x 8. T10 Paperbound **$1.25**

THE PSYCHOLOGY OF INVENTION IN THE MATHEMATICAL FIELD, J. Hadamard. Where do ideas come from? What role does the unconscious play? Are ideas best developed by mathematical reasoning, word reasoning, visualization? What are the methods used by Einstein, Poincaré, Galton, Riemann? How can these techniques be applied by others? Hadamard, one of the world's leading mathematicians, discusses these and other questions. xiii + 145pp. 5⅜ x 8. T107 Paperbound **$1.25**

FOUNDATIONS OF GEOMETRY, Bertrand Russell. Analyzing basic problems in the overlap area between mathematics and philosophy, Nobel laureate Russell examines the nature of geometrical knowledge, the nature of geometry, and the application of geometry to space. It covers the history of non-Euclidean geometry, philosophic interpretations of geometry—especially Kant—projective and metrical geometry. This is most interesting as the solution offered in 1897 by a great mind to a problem still current. New introduction by Prof. Morris Kline of N. Y. University. xii + 201pp. 5⅜ x 8. S232 Clothbound **$3.25**
S233 Paperbound **$1.60**

Relativity, quantum theory, nuclear physics

THE PRINCIPLE OF RELATIVITY, A. Einstein, H. Lorentz, M. Minkowski, H. Weyl. These are the 11 basic papers that founded the general and special theories of relativity, all translated into English. Two papers by Lorentz on the Michelson experiment, electromagnetic phenomena. Minkowski's SPACE & TIME, and Weyl's GRAVITATION & ELECTRICITY. 7 epoch-making papers by Einstein: ELECTROMAGNETICS OF MOVING BODIES, INFLUENCE OF GRAVITATION IN PROPAGATION OF LIGHT, COSMOLOGICAL CONSIDERATIONS, GENERAL THEORY, and 3 others. 7 diagrams. Special notes by A. Sommerfeld. 224pp. 5⅜ x 8.
S81 Paperbound **$1.75**

SPACE TIME MATTER, Hermann Weyl. "The standard treatise on the general theory of relativity," (Nature), written by a world-renowned scientist, provides a deep clear discussion of the logical coherence of the general theory, with introduction to all the mathematical tools needed: Maxwell, analytical geometry, non-Euclidean geometry, tensor calculus, etc. Basis is classical space-time, before absorption of relativity. Partial contents: Euclidean space, mathematical form, metrical continuum, relativity of time and space, general theory. 15 diagrams. Bibliography. New preface for this edition. xviii + 330pp. 5⅜ x 8.
S267 Paperbound **$1.85**

PRINCIPLES OF QUANTUM MECHANICS, W. V. Houston. Enables student with working knowledge of elementary mathematical physics to develop facility in use of quantum mechanics, understand published work in field. Formulates quantum mechanics in terms of Schroedinger's wave mechanics. Studies evidence for quantum theory, for inadequacy of classical mechanics, 2 postulates of quantum mechanics; numerous important, fruitful applications of quantum mechanics in spectroscopy, collision problems, electrons in solids; other topics. "One of the most rewarding features . . . is the interlacing of problems with text," Amer. J. of Physics. Corrected edition. 21 illus. Index. 296pp. 5⅜ x 8. S524 Paperbound **$1.85**

PHYSICAL PRINCIPLES OF THE QUANTUM THEORY, Werner Heisenberg. A Nobel laureate discusses quantum theory; Heisenberg's own work, Compton, Schroedinger, Wilson, Einstein, many others. Written for physicists, chemists who are not specialists in quantum theory, only elementary formulae are considered in the text; there is a mathematical appendix for specialists. Profound without sacrifice of clarity. Translated by C. Eckart, F. Hoyt. 18 figures. 192pp. 5⅜ x 8. S113 Paperbound **$1.25**

SELECTED PAPERS ON QUANTUM ELECTRODYNAMICS, edited by **J. Schwinger.** Facsimiles of papers which established quantum electrodynamics, from initial successes through today's position as part of the larger theory of elementary particles. First book publication in any language of these collected papers of Bethe, Bloch, Dirac, Dyson, Fermi, Feynman, Heisenberg, Kusch, Lamb, Oppenheimer, Pauli, Schwinger, Tomonoga, Weisskopf, Wigner, etc. 34 papers in all, 29 in English, 1 in French, 3 in German, 1 in Italian. Preface and historical commentary by the editor. xvii + 423pp. 6⅛ x 9¼. S444 Paperbound **$2.45**

THE FUNDAMENTAL PRINCIPLES OF QUANTUM MECHANICS, WITH ELEMENTARY APPLICATIONS, E. C. Kemble. An inductive presentation, for the graduate student or specialist in some other branch of physics. Assumes some acquaintance with advanced math; apparatus necessary beyond differential equations and advanced calculus is developed as needed. Although a general exposition of principles, hundreds of individual problems are fully treated, with applications of theory being interwoven with development of the mathematical structure. The author is the Professor of Physics at Harvard Univ. "This excellent book would be of great value to every student . . . a rigorous and detailed mathematical discussion of all of the principal quantum-mechanical methods . . . has succeeded in keeping his presentations clear and understandable," Dr. Linus Pauling, J. of the American Chemical Society. Appendices: calculus of variations, math. notes, etc. Indexes. 611pp. 5⅜ x 8.
S472 Paperbound **$2.95**

ATOMIC SPECTRA AND ATOMIC STRUCTURE, G. Herzberg. Excellent general survey for chemists, physicists specializing in other fields. Partial contents: simplest line spectra and elements of atomic theory, building-up principle and periodic system of elements, hyperfine structure of spectral lines, some experiments and applications. Bibilography. 80 figures. Index. xii + 257pp. 5⅜ x 8. S115 Paperbound **$1.95**

THE THEORY AND THE PROPERTIES OF METALS AND ALLOYS, N. F. Mott, H. Jones. Quantum methods used to develop mathematical models which show interrelationship of basic chemical phenomena with crystal structure, magnetic susceptibility, electrical, optical properties. Examines thermal properties of crystal lattice, electron motion in applied field, cohesion, electrical resistance, noble metals, para-, dia-, and ferromagnetism, etc. "Exposition . . . clear . . . mathematical treatment . . . simple," Nature. 138 figures. Bibliography. Index. xiii + 320pp. 5⅜ x 8. S456 Paperbound **$1.85**

FOUNDATIONS OF NUCLEAR PHYSICS, edited by **R. T. Beyer.** 13 of the most important papers on nuclear physics reproduced in facsimile in the original languages of their authors: the papers most often cited in footnotes, bibliographies. Anderson, Curie, Joliot, Chadwick, Fermi, Lawrence, Cockcroft, Hahn, Yukawa. UNPARALLELED BIBLIOGRAPHY. 122 double-columned pages, over 4,000 articles, books classified. 57 figures. 288pp. 6⅛ x 9¼.
S19 Paperbound **$1.75**

MESON PHYSICS, R. E. Marshak. Traces the basic theory, and explicity presents results of experiments with particular emphasis on theoretical significance. Phenomena involving mesons as virtual transitions are avoided, eliminating some of the least satisfactory predictions of meson theory. Includes production and study of π mesons at nonrelativistic nucleon energies, contrasts between π and μ mesons, phenomena associated with nuclear interaction of π mesons, etc. Presents early evidence for new classes of particles and indicates theoretical difficulties created by discovery of heavy mesons and hyperons. Name and subject indices. Unabridged reprint. viii + 378pp. 5⅜ x 8. S500 Paperbound **$1.95**

See also: **STRANGE STORY OF THE QUANTUM, B. Hoffmann; FROM EUCLID TO EDDINGTON, E. Whittaker; MATTER AND LIGHT, THE NEW PHYSICS, L. de Broglie; THE EVOLUTION OF SCIENTIFIC THOUGHT FROM NEWTON TO EINSTEIN, A. d'Abro; THE RISE OF THE NEW PHYSICS, A. d'Abro; THE THEORY OF GROUPS AND QUANTUM MECHANICS, H. Weyl; SUBSTANCE AND FUNCTION, & EINSTEIN'S THEORY OF RELATIVITY, E. Cassirer; FUNDAMENTAL FORMULAS OF PHYSICS, D. H. Menzel.**

Hydrodynamics

HYDRODYNAMICS, H. Dryden, F. Murnaghan, Harry Bateman. Published by the National Research Council in 1932 this enormous volume offers a complete coverage of classical hydrodynamics. Encyclopedic in quality. Partial contents: physics of fluids, motion, turbulent flow, compressible fluids, motion in 1, 2, 3 dimensions; viscous fluids rotating, laminar motion, resistance of motion through viscous fluid, eddy viscosity, hydraulic flow in channels of various shapes, discharge of gases, flow past obstacles, etc. Bibliography of over 2,900 items. Indexes. 23 figures. 634pp. 5⅜ x 8. S303 Paperbound **$2.75**

A TREATISE ON HYDRODYNAMICS, A. B. Basset. Favorite text on hydrodynamics for 2 generations of physicists, hydrodynamical engineers, oceanographers, ship designers, etc. Clear enough for the beginning student, and thorough source for graduate students and engineers on the work of d'Alembert, Euler, Laplace, Lagrange, Poisson, Green, Clebsch, Stokes, Cauchy, Helmholtz, J. J. Thomson, Love, Hicks, Greenhill, Besant, Lamb, etc. Great amount of documentation on entire theory of classical hydrodynamics. Vol I: theory of motion of frictionless liquids, vortex, and cyclic irrotational motion, etc. 132 exercises. Bibliography. 3 Appendixes. xii + 264pp. Vol II: motion in viscous liquids, harmonic analysis, theory of tides, etc. 112 exercises. Bibliography. 4 Appendixes. xv + 328pp. Two volume set. 5⅜ x 8.
S724 Vol I Paperbound **$1.75**
S725 Vol II Paperbound **$1.75**
The set **$3.50**

HYDRODYNAMICS, Horace Lamb. Internationally famous complete coverage of standard reference work on dynamics of liquids & gases. Fundamental theorems, equations, methods, solutions, background, for classical hydrodynamics. Chapters include Equations of Motion, Integration of Equations in Special Gases, Irrotational Motion, Motion of Liquid in 2 Dimensions, Motion of Solids through Liquid-Dynamical Theory, Vortex Motion, Tidal Waves, Surface Waves, Waves of Expansion, Viscosity, Rotating Masses of liquids. Excellently planned, arranged; clear, lucid presentation. 6th enlarged, revised edition. Index. Over 900 footnotes, mostly bibliographical. 119 figures. xv + 738pp. 6⅛ x 9¼. S256 Paperbound **$2.95**

See also: **FUNDAMENTAL FORMULAS OF PHYSICS, D. H. Menzel; THEORY OF FLIGHT, R. von Mises; FUNDAMENTALS OF HYDRO- AND AEROMECHANICS, L. Prandtl and O. G. Tietjens; APPLIED HYDRO- AND AEROMECHANICS, L. Prandtl and O. G. Tietjens; HYDRAULICS AND ITS APPLICATIONS, A. H. Gibson; FLUID MECHANICS FOR HYDRAULIC ENGINEERS, H. Rouse.**

Acoustics, optics, electromagnetics

ON THE SENSATIONS OF TONE, Hermann Helmholtz. This is an unmatched coordination of such fields as acoustical physics, physiology, experiment, history of music. It covers the entire gamut of musical tone. Partial contents: relation of musical science to acoustics, physical vs. physiological acoustics, composition of vibration, resonance, analysis of tones by sympathetic resonance, beats, chords, tonality, consonant chords, discords, progression of parts, etc. 33 appendixes discuss various aspects of sound, physics, acoustics, music, etc. Translated by A. J. Ellis. New introduction by Prof. Henry Margenau of Yale. 68 figures. 43 musical passages analyzed. Over 100 tables. Index. xix + 576pp. 6⅛ x 9¼.
S114 Paperbound **$2.95**

THE THEORY OF SOUND, Lord Rayleigh. Most vibrating systems likely to be encountered in practice can be tackled successfully by the methods set forth by the great Nobel laureate, Lord Rayleigh. Complete coverage of experimental, mathematical aspects of sound theory. Partial contents: Harmonic motions, vibrating systems in general, lateral vibrations of bars, curved plates or shells, applications of Laplace's functions to acoustical problems, fluid friction, plane vortex-sheet, vibrations of solid bodies, etc. This is the first inexpensive edition of this great reference and study work. Bibliography. Historical introduction by R. B. Lindsay. Total of 1040pp. 97 figures. 5⅜ x 8.
S292, S293, Two volume set, paperbound, **$4.00**

THE DYNAMICAL THEORY OF SOUND, H. Lamb. Comprehensive mathematical treatment of the physical aspects of sound, covering the theory of vibrations, the general theory of sound, and the equations of motion of strings, bars, membranes, pipes, and resonators. Includes chapters on plane, spherical, and simple harmonic waves, and the Helmholtz Theory of Audition. Complete and self-contained development for student and specialist; all fundamental differential equations solved completely. Specific mathematical details for such important phenomena as harmonics, normal modes, forced vibrations of strings, theory of reed pipes, etc. Index. Bibliography. 86 diagrams. viii + 307pp. 5⅜ x 8. S655 Paperbound **$1.50**

WAVE PROPAGATION IN PERIODIC STRUCTURES, L. Brillouin. A general method and application to different problems: pure physics, such as scattering of X-rays of crystals, thermal vibration in crystal lattices, electronic motion in metals; and also problems of electrical engineering. Partial contents: elastic waves in 1-dimensional lattices of point masses. Propagation of waves along 1-dimensional lattices. Energy flow. 2 dimensional, 3 dimensional lattices. Mathieu's equation. Matrices and propagation of waves along an electric line. Continuous electric lines. 131 illustrations. Bibliography. Index. xii + 253pp. 5⅜ x 8.
S34 Paperbound **$1.85**

THEORY OF VIBRATIONS, N. W. McLachlan. Based on an exceptionally successful graduate course given at Brown University, this discusses linear systems having 1 degree of freedom, forced vibrations of simple linear systems, vibration of flexible strings, transverse vibrations of bars and tubes, transverse vibration of circular plate, sound waves of finite amplitude, etc. Index. 99 diagrams. 160pp. 5⅜ x 8. S190 Paperbound **$1.35**

LOUD SPEAKERS: THEORY, PERFORMANCE, TESTING AND DESIGN, N. W. McLachlan. Most comprehensive coverage of theory, practice of loud speaker design, testing; classic reference, study manual in field. First 12 chapters deal with theory, for readers mainly concerned with math. aspects; last 7 chapters will interest reader concerned with testing, design. Partial contents: principles of sound propagation, fluid pressure on vibrators, theory of moving-coil principle, transients, driving mechanisms, response curves, design of horn type moving coil speakers, electrostatic speakers, much more. Appendix. Bibliography. Index. 165 illustrations, charts. 411pp. 5⅜ x 8. S588 Paperbound **$2.25**

MICROWAVE TRANSMISSION, J. S. Slater. First text dealing exclusively with microwaves, brings together points of view of field, circuit theory, for graduate student in physics, electrical engineering, microwave technician. Offers valuable point of view not in most later studies. Uses Maxwell's equations to study electromagnetic field, important in this area. Partial contents: infinite line with distributed parameters, impedance of terminated line, plane waves, reflections, wave guides, coaxial line, composite transmission lines, impedance matching, etc. Introduction. Index. 76 illus. 319pp. 5⅜ x 8.
S564 Paperbound **$1.50**

THE ANALYSIS OF SENSATIONS, Ernst Mach. Great study of physiology, psychology of perception, shows Mach's ability to see material freshly, his "incorruptible skepticism and independence." (Einstein). Relation of problems of psychological perception to classical physics, supposed dualism of physical and mental, principle of continuity, evolution of senses, will as organic manifestation, scores of experiments, observations in optics, acoustics, music, graphics, etc. New introduction by T. S. Szasz, M. D. 58 illus. 300-item bibliography. Index. 404pp. 5⅜ x 8. S525 Paperbound **$1.75**

APPLIED OPTICS AND OPTICAL DESIGN, A. E. Conrady. With publication of vol. 2, standard work for designers in optics is now complete for first time. Only work of its kind in English; only detailed work for practical designer and self-taught. Requires, for bulk of work, no math above trig. Step-by-step exposition, from fundamental concepts of geometrical, physical optics, to systematic study, design, of almost all types of optical systems. Vol. 1: all ordinary ray-tracing methods; primary aberrations; necessary higher aberration for design of telescopes, low-power microscopes, photographic equipment. Vol. 2: (Completed from author's notes by R. Kingslake, Dir. Optical Design, Eastman Kodak.) Special attention to high-power microscope, anastigmatic photographic objectives. "An indispensable work," J., Optical Soc. of Amer. "As a practical guide this book has no rival," Transactions, Optical Soc. Index. Bibliography. 193 diagrams. 852pp. 6⅛ x 9¼. Vol. 1 T611 Paperbound **$2.95**
Vol. 2 T612 Paperbound **$2.95**

THE THEORY OF OPTICS, Paul Drude. One of finest fundamental texts in physical optics, classic offers thorough coverage, complete mathematical treatment of basic ideas. Includes fullest treatment of application of thermodynamics to optics; sine law in formation of images, transparent crystals, magnetically active substances, velocity of light, apertures, effects depending upon them, polarization, optical instruments, etc. Introduction by A. A. Michelson. Index. 110 illus. 567pp. 5⅜ x 8. S532 Paperbound **$2.45**

OPTICKS, Sir Isaac Newton. In its discussions of light, reflection, color, refraction, theories of wave and corpuscular theories of light, this work is packed with scores of insights and discoveries. In its precise and practical discussion of construction of optical apparatus, contemporary understandings of phenomena it is truly fascinating to modern physicists, astronomers, mathematicians. Foreword by Albert Einstein. Preface by I. B. Cohen of Harvard University. 7 pages of portraits, facsimile pages, letters, etc. cxvi + 414pp. 5⅜ x 8. S205 Paperbound **$2.00**

OPTICS AND OPTICAL INSTRUMENTS: AN INTRODUCTION WITH SPECIAL REFERENCE TO PRACTICAL APPLICATIONS, B. K. Johnson. An invaluable guide to basic practical applications of optical principles, which shows how to set up inexpensive working models of each of the four main types of optical instruments—telescopes, microscopes, photographic lenses, optical projecting systems. Explains in detail the most important experiments for determining their accuracy, resolving power, angular field of view, amounts of aberration, all other necessary facts about the instruments. Formerly "Practical Optics." Index. 234 diagrams. Appendix. 224pp. 5⅜ x 8. S642 Paperbound **$1.65**

PRINCIPLES OF PHYSICAL OPTICS, Ernst Mach. This classical examination of the propagation of light, color, polarization, etc. offers an historical and philosophical treatment that has never been surpassed for breadth and easy readability. Contents: Rectilinear propagation of light. Reflection, refraction. Early knowledge of vision. Dioptrics. Composition of light. Theory of color and dispersion. Periodicity. Theory of interference. Polarization. Mathematical representation of properties of light. Propagation of waves, etc. 279 illustrations, 10 portraits. Appendix. Indexes. 324pp. 5⅜ x 8. S178 Paperbound **$1.75**

FUNDAMENTALS OF ELECTRICITY AND MAGNETISM, L. B. Loeb. For students of physics, chemistry, or engineering who want an introduction to electricity and magnetism on a higher level and in more detail than general elementary physics texts provide. Only elementary differential and integral calculus is assumed. Physical laws developed logically, from magnetism to electric currents, Ohm's law, electrolysis, and on to static electricity, induction, etc. Covers an unusual amount of material; one third of book on modern material: solution of wave equation, photoelectric and thermionic effects, etc. Complete statement of the various electrical systems of units and interrelations. 2 Indexes. 75 pages of problems with answers stated. Over 300 figures and diagrams. xix +669pp. 5⅜ x 8. S745 Paperbound **$2.75**

THE ELECTROMAGNETIC FIELD, Max Mason & Warren Weaver. Used constantly by graduate engineers. Vector methods exclusively: detailed treatment of electrostatics, expansion methods, with tables converting any quantity into absolute electromagnetic, absolute electrostatic, practical units. Discrete charges, ponderable bodies, Maxwell field equations, etc. Introduction. Indexes. 416pp. 5⅜ x 8. S185 Paperbound **$2.00**

ELECTRICAL THEORY ON THE GIORGI SYSTEM, P. Cornelius. A new clarification of the fundamental concepts of electricity and magnetism, advocating the convenient m.k.s. system of units that is steadily gaining followers in the sciences. Illustrating the use and effectiveness of his terminology with numerous applications to concrete technical problems, the author here expounds the famous Giorgi system of electrical physics. His lucid presentation and well-reasoned, cogent argument for the universal adoption of this system form one of the finest pieces of scientific exposition in recent years. 28 figures. Index. Conversion tables for translating earlier data into modern units. Translated from 3rd Dutch edition by L. J. Jolley. x + 187pp. 5½ x 8¾. S909 Clothbound **$6.00**

THEORY OF ELECTRONS AND ITS APPLICATION TO THE PHENOMENA OF LIGHT AND RADIANT HEAT, H. Lorentz. Lectures delivered at Columbia University by Nobel laureate Lorentz. Unabridged, they form a historical coverage of the theory of free electrons, motion, absorption of heat, Zeeman effect, propagation of light in molecular bodies, inverse Zeeman effect, optical phenomena in moving bodies, etc. 109 pages of notes explain the more advanced sections. Index. 9 figures. 352pp. 5⅜ x 8. S173 Paperbound **$1.85**

TREATISE ON ELECTRICITY AND MAGNETISM, James Clerk Maxwell. For more than 80 years a seemingly inexhaustible source of leads for physicists, mathematicians, engineers. Total of 1082pp. on such topics as Measurement of Quantities, Electrostatics, Elementary Mathematical Theory of Electricity, Electrical Work and Energy in a System of Conductors, General Theorems, Theory of Electrical Images, Electrolysis, Conduction, Polarization, Dielectrics, Resistance, etc. "The greatest mathematical physicist since Newton," Sir James Jeans. 3rd edition. 107 figures, 21 plates. 1082pp. 5⅜ x 8. S636-7, 2 volume set, paperbound **$4.00**

See also: **FUNDAMENTAL FORMULAS OF PHYSICS, D. H. Menzel; MATHEMATICAL ANALYSIS OF ELECTRICAL & OPTICAL WAVE MOTION, H. Bateman.**

Mechanics, dynamics, thermodynamics, elasticity

MECHANICS VIA THE CALCULUS, P. W. Norris, W. S. Legge. Covers almost everything, from linear motion to vector analysis: equations determining motion, linear methods, compounding of simple harmonic motions, Newton's laws of motion, Hooke's law, the simple pendulum, motion of a particle in 1 plane, centers of gravity, virtual work, friction, kinetic energy of rotating bodies, equilibrium of strings, hydrostatics, sheering stresses, elasticity, etc. 550 problems. 3rd revised edition. xii + 367pp. 6 x 9. S207 Clothbound **$3.95**

MECHANICS, J. P. Den Hartog. Already a classic among introductory texts, the M.I.T. professor's lively and discursive presentation is equally valuable as a beginner's text, an engineering student's refresher, or a practicing engineer's reference. Emphasis in this highly readable text is on illuminating fundamental principles and showing how they are embodied in a great number of real engineering and design problems: trusses, loaded cables, beams, jacks, hoists, etc. Provides advanced material on relative motion and gyroscopes not usual in introductory texts. "Very thoroughly recommended to all those anxious to improve their real understanding of the principles of mechanics." MECHANICAL WORLD. Index. List of equations. 334 problems, all with answers. Over 550 diagrams and drawings. ix + 462pp. 5⅜ x 8.
S754 Paperbound **$2.00**

THEORETICAL MECHANICS: AN INTRODUCTION TO MATHEMATICAL PHYSICS, J. S. Ames, F. D. Murnaghan. A mathematically rigorous development of theoretical mechanics for the advanced student, with constant practical applications. Used in hundreds of advanced courses. An unusually thorough coverage of gyroscopic and baryscopic material, detailed analyses of the Corilis acceleration, applications of Lagrange's equations, motion of the double pendulum, Hamilton-Jacobi partial differential equations, group velocity and dispersion, etc. Special relativity is also included. 159 problems. 44 figures. ix + 462pp. 5⅜ x 8.
S461 Paperbound **$2.00**

THEORETICAL MECHANICS: STATICS AND THE DYNAMICS OF A PARTICLE, W. D. MacMillan. Used for over 3 decades as a self-contained and extremely comprehensive advanced undergraduate text in mathematical physics, physics, astronomy, and deeper foundations of engineering. Early sections require only a knowledge of geometry; later, a working knowledge of calculus. Hundreds of basic problems, including projectiles to the moon, escape velocity, harmonic motion, ballistics, falling bodies, transmission of power, stress and strain, elasticity, astronomical problems. 340 practice problems plus many fully worked out examples make it possible to test and extend principles developed in the text. 200 figures. xvii + 430pp. 5⅜ x 8.
S467 Paperbound **$2.00**

THEORETICAL MECHANICS: THE THEORY OF THE POTENTIAL, W. D. MacMillan. A comprehensive, well balanced presentation of potential theory, serving both as an introduction and a reference work with regard to specific problems, for physicists and mathematicians. No prior knowledge of integral relations is assumed, and all mathematical material is developed as it becomes necessary. Includes: Attraction of Finite Bodies; Newtonian Potential Function; Vector Fields, Green and Gauss Theorems; Attractions of Surfaces and Lines; Surface Distribution of Matter; Two-Layer Surfaces; Spherical Harmonics; Ellipsoidal Harmonics; etc. "The great number of particular cases . . . should make the book valuable to geophysicists and others actively engaged in practical applications of the potential theory," Review of Scientific Instruments. Index. Bibliography. xiii + 469pp. 5⅜ x 8.
S486 Paperbound **$2.25**

THEORETICAL MECHANICS: DYNAMICS OF RIGID BODIES, W. D. MacMillan. Theory of dynamics of a rigid body is developed, using both the geometrical and analytical methods of instruction. Begins with exposition of algebra of vectors, it goes through momentum principles, motion in space, use of differential equations and infinite series to solve more sophisticated dynamics problems. Partial contents: moments of inertia, systems of free particles, motion parallel to a fixed plane, rolling motion, method of periodic solutions, much more. 82 figs. 199 problems. Bibliography. Indexes. xii + 476pp. 5⅜ x 8.
S641 Paperbound **$2.00**

MATHEMATICAL FOUNDATIONS OF STATISTICAL MECHANICS, A. I. Khinchin. Offering a precise and rigorous formulation of problems, this book supplies a thorough and up-to-date exposition. It provides analytical tools needed to replace cumbersome concepts, and furnishes for the first time a logical step-by-step introduction to the subject. Partial contents: geometry & kinematics of the phase space, ergodic problem, reduction to theory of probability, application of central limit problem, ideal monatomic gas, foundation of thermo-dynamics, dispersion and distribution of sum functions. Key to notations. Index. viii + 179pp. 5⅜ x 8.
S147 Paperbound **$1.35**

ELEMENTARY PRINCIPLES IN STATISTICAL MECHANICS, J. W. Gibbs. Last work of the great Yale mathematical physicist, still one of the most fundamental treatments available for advanced students and workers in the field. Covers the basic principle of conservation of probability of phase, theory of errors in the calculated phases of a system, the contributions of Clausius, Maxwell, Boltzmann, and Gibbs himself, and much more. Includes valuable comparison of statistical mechanics with thermodynamics: Carnot's cycle, mechanical definitions of entropy, etc. xvi + 208pp. 5⅜ x 8.
S707 Paperbound **$1.45**

THE DYNAMICS OF PARTICLES AND OF RIGID, ELASTIC, AND FLUID BODIES; BEING LECTURES ON MATHEMATICAL PHYSICS, A. G. Webster. The reissuing of this classic fills the need for a comprehensive work on dynamics. A wide range of topics is covered in unusually great depth, applying ordinary and partial differential equations. Part I considers laws of motion and methods applicable to systems of all sorts; oscillation, resonance, cyclic systems, etc. Part 2 is a detailed study of the dynamics of rigid bodies. Part 3 introduces the theory of potential; stress and strain, Newtonian potential functions, gyrostatics, wave and vortex motion, etc. Further contents: Kinematics of a point; Lagrange's equations; Hamilton's principle; Systems of vectors; Statics and dynamics of deformable bodies; much more, not easily found together in one volume. Unabridged reprinting of 2nd edition. 20 pages of notes on differential equations and the higher analysis. 203 illustrations. Selected bibliography. Index. xi + 588pp. 5⅜ x 8.
S522 Paperbound **$2.35**

A TREATISE ON DYNAMICS OF A PARTICLE, E. J. Routh. Elementary text on dynamics for beginning mathematics or physics student. Unusually detailed treatment from elementary definitions to motion in 3 dimensions, emphasizing concrete aspects. Much unique material important in recent applications. Covers impulsive forces, rectilinear and constrained motion in 2 dimensions, harmonic and parabolic motion, degrees of freedom, closed orbits, the conical pendulum, the principle of least action, Jacobi's method, and much more. Index. 559 problems, many fully worked out, incorporated into text. xiii + 418pp. 5⅜ x 8.
S696 Paperbound **$2.25**

DYNAMICS OF A SYSTEM OF RIGID BODIES (Elementary Section), E. J. Routh. Revised 7th edition of this standard reference. This volume covers the dynamical principles of the subject, and its more elementary applications: finding moments of inertia by integration, foci of inertia, d'Alembert's principle, impulsive forces, motion in 2 and 3 dimensions, Lagrange's equations, relative indicatrix, Euler's theorem, large tautochronous motions, etc. Index. 55 figures. Scores of problems. xv + 443pp. 5⅜ x 8. S664 Paperbound **$2.35**

DYNAMICS OF A SYSTEM OF RIGID BODIES (Advanced Section), E. J. Routh. Revised 6th edition of a classic reference aid. Much of its material remains unique. Partial contents: moving axes, relative motion, oscillations about equilibrium, motion. Motion of a body under no forces, any forces. Nature of motion given by linear equations and conditions of stability. Free, forced vibrations, constants of integration, calculus of finite differences, variations, precession and nutation, motion of the moon, motion of string, chain, membranes. 64 figures. 498pp. 5⅜ x 8.
S229 Paperbound **$2.35**

DYNAMICAL THEORY OF GASES, James Jeans. Divided into mathematical and physical chapters for the convenience of those not expert in mathematics, this volume discusses the mathematical theory of gas in a steady state, thermodynamics, Boltzmann and Maxwell, kinetic theory, quantum theory, exponentials, etc. 4th enlarged edition, with new material on quantum theory, quantum dynamics, etc. Indexes. 28 figures. 444pp. 6⅛ x 9¼.
S136 Paperbound **$2.45**

FOUNDATIONS OF POTENTIAL THEORY, O. D. Kellogg. Based on courses given at Harvard this is suitable for both advanced and beginning mathematicians. Proofs are rigorous, and much material not generally avialable elsewhere is included. Partial contents: forces of gravity, fields of force, divergence theorem, properties of Newtonian potentials at points of free space, potentials as solutions of Laplace's equations, harmonic functions, electrostatics, electric images, logarithmic potential, etc. One of Grundlehren Series. ix + 384pp. 5⅜ x 8.
S144 Paperbound **$1.98**

THERMODYNAMICS, Enrico Fermi. Unabridged reproduction of 1937 edition. Elementary in treatment; remarkable for clarity, organization. Requires no knowledge of advanced math beyond calculus, only familiarity with fundamentals of thermometry, calorimetry. Partial Contents: Thermodynamic systems; First & Second laws of thermodynamics; Entropy; Thermodynamic potentials: phase rule, reversible electric cell; Gaseous reactions: van't Hoff reaction box, principle of LeChatelier; Thermodynamics of dilute solutions: osmotic & vapor pressures, boiling & freezing points; Entropy constant. Index. 25 problems. 24 illustrations. x + 160pp. 5⅜ x 8.
S361 Paperbound **$1.75**

THE THERMODYNAMICS OF ELECTRICAL PHENOMENA IN METALS and A CONDENSED COLLECTION OF THERMODYNAMIC FORMULAS, P. W. Bridgman. Major work by the Nobel Prizewinner: stimulating conceptual introduction to aspects of the electron theory of metals, giving an intuitive understanding of fundamental relationships concealed by the formal systems of Onsager and others. Elementary mathematical formulations show clearly the fundamental thermodynamical relationships of the electric field, and a complete phenomenological theory of metals is created. This is the work in which Bridgman announced his famous "thermomotive force" and his distinction between "driving" and "working" electromotive force. We have added in this Dover edition the author's long unavailable tables of thermodynamic formulas, extremely valuable for the speed of reference they allow. Two works bound as one. Index. 33 figures. Bibliography. xviii + 256pp. 5⅜ x 8. S723 Paperbound **$1.65**

REFLECTIONS ON THE MOTIVE POWER OF FIRE, by Sadi Carnot, and other papers on the 2nd law of thermodynamics by E. Clapeyron and R. Clausius. Carnot's "Reflections" laid the groundwork of modern thermodynamics. Its non-technical, mostly verbal statements examine the relations between heat and the work done by heat in engines, establishing conditions for the economical working of these engines. The papers by Clapeyron and Clausius here reprinted added further refinements to Carnot's work, and led to its final acceptance by physicists. Selections from posthumous manuscripts of Carnot are also included. All papers in English. New introduction by E. Mendoza. 12 illustrations. xxii + 152pp. 5⅜ x 8.
S661 Paperbound **$1.50**

TREATISE ON THERMODYNAMICS, Max Planck. Based on Planck's original papers this offers a uniform point of view for the entire field and has been used as an introduction for students who have studied elementary chemistry, physics, and calculus. Rejecting the earlier approaches of Helmholtz and Maxwell, the author makes no assumptions regarding the nature of heat, but begins with a few empirical facts, and from these deduces new physical and chemical laws. 3rd English edition of this standard text by a Nobel laureate. xvi + 297pp. 5⅜ x 8.
S219 Paperbound **$1.75**

THE THEORY OF HEAT RADIATION, Max Planck. A pioneering work in thermodynamics, providing basis for most later work. Nobel Laureate Planck writes on Deductions from Electrodynamics and Thermodynamics, Entropy and Probability, Irreversible Radiation Processes, etc. Starts with simple experimental laws of optics, advances to problems of spectral distribution of energy and irreversibility. Bibliography. 7 illustrations, xiv + 224pp. 5⅜ x 8.
S546 Paperbound **$1.50**

A HISTORY OF THE THEORY OF ELASTICITY AND THE STRENGTH OF MATERIALS, I. Todhunter and K. Pearson. For over 60 years a basic reference, unsurpassed in scope or authority. Both a history of the mathematical theory of elasticity from Galileo, Hooke, and Mariotte to Saint Venant, Kirchhoff, Clebsch, and Lord Kelvin and a detailed presentation of every important mathematical contribution during this period. Presents proofs of thousands of theorems and laws, summarizes every relevant treatise, many unavailable elsewhere. Practically a book apiece is devoted to modern founders: Saint Venant, Lame, Boussinesq, Rankine, Lord Kelvin, F. Neumann, Kirchhoff, Clebsch. Hundreds of pages of technical and physical treatises on specific applications of elasticity to particular materials. Indispensable for the mathematician, physicist, or engineer working with elasticity. Unabridged, corrected reprint of original 3-volume 1886-1893 edition. Three volume set. Two indexes. Appendix to Vol. I. Total of 2344pp. 5⅜ x 8⅜.
S914–916 The set, Clothbound **$12.50**

THE MATHEMATICAL THEORY OF ELASTICITY, A. E. H. Love. A wealth of practical illustration combined with thorough discussion of fundamentals—theory, application, special problems and solutions. Partial Contents: Analysis of Strain & Stress, Elasticity of Solid Bodies, Elasticity of Crystals, Vibration of Spheres, Cylinders, Propagation of Waves in Elastic Solid Media, Torsion, Theory of Continuous Beams, Plates. Rigorous treatment of Volterra's theory of dislocations, 2-dimensional elastic systems, other topics of modern interest. "For years the standard treatise on elasticity," AMERICAN MATHEMATICAL MONTHLY. 4th revised edition. Index. 76 figures. xviii + 643pp. 6⅛ x 9¼.
S174 Paperbound **$2.95**

RAYLEIGH'S PRINCIPLE AND ITS APPLICATIONS TO ENGINEERING, G. Temple & W. Bickley. Rayleigh's principle developed to provide upper and lower estimates of true value of fundamental period of a vibrating system, or condition of stability of elastic systems. Illustrative examples; rigorous proofs in special chapters. Partial contents: Energy method of discussing vibrations, stability. Perturbation theory, whirling of uniform shafts. Criteria of elastic stability. Application of energy method. Vibrating systems. Proof, accuracy, successive approximations, application of Rayleigh's principle. Synthetic theorems. Numerical, graphical methods. Equilibrium configurations, Ritz's method. Bibliography. Index. 22 figures. ix + 156pp. 5⅜ x 8.
S307 Paperbound **$1.50**

INVESTIGATIONS ON THE THEORY OF THE BROWNIAN MOVEMENT, Albert Einstein. Reprints from rare European journals. 5 basic papers, including the Elementary Theory of the Brownian Movement, written at the request of Lorentz to provide a simple explanation. Translated by A. D. Cowper. Annotated, edited by R. Fürth. 33pp. of notes elucidate, give history of previous investigations. Author, subject indexes. 62 footnotes. 124pp. 5⅜ x 8.
S304 Paperbound **$1.25**

See also: **FUNDAMENTAL FORMULAS OF PHYSICS, D. H. Menzel.**

ENGINEERING

THEORY OF FLIGHT, Richard von Mises. Remains almost unsurpassed as balanced, well-written account of fundamental fluid dynamics, and situations in which air compressibility effects are unimportant. Stressing equally theory and practice, avoiding formidable mathematical structure, it conveys a full understanding of physical phenomena and mathematical concepts. Contains perhaps the best introduction to general theory of stability. "Outstanding," Scientific, Medical, and Technical Books. New introduction by K. H. Hohenemser. Bibliographical, historical notes. Index. 408 illustrations. xvi + 620pp. 5⅜ x 8⅜. S541 Paperbound **$2.85**

THEORY OF WING SECTIONS, I. H. Abbott, A. E. von Doenhoff. Concise compilation of subsonic aerodynamic characteristics of modern NASA wing sections, with description of their geometry, associated theory. Primarily reference work for engineers, students, it gives methods, data for using wing-section data to predict characteristics. Particularly valuable: chapters on thin wings, airfoils; complete summary of NACA's experimental observations, system of construction families of airfoils. 350pp. of tables on Basic Thickness Forms, Mean Lines, Airfoil Ordinates, Aerodynamic Characteristics of Wing Sections. Index. Bibliography. 191 illustrations. Appendix. 705pp. 5⅜ x 8. S558 Paperbound **$2.95**

SUPERSONIC AERODYNAMICS, E. R. C. Miles. Valuable theoretical introduction to the supersonic domain, with emphasis on mathematical tools and principles, for practicing aerodynamicists and advanced students in aeronautical engineering. Covers fundamental theory, divergence theorem and principles of circulation, compressible flow and Helmholtz laws, the Prandtl-Busemann graphic method for 2-dimensional flow, oblique shock waves, the Taylor-Maccoll method for cones in supersonic flow, the Chaplygin method for 2-dimensional flow, etc. Problems range from practical engineering problems to development of theoretical results. "Rendered outstanding by the unprecedented scope of its contents . . . has undoubtedly filled a vital gap," AERONAUTICAL ENGINEERING REVIEW. Index. 173 problems, answers. 106 diagrams. 7 tables. xii + 255pp. 5⅜ x 8.
S214 Paperbound **$1.45**

WEIGHT-STRENGTH ANALYSIS OF AIRCRAFT STRUCTURES, F. R. Shanley. Scientifically sound methods of analyzing and predicting the structural weight of aircraft and missiles. Deals directly with forces and the distances over which they must be transmitted, making it possible to develop methods by which the minimum structural weight can be determined for any material and conditions of loading. Weight equations for wing and fuselage structures. Includes author's original papers on inelastic buckling and creep buckling. "Particularly successful in presenting his analytical methods for investigating various optimum design principles," AERONAUTICAL ENGINEERING REVIEW. Enlarged bibliography. Index. 199 figures. xiv + 404pp. 5⅝ x 8⅜. S660 Paperbound **$2.45**

INTRODUCTION TO THE STATISTICAL DYNAMICS OF AUTOMATIC CONTROL SYSTEMS, V. V. Solodovnikov. First English publication of text-reference covering important branch of automatic control systems—random signals; in its original edition, this was the first comprehensive treatment. Examines frequency characteristics, transfer functions, stationary random processes, determination of minimum mean-squared error, of transfer function for a finite period of observation, much more. Translation edited by J. B. Thomas, L. A. Zadeh. Index. Bibliography. Appendix. xxii + 308pp. 5⅜ x 8. S420 Paperbound **$2.25**

TENSORS FOR CIRCUITS, Gabriel Kron. A boldly original method of analysing engineering problems, at center of sharp discussion since first introduced, now definitely proved useful in such areas as electrical and structural networks on automatic computers. Encompasses a great variety of specific problems by means of a relatively few symbolic equations. "Power and flexibility . . . becoming more widely recognized," Nature. Formerly "A Short Course in Tensor Analysis." New introduction by B. Hoffmann. Index. Over 800 diagrams. xix + 250pp. 5⅜ x 8. S534 Paperbound **$1.85**

DESIGN AND USE OF INSTRUMENTS AND ACCURATE MECHANISM, T. N. Whitehead. For the instrument designer, engineer; how to combine necessary mathematical abstractions with independent observation of actual facts. Partial contents: instruments & their parts, theory of errors, systematic errors, probability, short period errors, erratic errors, design precision, kinematic, semikinematic design, stiffness, planning of an instrument, human factor, etc. Index. 85 photos, diagrams. xii + 288pp. 5⅜ x 8. S270 Paperbound **$1.95**

APPLIED ELASTICITY, J. Prescott. Provides the engineer with the theory of elasticity usually lacking in books on strength of materials, yet concentrates on those portions useful for immediate application. Develops every important type of elasticity problem from theoretical principles. Covers analysis of stress, relations between stress and strain, the empirical basis of elasticity, thin rods under tension or thrust, Saint Venant's theory, transverse oscillations of thin rods, stability of thin plates, cylinders with thin walls, vibrations of rotating disks, elastic bodies in contact, etc. "Excellent and important contribution to the subject, not merely in the old matter which he has presented in new and refreshing form, but also in the many original investigations here published for the first time," NATURE. Index. 3 Appendixes. vi + 672pp. 5⅜ x 8. S726 Paperbound **$2.95**

STRENGTH OF MATERIALS, J. P. Den Hartog. Distinguished text prepared for M.I.T. course, ideal as introduction, refresher, reference, or self-study text. Full clear treatment of elementary material (tension, torsion, bending, compound stresses, deflection of beams, etc.), plus much advanced material on engineering methods of great practical value: full treatment of the Mohr circle, lucid elementary discussions of the theory of the center of shear and the "Myosotis" method of calculating beam deflections, reinforced concrete, plastic deformations, photoelasticity, etc. In all sections, both general principles and concrete applications are given. Index. 186 figures (160 others in problem section). 350 problems, all with answers. List of formulas. viii + 323pp. 5⅜ x 8. S755 Paperbound **$1.95**

PHOTOELASTICITY: PRINCIPLES AND METHODS, H. T. Jessop, F. C. Harris. For the engineer, for specific problems of stress analysis. Latest time-saving methods of checking calculations in 2-dimensional design problems, new techniques for stresses in 3 dimensions, and lucid description of optical systems used in practical photoelasticity. Useful suggestions and hints based on on-the-job experience included. Partial contents: strained and stress-strain relations, circular disc under thrust along diameter, rectangular block with square hole under vertical thrust, simply supported rectangular beam under central concentrated load, etc. Theory held to minimum, no advanced mathematical training needed. Index. 164 illustrations. viii + 184pp. 6⅛ x 9¼. S137 Clothbound **$3.75**

MECHANICS OF THE GYROSCOPE, THE DYNAMICS OF ROTATION, R. F. Deimel, Professor of Mechanical Engineering at Stevens Institute of Technology. Elementary general treatment of dynamics of rotation, with special application of gyroscopic phenomena. No knowledge of vectors needed. Velocity of a moving curve, acceleration to a point, general equations of motion, gyroscopic horizon, free gyro, motion of discs, the damped gyro, 103 similar topics. Exercises. 75 figures. 208pp. 5⅜ x 8. S66 Paperbound **$1.65**
S144 Paperbound **$1.98**

A TREATISE ON GYROSTATICS AND ROTATIONAL MOTION: THEORY AND APPLICATIONS, Andrew Gray. Most detailed, thorough book in English, generally considered definitive study. Many problems of all sorts in full detail, or step-by-step summary. Classical problems of Bour, Lottner, etc.; later ones of great physical interest. Vibrating systems of gyrostats, earth as a top, calculation of path of axis of a top by elliptic integrals, motion of unsymmetrical top, much more. Index. 160 illus. 550pp. 5⅜ x 8. S589 Paperbound **$2.75**

K. Pearson; THEORY AND OPERATION OF THE SLIDE RULE, J. P. Ellis; DIFFERENTIAL EQUATIONS FOR ENGINEERS, P. Franklin; MATHEMATICAL METHODS FOR SCIENTISTS AND ENGINEERS, L. P. Smith; APPLIED MATHEMATICS FOR RADIO AND COMMUNICATIONS ENGINEERS, C. E. Smith; MATHEMATICS OF MODERN ENGINEERING, E. G. Keller, R. E. Doherty; THEORY OF FUNCTIONS AS APPLIED TO ENGINEERING PROBLEMS, R. Rothe, F. Ollendorff, K. Pohlhausen.

CHEMISTRY AND PHYSICAL CHEMISTRY

ORGANIC CHEMISTRY, F. C. Whitmore. The entire subject of organic chemistry for the practicing chemist and the advanced student. Storehouse of facts, theories, processes found elsewhere only in specialized journals. Covers aliphatic compounds (500 pages on the properties and synthetic preparation of hydrocarbons, halides, proteins, ketones, etc.), alicyclic compounds, aromatic compounds, heterocyclic compounds, organophosphorus and organometallic compounds. Methods of synthetic preparation analyzed critically throughout. Includes much of biochemical interest. "The scope of this volume is astonishing," INDUSTRIAL AND ENGINEERING CHEMISTRY. 12,000-reference index. 2387-item bibliography. Total of x + 1005pp. 5⅜ x 8. Two volume set. S700 Vol I Paperbound **$2.00**
S701 Vol II Paperbound **$2.00**
The set **$4.00**

THE PRINCIPLES OF ELECTROCHEMISTRY, D. A. MacInnes. Basic equations for almost every subfield of electrochemistry from first principles, referring at all times to the soundest and most recent theories and results; unusually useful as text or as reference. Covers coulometers and Faraday's Law, electrolytic conductance, the Debye-Hueckel method for the theoretical calculation of activity coefficients, concentration cells, standard electrode potentials, thermodynamic ionization constants, pH, potentiometric titrations, irreversible phenomena, Planck's equation, and much more. "Excellent treatise," AMERICAN CHEMICAL SOCIETY JOURNAL. "Highly recommended," CHEMICAL AND METALLURGICAL ENGINEERING. 2 Indices. Appendix. 585-item bibliography. 137 figures. 94 tables. ii + 478pp. 5⅝ x 8⅜.
S52 Paperbound **$2.35**

THE CHEMISTRY OF URANIUM: THE ELEMENT, ITS BINARY AND RELATED COMPOUNDS, J. J. Katz and E. Rabinowitch. Vast post-World War II collection and correlation of thousands of AEC reports and published papers in a useful and easily accessible form, still the most complete and up-to-date compilation. Treats "dry uranium chemistry," occurrences, preparation, properties, simple compounds, isotopic composition, extraction from ores, spectra, alloys, etc. Much material available only here. Index. Thousands of evaluated bibliographical references. 324 tables, charts, figures. xxi + 609pp. 5⅜ x 8. S757 Paperbound **$2.95**

KINETIC THEORY OF LIQUIDS, J. Frenkel. Regarding the kinetic theory of liquids as a generalization and extension of the theory of solid bodies, this volume covers all types of arrangements of solids, thermal displacements of atoms, interstitial atoms and ions, orientational and rotational motion of molecules, and transition between states of matter. Mathematical theory is developed close to the physical subject matter. 216 bibliographical footnotes. 55 figures. xi + 485pp. 5⅜ x 8. S94 Clothbound **$3.95**
S95 Paperbound **$2.45**

POLAR MOLECULES, Pieter Debye. This work by Nobel laureate Debye offers a complete guide to fundamental electrostatic field relations, polarizability, molecular structure. Partial contents: electric intensity, displacement and force, polarization by orientation, molar polarization and molar refraction, halogen-hydrides, polar liquids, ionic saturation, dielectric constant, etc. Special chapter considers quantum theory. Indexed. 172pp. 5⅜ x 8.
S64 Paperbound **$1.50**

ELASTICITY, PLASTICITY AND STRUCTURE OF MATTER, R. Houwink. Standard treatise on rheological aspects of different technically important solids such as crystals, resins, textiles, rubber, clay, many others. Investigates general laws for deformations; determines divergences from these laws for certain substances. Covers general physical and mathematical aspects of plasticity, elasticity, viscosity. Detailed examination of deformations, internal structure of matter in relation to elastic and plastic behavior, formation of solid matter from a fluid, conditions for elastic and plastic behavior of matter. Treats glass, asphalt, gutta percha, balata, proteins, baker's dough, lacquers, sulphur, others. 2nd revised, enlarged edition. Extensive revised bibliography in over 500 footnotes. Index. Table of symbols. 214 figures. xviii + 368pp. 6 x 9¼. S385 Paperbound **$2.45**

THE PHASE RULE AND ITS APPLICATION, Alexander Findlay. Covering chemical phenomena of 1, 2, 3, 4, and multiple component systems, this "standard work on the subject" (NATURE, London), has been completely revised and brought up to date by A. N. Campbell and N. O. Smith. Brand new material has been added on such matters as binary, tertiary liquid equilibria, solid solutions in ternary systems, quinary systems of salts and water Completely revised to triangular coordinates in ternary systems, clarified graphic representation, solid models, etc. 9th revised edition. Author, subject indexes. 236 figures. 505 footnotes, mostly bibliographic. xii + 494pp. 5⅜ x 8. S91 Paperbound **$2.45**

TERNARY SYSTEMS: INTRODUCTION TO THE THEORY OF THREE COMPONENT SYSTEMS, G. Masing. Furnishes detailed discussion of representative types of 3-components systems, both in solid models (particularly metallic alloys) and isothermal models. Discusses mechanical mixture without compounds and without solid solutions; unbroken solid solution series; solid solutions with solubility breaks in two binary systems; iron-silicon-aluminum alloys; allotropic forms of iron in ternary system; other topics. Bibliography. Index. 166 illustrations. 178pp. 5⅜ x 8⅜. S631 Paperbound **$1.45**

THE STORY OF ALCHEMY AND EARLY CHEMISTRY, J. M. Stillman. An authoritative, scholarly work, highly readable, of development of chemical knowledge from 4000 B.C. to downfall of phlogiston theory in late 18th century. Every important figure, many quotations. Brings alive curious, almost incredible history of alchemical beliefs, practices, writings of Arabian Prince Oneeyade, Vincent of Beauvais, Geber, Zosimos, Paracelsus, Vitruvius, scores more. Studies work, thought of Black, Cavendish, Priestley, Van Helmont, Bergman, Lavoisier, Newton, etc. Index. Bibliography. 579pp. 5⅜ x 8. S628 Paperbound **$2.45**

See also: **ATOMIC SPECTRA AND ATOMIC STRUCTURE, G. Herzberg; INVESTIGATIONS ON THE THEORY OF THE BROWNIAN MOVEMENT, A. Einstein; TREATISE ON THERMODYNAMICS, M. Planck.**

ASTRONOMY AND ASTROPHYSICS

AN ELEMENTARY SURVEY OF CELESTIAL MECHANICS, Y. Ryabov. Elementary exposition of gravitational theory and celestial mechanics. Historical introduction and coverage of basic principles, including: the elliptic, the orbital plane, the 2- and 3-body problems, the discovery of Neptune, planetary rotation, the length of the day, the shapes of galaxies, satellites (detailed treatment of Sputnik I), etc. First American reprinting of successful Russian popular exposition. Elementary algebra and trigonometry helpful, but not necessary; presentation chiefly verbal. Appendix of theorem proofs. 58 figures. 165pp. 5⅜ x 8. T756 Paperbound **$1.25**

THE SKY AND ITS MYSTERIES, E. A. Beet. One of most lucid books on mysteries of universe; deals with astronomy from earliest observations to latest theories of expansion of universe, source of stellar energy, birth of planets, origin of moon craters, possibility of life on other planets. Discusses effects of sunspots on weather; distances, ages of several stars; master plan of universe; methods and tools of astronomers; much more. "Eminently readable book," London Times. Extensive bibliography. Over 50 diagrams. 12 full-page plates, fold-out star map. Introduction. Index, 238pp. 5¼ x 7½. T627 Clothbound **$3.00**

THE REALM OF THE NEBULAE, E. Hubble. One of the great astronomers of our time records his formulation of the concept of "island universes," and its impact on astronomy. Such topics are covered as the velocity-distance relation; classification, nature, distances, general field of nebulae; cosmological theories; nebulae in the neighborhood of the Milky Way. 39 photos of nebulae, nebulae clusters, spectra of nebulae, and velocity distance relations shown by spectrum comparison. "One of the most progressive lines of astronomical research," The Times (London). New introduction by A. Sandage. 55 illustrations. Index. iv + 201pp. 5⅜ x 8. S455 Paperbound **$1.50**

OUT OF THE SKY, H. H. Nininger. A non-technical but comprehensive introduction to "meteoritics", the young science concerned with all aspects of the arrival of matter from outer space. Written by one of the world's experts on meteorites, this work shows how, despite difficulties of observation and sparseness of data, a considerable body of knowledge has arisen. It defines meteors and meteorites; studies fireball clusters and processions, meteorite composition, size, distribution, showers, explosions, origins, craters, and much more. A true connecting link between astronomy and geology. More than 175 photos, 22 other illustrations. References. Bibliography of author's publications on meteorites. Index. viii + 336pp. 5⅜ x 8. T519 Paperbound **$1.85**

SATELLITES AND SCIENTIFIC RESEARCH, D. King-Hele. Non-technical account of the manmade satellites and the discoveries they have yielded up to the spring of 1959. Brings together information hitherto published only in hard-to-get scientific journals. Includes the life history of a typical satellite, methods of tracking, new information on the shape of the earth, zones of radiation, etc. Over 60 diagrams and 6 photographs. Mathematical appendix. Bibliography of over 100 items. Index. xii + 180pp. 5⅜ x 8½. T703 Clothbound **$4.00**

HOW TO MAKE A TELESCOPE, Jean Texereau. Enables the most inexperienced to choose, design, and build an f/6 or f/8 Newtonian type reflecting telescope, with an altazimuth Couder mounting, suitable for lunar, planetary, and stellar observation. A practical step-by-step course covering every operation and every piece of equipment. Basic principles of geometric and physical optics are discussed (though unnecessary to construction), and the merits of reflectors and refractors compared. A thorough discussion of eyepieces, finders, grinding, installation, testing, using the instrument, etc. 241 figures and 38 photos show almost every operation and tool. Potential errors are anticipated as much as possible. Foreword by A. Couder. Bibliography and sources of supply listing. Index. xiii + 191pp. 6¼ x 10. T464 Clothbound **$3.50**

AN INTRODUCTORY TREATISE ON DYNAMICAL ASTRONOMY, H. C. Plummer. Unusually wide connected and concise coverage of nearly every significant branch of dynamical astronomy, stressing basic principles throughout: determination of orbits, planetary theory, lunar theory, precession and nutation, and many of their applications. Hundreds of formulas and theorems worked out completely, important methods thoroughly explained. Covers motion under a central attraction, orbits of double stars and spectroscopic binaries, the libration of the moon, and much more. Index. 8 diagrams. xxi + 343pp. 5⅝ x 8⅜. S689 Paperbound **$2.35**

A COMPENDIUM OF SPHERICAL ASTRONOMY, S. Newcomb. Long a standard collection of basic methods and formulas most useful to the working astronomer, and clear full text for students. Includes the most important common approximations; 40 pages on the method of least squares; general theory of spherical coordinates; parallax; aberration; astronomical refraction; theory of precession; proper motion of the stars; methods of deriving positions of stars; and much more. Index. 9 Appendices of tables, formulas, etc. 36 figures. xviii + 444pp. 5⅜ x 8.
S690 Paperbound **$2.25**

AN INTRODUCTORY TREATISE ON THE LUNAR THEORY, E. W. Brown. Indispensable for all scientists and engineers interested in orbital calculation, satellites, or navigation of space. Only work in English to explain in detail 5 major mathematical approaches to the problem of 3 bodies, those of Laplace, de Pontécoulant, Hansen, Delaunay, and Hill. Covers expressions for mutual attraction, equations of motion, forms of solution, variations of the elements in disturbed motion, the constants and their interpretations, planetary and other disturbing influences, etc. Index. Bibliography. Tables. xvi + 292pp. 5⅝ x 8⅜.
S666 Paperbound **$2.00**

LES METHODES NOUVELLES DE LA MECANIQUE CELESTE, H. Poincaré. Complete text (in French) of one of Poincaré's most important works. This set revolutionized celestial mechanics: first use of integral invariants, first major application of linear differential equations, study of periodic orbits, lunar motion and Jupiter's satellites, three body problem, and many other important topics. "Started a new era . . . so extremely modern that even today few have mastered his weapons," E. T. Bell. Three volumes. Total 1282pp. 6⅛ x 9¼.
Vol. 1. S401 Paperbound **$2.75**
Vol. 2. S402 Paperbound **$2.75**
Vol. 3. S403 Paperbound **$2.75**
The set **$7.50**

SPHERICAL AND PRACTICAL ASTRONOMY, W. Chauvenet. First book in English to apply mathematical techniques to astronomical problems is still standard work. Covers almost entire field, rigorously, with over 300 examples worked out. Vol. 1, spherical astronomy, applications to nautical astronomy; determination of hour angles, parallactic angle for known stars; interpolation; parallax; laws of refraction; predicting eclipses; precession, nutation of fixed stars; etc. Vol. 2, theory, use, of instruments; telescope; measurement of arcs, angles in general; electro-chronograph; sextant, reflecting circles; zenith telescope; etc. 100-page appendix of detailed proof of Gauss' method of least squares. 5th revised edition. Index. 15 plates, 20 tables. 1340pp. 5⅜ x 8. Vol. 1 S618 Paperbound **$2.75**
Vol. 2 S619 Paperbound **$2.75**
The set **$5.50**

THE INTERNAL CONSTITUTION OF THE STARS, Sir A. S. Eddington. Influence of this has been enormous; first detailed exposition of theory of radiative equilibrium for stellar interiors, of all available evidence for existence of diffuse matter in interstellar space. Studies quantum theory, polytropic gas spheres, mass-luminosity relations, variable stars, etc. Discussions of equations paralleled with informal exposition of intimate relationship of astrophysics with great discoveries in atomic physics, radiation. Introduction. Appendix. Index. 421pp. 5⅜ x 8.
S563 Paperbound **$2.25**

ASTRONOMY OF STELLAR ENERGY AND DECAY, Martin Johnson. Middle level treatment of astronomy as interpreted by modern atomic physics. Part One is non-technical, examines physical properties, source of energy, spectroscopy, fluctuating stars, various models and theories, etc. Part Two parallels these topics, providing their mathematical foundation. "Clear, concise, and readily understandable," American Library Assoc. Bibliography. 3 indexes. 29 illustrations. 216pp. 5⅜ x 8. S537 Paperbound **$1.50**

RADIATIVE TRANSFER, S. Chandrasekhar. Definitive work in field provides foundation for analysis of stellar atmospheres, planetary illumination, sky radiation; to physicists, a study of problems analogous to those in theory of diffusion of neutrons. Partial contents: equation of transfer, isotropic scattering, H-functions, diffuse reflection and transmission, Rayleigh scattering, X, Y functions, radiative equilibrium of stellar atmospheres. Extensive bibliography. 3 appendices. 35 tables. 35 figures. 407pp. 5⅝ x 8⅜. S599 Paperbound **$2.25**

AN INTRODUCTION TO THE STUDY OF STELLAR STRUCTURE, Subrahmanyan Chandrasekhar. Outstanding treatise on stellar dynamics by one of world's greatest astrophysicists. Uses classical & modern math methods to examine relationship between loss of energy, the mass, and radius of stars in a steady state. Discusses thermodynamic laws from Caratheodory's axiomatic standpoint; adiabatic, polytropic laws; work of Ritter, Emden, Kelvin, others; Stroemgren envelopes as starter for theory of gaseous stars; Gibbs statistical mechanics (quantum); degenerate stellar configuration & theory of white dwarfs, etc. "Highest level of scientific merit," BULLETIN, AMER. MATH. SOC. Bibliography. Appendixes. Index. 33 figures. 509pp. 5⅜ x 8. S413 Paperbound **$2.75**